THE BRIDGE AND THE CITY

A UNIVERSAL LOVE STORY

Daniel Biau

A French version of this book, entitled "Le Pont et la Ville" was published in Paris in 2012 by Presses des Ponts.

Disclaimer

Photos have been duly credited to their authors, but errors are always possible and should be signaled to the publisher. Non-credited photos belong to the personal collections of the author.

ISBN: 978-1-62550-148-6

       978-1-62550-210-0

Printed in the United States of America by Llumina Press

Library of Congress Control Number: 2014906136

ACKNOWLEDGEMENTS

The author wishes to thank the many colleagues who have provided information and contacts in the concerned cities and the artists and photographers who have greatly contributed to the illustration of this book. All cannot be mentioned but several of them deserve a special recognition:

Alioune Badiane, Senegal; Nefise Bazoglu, Turkey; Rusmir Ćišić, Bosnia-Herzegovina; Bernard Gambini, France; Naoko Goto, Japan; Dominique Héron, Veolia Environnement, France; Teruo Hirano, Japan; Mike Jones, United Kingdom; Heinz Kull, Germany; Gillian Lach, photographer, Brazil; Sudipto Mukerjee, India; Mrs. Nga Nguyen, Vietnam/France; Quang Nguyen, Vietnam; Tatiana Roskhosnaya, Russian Federation; Jianguo Shen, China; Mansour Tall, Senegal; Farouk Tebbal, Algeria; Rasna Warah, Kenya; Li Zili, painter, France/China.

TABLE OF CONTENTS

Introduction

In the beginning there was the river. Human beings created the city. The city was in need of water: she settled near the river. Aquatic nature and architectural culture met for centuries. But this union also created a division between the two banks of the river. Bridging these banks would become one of the major challenges facing urban societies.

OF BRIDGES AND MEN

For centuries bridges have constituted an essential link between both geographically distinct territories and sometimes hostile communities. They have been an important factor of exchange, contact and communication between peoples. Bridges constitute an essential physical response to the need for human interaction in diverse environments. Finding ways to cross over to the other side of a waterway via bridges has been a major task of engineers for centuries, and even today, bridge builders are viewed with a certain amount of awe and respect. Indeed, bridges are among the largest and most complex objects ever invented by man. Often they appear to challenge the laws of gravity and to "overcome nature". Bridges also symbolize love, longing, friendship and unity, and, therefore, evoke a lot of emotions. As architectural objects, bridges directly reflect the technical progress and aesthetic values of their time and, therefore, the socio-cultural context of their construction. They are the product – and often an important landmark – of the civilizations that built and designed them.

As a former director at UN-Habitat, the UN City Agency, an organization whose stated objectives are peace and development, I am convinced that bridges, by their very nature and *raison d'être*, contribute to these two objectives of the human community. They foster peace among human beings by linking populations across waterways, and they contribute to socio-economic development by providing infrastructure that is essential to production and exchange. Bridges are indicators of coexistence and progress, though they have also played a part in conflict, having been used by armies to facilitate the movement of troops and to conquer territories. They are powerful symbols of culture, of solidarity between societies separated by nature, of freedom of movement, of openness, and of reciprocity.

The idea of this book was born on 23 July 2004 in Mostar, Bosnia Herzegovina. On that day, the reconciliation bridge was solemnly inaugurated after having been reconstructed. It had been destroyed by the Croatian army eleven years earlier in one of the most ferocious battles of the Balkan war, the last European war of the twentieth century. The old bridge, erected by the Ottomans in 1566, had been identically restored with the assistance of the international community and its shining new arch symbolized the end of a terrible ethnic conflict.

Mostar, 23 July 2004

I decided on that day to identify, visit and document the most beautiful bridges on the planet, the most extraordinary urban bridges. In my mind, these bridges had to share several characteristics: be located in an urban setting where communities had lived and still live together; possess a strong historical and cultural content; have an original architecture adapted to their environment; and play (or have played) an economic role in the development of the city in which they are located. They had to combine technological intelligence and poetry to give meaning and identity to an urban site; they should have added a new dimension to a city. This is how I understood their beauty.

I have been very selective but have highlighted examples from all regions of the world, not just Europe and North America. This book does not focus on modern bridges that are known for their technical performance as these bridges are described in a number of publications targeting a professional audience. I did not try to produce a book on "the greatest bridges of the world" because there are already several such books around (and which I am sure all bridge-addicts are aware of). These books usually stress the technical and sometimes aesthetic aspects of bridges, but rarely make any distinction between urban and rural bridges or between urban and strictly infrastructural bridges. In contrast, I have tried to demonstrate how a bridge as an economic and social undertaking can be a key part of the urban fabric and can contribute to shaping urban development patterns. I have arbitrarily set the total number of chapters to 24 to correspond with the 24 time zones which organize time in our world. Since the selection is naturally subjective, this book could be considered as the first part of a "loving dictionary of urban bridges".

I have chosen the bridges based on the beauty of their host cities and on their contribution to the evolution of these agglomerations. This has not been very difficult because there is a nearly perfect correlation between spectacular cities and spectacular bridges. The most fascinating cities of Europe (Paris, Rome, Istanbul, Saint Petersburg, Prague, London) all possess fantastic bridges.

Prague, Charles Bridge, fourteenth century

The same applies to North America (New York, San Francisco) and to other regions of the world. Besides, and this is how they take on strategic value, the most famous bridges have almost always been built at a critical point in the history of their host cities. We could argue that "the bridge makes the city" because in history the city often takes on a new dimension when its "grand" bridge is inaugurated. This was the case in Prague and Florence in the fourteenth century, in Mostar and Venice in the sixteenth century, in Paris and Isfahan in the seventeenth century, in New York and London in the nineteenth century and in Sydney, San Francisco and Shanghai in the twentieth century. Bridges constitute the milestones, the buttonholes and laces of the urban fabric, the signatures of the built environment.

Most cities have been established near rivers in order to have easy access to water, or along coastlines for commercial reasons, and sometimes around oases. Up until the nineteenth century, very few cities ignored the essential need to have access to drinking water, and thus most were established near a water source. Rivers, both wide and narrow, have not just provided water, but have also provided means of communication, transport and commerce. However, they have also physically divided people and territories, thereby representing an obstacle to social relations. Bridge builders have, therefore, had to solve two "perpendicular" problems: they have had to let river traffic through while linking the two banks of a river as permanently as possible. Amsterdam and Saint Petersburg are telling illustrations of this double constraint.

Many cities have been developed on a single side of a river in an attempt to protect their inhabitants from flooding. On the other bank working-class areas emerged spontaneously as suburbs or "faubourgs". Examples include the Trastevere in Rome, Oltrarno in Florence, Brooklyn in New York, Pest in Budapest and Pudong in Shanghai. Meanwhile, in other cities, such as Paris, Prague and Zurich, the two banks were linked from the outset, the river being the cradle of the city and its initial core. Two very different evolutions. A notable exception is Rio de Janeiro, a city with a particularly misleading name as the waterway, which was considered the mouth of a river by Portuguese explorers in 1502 was, in fact, the Guanabara Bay. On the other hand the rivers of New York, London and Shanghai are affected by sea tides; these agglomerations were port-cities long before they became bridge-cities.

I have selected the following 24 cities and their signature bridges:

- In **Western Europe**:

Rome and its Ponte Sant'Angelo (or Aelius), built in 134 and renovated between 1667 and 1671;

Florence and its Ponte Vecchio, built in 1345;

Venice and its Ponte di Rialto, built between 1588 and 1591;

Paris and its Pont-Neuf, built between 1597 and 1607;

Amsterdam and its Magere Brug, built between 1871 and 1878;

Porto and its Dom Luis Bridge, built between 1885 and 1886;

London and its Tower Bridge, built between 1886 and 1894.

- In **Central and Eastern Europe**:

Prague and its Charles Bridge, built between 1357 and 1402;

Mostar and its Stari Most, built between 1557 and 1566, destroyed in 1993, rebuilt between 2003 and 2004;

Budapest and its Chain Bridge, built between 1838 and 1849, destroyed in 1945, rebuilt in 1949;

Saint Petersburg and its Trinity Bridge, built between 1897 and 1903.

- In **Africa:**

Saint-Louis du Sénégal and its Faidherbe Bridge, built between 1894 and 1897, renovated between 2010 and 2011;

Constantine and its Sidi Rached Bridge, built between 1908 and 1912;

Cairo and its Qasr El-Nile (or Tahrir) Bridge, built between 1931 and 1933;

- In the **Near East and Middle East:**

Isfahan and its Khaju Bridge, built in 1650;

Istanbul and its Bosphorus Bridge, built between 1970 and 1973;

- In **Asia:**

Hanoi and its Long Bien Bridge, built between 1899 and 1902;

Calcutta and its Howrah Bridge, built between 1937 and 1943;

Hiroshima and its Peace Bridge, built in 1952;

Shanghai and its Nanpu Bridge, built between 1990 and 1991.

- In **Australia:**

Sydney and its Harbour Bridge, built between 1926 and 1932.

- In **South America:**

Rio de Janeiro and its Arcos de Lapa, built between 1744 and 1750.

- In **North America**:

New York and its Brooklyn Bridge, built between 1869 and 1883;

San Francisco and its Bay Bridge, built between 1933 and 1936.

A BRIDGE BY OTHER NAMES
Arabic: *kobri, kantara, jisr*
Bengali: *setu*
Chinese: *qiao*
Dutch: *brug*
Farsi: *pole*
French: *pont*
German: *brücke*
Greek: *gefura*
Hindi: *pul*
Hungarian: *hid*
Indonesian: *jembatan*
Italian: *ponte*
Japanese: *hashi, kyō*
Latin: *pons*
Portuguese: *ponte*
Russian / Slavic: *most*
Spanish: *puente*
Swahili: *daraja*
Thai: *saphan*
Turkish: *köprüsü*
Vietnamese: Câu

The selection of the above bridges has been a bit tricky, particularly those in Europe and North America, regions which count many remarkable monuments and cities. In some cities, such as Isfahan and Istanbul, I have had to focus on two bridges. In other cases, such as Hiroshima, I have tried to broaden the analysis to the national level.

For each bridge I have looked at the history of its birth, its construction and its design, but also its function and its socio-economic and cultural impact on the city in which it is located. I believe that I have empirically demonstrated that "the bridge makes the city." And doing so has given me the opportunity to contribute to the universal History of the City, a collective and never-ending venture. Sometimes I have amplified the didactic aspect of the narrative through information boxes on the evolution of large cities around the world, recalling from my academic and professional career the student's appreciation of synthesis.

With many photos, but also drawings and reproductions of stamps and paintings, from Canaletto to Auguste Renoir, I wanted the reader to fully visualize the beauty and poetry of these artistic structures. I have tried to present photos of high quality, day and night views from the ground and the sky, inserting bridges within their urban environment, knowing that a good picture is often worth a thousand words[1]. I wish to mention in this regard a rich databank of digital images, Shutterstock, on which I relied to illustrate this book. I also quoted some excerpts from literary works that lift the veil on the mystery of intersecting human and aquatic currents that all bridges symbolize. Finally, I traced some genius designers who have marked history, from Jean-Rodolphe Perronet and Gustave Eiffel to John Roebling and Othmar Ammann, but also some political leaders who decided to build bridges and sometimes cities, often against all odds – for instance in Isfahan, Saint-Petersburg and Budapest.

I have presented the bridges and towns in chronological order, from the oldest bridge to the most recent, in 24 inter-related monographs. By combining the history of these cities I hope to have painted a fairly comprehensive picture of the major stages of urbanization on our planet, including the challenges and successes of this process over thousands of years.

Finally, it is important to remember that between two revolutionary discoveries, the great Isaac Newton had alerted his fellow citizens with this admonition: "We build too many walls and not enough bridges." Despite hundreds of thousands of bridges that have emerged since the discovery of the laws of universal gravitation, the warning remains extremely valid even today[2].

---

1 I prefer the night shots that showcase the dynamic face of the city, its pride and its "sex appeal", and that conceals its sordid face, its waste and its wounds. Long exposure views, taken at dusk when the sky turns dark blue, and when natural and artificial lights are balanced, beautify the urban landscape. They combine multiple brightness levels and different color temperatures, and by selecting the most mysterious or surprising areas, reveal the various faces of the city's magic. The French company Citelum, specializing in the improvement of public lighting, has demonstrated its expertise from Shanghai to London, via Prague, Salvador de Bahia and Madrid. Demand is growing rapidly. My experience as a polymorphic urban taster allows me to advise all those who would use this book as a travel guide: a city should preferably be discovered "around midnight", in line with a famous jazz ballad, and in the company of a local friend who knows the multifarious flavors of the place and can share it with you. This applies not only to the White Nights in Saint-Petersburg, but also to New York, Paris, Tokyo, Istanbul and all the cities of our fantastic urban planet. As explained by the great photographer Brassaï (1899-1984): "The night suggests, it does not show. Night disturbs us and surprises us with its strangeness, it releases forces within you that in daytime are dominated by reason."
2 On 9 November 1989, when the border between the two Berlins opened, East Berliners rushed to the Bornholmer Strasse and crossed the Bösebrücke at 10:30 p.m. to reach West Berlin. Crossing this bridge was the first step on the road to reconciliation, a symbol of unity. The wall, created on 13 August 1961, was then torn down and its pieces offered as souvenirs to collectors. There is symmetric literature on the walls that divide cities or territories, from the Berlin Wall to those in Baghdad, Tijuana, Ciudad Juarez, Belfast, Nicosia, Padua, Ceuta and the high wall that today encircles Palestine. The references are quite numerous, including: Thierry Paquot (Les Murs de la Peur, Le Monde Diplomatique, 0ctober 2006); Charles Bowden (Our Walls, Ourselves, National Geographic, May 2007); René Backmann (A Wall in Palestine, Picador, 2010); Wendy Brown (Walled States, Waning Sovereignty, Zone books, 2010); Kai Wiedenhöfer (Wall, Steidl, 2007); Alexandra Novosseloff and Frank Neisse (Des murs entre les Hommes, Documentation Française, 2007); and Claude Quétel (Murs: une autre Histoire des Hommes, Perrin, 2012). One might add "Fortress America, Gated Communities in the United States", by Edward J. Blakely and Mary G. Snyder (Brookings Institute Press, 1999). The same message emanates from all these publications: "Walls are a protection, often imaginary, but also a cage, sometimes very real."

The Urbanization of the World

Before discussing bridges and their impact on cities, we must put the city itself in its historical context. Indeed bridges appeared only when they became necessary for intra-urban and inter-urban communications and when it was technically possible to build them. Similarly, cities emerged when they became necessary for economic and social development, and for the functioning of the State. The history of cities is the history both of humankind and of a fascinating geography. It is simply the history and geography of the world. However, relatively little research has been specifically devoted to urban history. For example, it is almost impossible to find in-depth publications on the long history of Indian cities, a country which nevertheless produced many historical works.

Historians have shown that the evolution of the village into the city was primarily the result of a political and social transformation, moving from a world of clans and tribes that produced little surplus to a world of classes where the State was an instrument of monarchical power, and where cities formed the territory of that power. Kings of antiquity were the first founders of cities in Mesopotamia and Egypt. And these cities were to symbolize their power through prestigious buildings erected by thousands of slaves. These cities were to attract people and to become the most dynamic hotbeds of innovation and intellectual progress. If Catal Huyuk in Anatolia and Jericho in Palestine are considered the oldest towns, it is generally accepted that Uruk in Mesopotamia was the first city in history. It is estimated that 5,000 years ago this fortified Sumerian city-state, which gave its name to Iraq, had 40,000 inhabitants. Under King Gilgamesh (2700 BCE), Uruk built monumental buildings and invented writing. It was on the banks of the Euphrates, in the Fertile Crescent, that mankind entered the age of cities.

Tags on the Israeli wall surrounding the West Bank

Babel Tower, Babylon, six-teenth century painting

Chinese cities were then born in the no less fertile Yellow River basin. The Egypt of the Pharaohs followed, building Memphis two thousand years before our era, and also the Indus Valley civilization (Harappa, 2600-1900 BCE) which disappeared almost without trace. Babylon, a capital from 1750 BCE, remained for centuries the largest city in the world.

It hosted more than 200,000 people in 600 BCE, before it fell to the Persian king Cyrus the Great in 539 BCE and entered its slow decline. A century later the Greeks would associate the city, the *polis*, with democracy, public space and citizenship. Of course slaves, women and foreigners were excluded from that democracy, but planning (as an inexact science of the organization of the built environment) was born in Athens, which had 100,000 inhabitants at its peak. Alexandria, founded by Alexander the Great in 332 BCE, quickly became one of the largest cities in the world with more than 300,000 inhabitants in the third century BCE, and the first truly cosmopolitan metropolis. At the same time the capital of the Mauryan empire, Pataliputra (now Patna) on the Ganges hosted roughly the same number of inhabitants. It remained the empire's capital for several centuries until the reign of the Guptas (320-550 CE).

The Phoenicians of Tyre had meanwhile founded Carthage (near today's Tunis) in 814 BCE, in direct competition with the Greek cities and later with Rome for control of the Mediterranean trade. The Punic Wars waged by Rome resulted in the total destruction of Carthage in 146 BCE. Three-quarters of its inhabitants (150,000 of 200,000) were killed, the others enslaved. Carthage, the richest city of the Mediterranean ring, was razed. But its vanished prosperity may have announced a future Lebanese emigration to Africa. Like the phoenix, the Phoenicians could also rise from the ashes.

Nineveh, capital of Assyria, lithograph of James Fergusson, nineteenth century

Rome then took over as the undisputed leader of the movement of urban invention, definitively combining city and civilization. Among the many Roman innovations, we must mention urban design, land registration, multi-story buildings, aqueducts, sewers for the rich (cloaca maxima), slums for the poor, and solid urban bridges. Rome was perhaps the first "million-plus" city at the very beginning of our era. With the rise of the Christian religion, she then became the "Eternal City". Rome could be considered the mother of all cities. But its decline between the third and the fifth century was inexorable, resulting from the vastness of an empire (three-and-a-half million square kilometers at its peak) covering the entire Mediterranean basin, most of Gaul and (Great) Britain, which became unmanageable. This left the southern European cities prey to Germanic invaders.

New outbreaks of urban life then moved eastward, especially to Byzantium, which became Constantinople in 330 CE.

Istanbul, Blue Mosque (1609)

The capital of Emperor Constantine, who converted to Christianity, was on several occasions the largest city in the world, with more than 400,000 people in 500 and between 1120 and 1150, and with 700,000 inhabitants from 1650 to 1700. Simultaneously, Asian cities began to grow, especially in the Yellow River basin, first with two ancient capitals: Luoyang, perhaps the world's second largest city after Rome in the year 100; and Xi'ān/Chang'ān, capital of the Tang dynasty from the seventh to the tenth century and one of the largest cities in the world in the year 700.

Xi'an, first Chinese capital
©bbbar/Shutterstock

Paris, view from
Notre-Dame towers

These were followed by Kaifeng after 960 and Hangzhou/Lin'an, the Song capital, after 1135. Islamic cities of the Middle East and Andalusia then began to grow rapidly at the end of the first millennium. It is estimated that Baghdad, which had taken over her neighbor Ctesiphon (the capital of the Sassanid Empire of Iran, including Afghanistan and Mesopotamia, from the third to the sixth century) was the largest city in the world in the year 900 with nearly one million inhabitants. Meanwhile Cordoba, with its 300,000 inhabitants, far outstripped Venice as the largest city in Europe by the year 1000.

In the twelfth century a number of European villages began to evolve into market towns, paying royalties to feudal lords in exchange for protection. Merchants banded together to defend their interests, to fund universities and cathedrals, and to obtain municipal charters. The bourgeoisie was born and with it the city of the Middle Ages, with its streets, squares, shops, artisans, and guilds. During the thirteenth and fourteenth centuries Gothic architecture blazed from Paris to Prague, reflecting a new prosperity and the strength of the Church.

European urbanization, however, went on standby between 1340 and 1490 because of wars, epidemics and famines. The modern era symbolically began in 1492, simultaneously in Grenada and the Caribbean. Italy, at the crossroads of trade between East and West, had in the meantime brought the world a new cultural revolution, the Renaissance and its humanism. Classical architectural design – its harmonious proportions, ancient columns, and domes – entered the city, in Florence first, and then in all the northern cities of the peninsula. The architectural profession emerged and earned recognition.

Venice, San Giorgio Mag-
giore (1568) ©Oliver Hoff-
mann/Shutterstock

Renaissance embodied the power and wealth of cities, but it also reflected a degree of aristocratic decentralization. Monarchs would regain their influence during the sixteenth and seventeenth centuries, renewing the role of capital cities to glorify their power. As in Rome, with the Popes (Sixtus V, 1580), in Paris with Henri IV (1600) and Louis XIV (1670), in Vienna with the Habsburgs, in Madrid with Philip II (1580), but also in Isfahan with Shah Abbas (1620) and in Istanbul with Süleyman the Magnificent (1550), kings and emperors would appeal to experts to plan their cities and would vest urbanism with true respect and legitimacy.

At the other end of the world it is estimated that Beijing (Dadu), rebuilt by the Mongols in the thirteenth century, was probably the largest city in the world in 1400, with half a million inhabitants.

Beijing, the Forbidden City
©Hung Chung Chih/
Shutterstock

It would succeed Nanjing in 1421 as the capital of the Ming dynasty, and would have one million inhabitants in the eighteenth century. Meanwhile Japan was to urbanize slowly from the eighteenth century and Edo-Tokyo, its administrative capital since 1603, would host 700,000 inhabitants by 1800. Most cities in Japan began as port cities, and would remain so, though with diversification of their economy, and would later become centers of industry and manufacturing. Beijing's population would be overtaken by London's by around 1825, while Tokyo's exploded during the twentieth century, reaching 35 million inhabitants in the year 2000.

The Baroque city of the seventeenth century expressed the strength of absolutism and its power to shape the urban landscape, including in Latin America where this is most evident in the beautiful, ornate churches of Brazil, Mexico and Ecuador. Baroque architecture represented a clear break with the humanism of the Renaissance. Its richest and most spectacular and impressive forms, sometimes with a deceptive appearance, were ideal means of glorifying the greatness of Catholicism and its kings. Just as Baroque exuberance and sensuality had emerged from the centralization of power and the wealth extracted from the colonies, so the coordination of architecture and the splendor of grandiose monuments and public spaces constituted the swan song of the absolute monarchy. Indeed fast-emerging urban planning had new objectives, beyond the glorification of the monarch; it would have to facilitate the industrial revolution and thus rationalize and functionalize urban areas to meet the needs of the capitalist economy with its expanding markets. The first engineering school, fittingly called Ecole des Ponts et Chaussées (School of Bridges and Roads), was founded in Paris in 1747 to help link French towns and cities with each other.

The Enlightenment would thus unify science and culture in Europe and initiate a real urban transition. This began with the founding of Saint Petersburg out of the northern swamps in 1703 and ended with Washington in 1793, confirming the honored status of the professions of town planner and civil engineer. During the

American and French revolutions, the contemporary city was in the making and the center of gravity of European urbanization was moving northwest (towards London and Amsterdam) due to the intensification of the transatlantic trade. Washington was the last Baroque city while London, the unplanned city *par excellence*, became the capital of the world. While only 10% of the world's population was urban in 1789, this share would grow rapidly in the nineteenth century. As industrialization increased the need for urban labor, urbanization levels jumped to 30% in 1900. Transportation would play a major role in this process through the development of roads and the construction of bridges.

The modern city of the nineteenth century was, therefore, marked by an inflow of rural populations, which resulted in the urbanization of poverty and the growth of slums, which tended to emerge around factories fuelling the industrial revolution. This spawned several inter-related trends: the spatial exclusion of the so-called "dangerous classes"; radical urban restructuring through major projects; new technologies and industrial materials (steel and cement); the creation of suburbs and slums; the very rapid growth of American cities (New York, Chicago) and the birth of colonial cities during the second half of the century; the emergence of an urban culture and of social movements; the return of classicism in architecture; and, through the commercialization of land and housing, the triumph of marketable space as a means of production, reproduction and enrichment. Until the Second World War the industrial city retained all of these characteristics.

New York, Chrysler Building (1930) ©Songquan Deng/ Shutterstock

From 1960 onwards there would then be an explosion of "Third World cities", which is still underway in Asia and Africa, and the gradual de-industrialization and population stabilization in northern cities. Tokyo became the largest city in the world from 1960 onwards, outstripping New York, although its recent growth results more from densification of urban interstices than from territorial expansion.

Almost a third of the urban world, a billion people, will enter the third millennium in overcrowded, unhealthy and often dangerous informal settlements. Experts will speak of a "planet of slums" while conflicts will also tend to urbanize, from Baghdad to Beirut, Belfast to Mostar, Kigali to Freetown and Bangui, Nicosia to Jerusalem, Tripoli to Homs and Aleppo.

The urbanization of the Western world has spread like a wave from East to West. Starting from Mesopotamia (now Iraq), for over two millennia, this wave was centered around the Mediterranean, heading for Egypt and Greece, then to Carthage and Rome. This was followed by a significant return – as if to recharge - to Constantinople, the gateway to the East and to the Arab world, before reaching France in the sixteenth and seventeenth centuries, England in the eighteenth and nineteenth centuries, and finally the United States in the nineteenth and twentieth centuries. One could almost argue that this wave then crossed the Pacific to reach Japan in the twentieth century, where it met the Asian wave and grew into a tsunami. The western wave started due to climatic reasons (agricultural surplus and irrigation), followed by political reasons (at the time of Athens and Rome), cultural renewal (the rise of the Arab civilization), and finally economic reasons (Paris and London were the driving forces of capitalism). This conquest of the West took place spontaneously, as a logical result and engine of socio-economic development. In contrast, Chinese cities conquered the eastern part of the country, starting from Xi'an and Luoyang in the Yellow River basin, then to the south (Nanjing and Hangzhou), and finally linking Beijing to the Yangtze Basin.

The first African cities were born in the interior of the continent (Axum, Gao, Timbuktu, Djenne, Ife). But after the creation of dozens of ports by colonial powers, urbanization has had some difficulty returning inland (as attempted with Abuja). Latin America has witnessed a similar trend, from the major capitals of autarchic, inward-looking empires (such as Tenochtitlan, one of the largest cities in the world in 1500, and Cuzco) to coastal additions. Nonetheless large cities, such as Mexico City, Sao Paulo, Bogota, Quito and Santiago, have developed in the interior of the continent. The Indian sub-continent, on its part, has progressively urbanized, beginning in the sixteenth century under the Mughals, from the northwest (the Indus Valley and Lahore) towards the center (Delhi was founded in 993, followed by Agra, Akbar's capital in the sixteenth and seventeenth centuries). Urbanization then spread to the south (Bombay, founded in the fifteenth century by the Portuguese, and Madras, founded in 1640) and finally to the east (Calcutta, the capital of Bengal, founded by the English in 1690).

Around the world, cities have always been centers of progress and innovation, thanks to the density of social relationships that they facilitate. To function properly, they have always required communication infrastructure. Thousands of bridges have helped to meet this critical need.

Footbridge in Nepal
©Daniel Prudek/Shutterstock.

CHANGING BRIDGING PATTERNS

While footbridges have existed since the dawn of time, especially in wooded and mountainous areas, bridges of larger capacity seem to have appeared around the sixth century BCE. In 513 BCE, the Persian king Darius built a pontoon bridge over the Bosphorus, consisting of wooden spans lying on many interconnected boats, on the site of the present Fatih Sultan Mehmet suspension bridge. These bridges of boats are still used today by military engineers to cross rivers in a minimum time. In the fifth century BCE Herodotus described a bridge on the Euphrates in Babylon as consisting of stone piers supporting movable wooden beams. In the third century BCE the Chinese created bridges with suspended braided vines (one can still see footbridges of this kind in Nepal).

A century later the Romans developed the first bridges and aqueducts with semi-circular stone arches, an Etruscan technique using wooden supports. The Romans also used temporary enclosures or cofferdams to build bridge foundations under water, as well as lime-pozzolana cements. These were major innovations.

The first global city, Rome, invented the architecture and the basic technique of bridge-building 2,000 years ago. Bridges were erected throughout the Roman Empire, with France's Pont du Gard and Spain's Segovia Aqueduct providing the best standing evidence of this era.

Rome, Ponte Fabricius, the oldest urban bridge in the world (62 BCE)

Many other Roman bridges are still in use, particularly in Spain, when there has been adequate maintenance. These masonry bridges, built arch by arch and pier by pier, dominated the world for two millennia until the eighteenth century. Unlike cathedrals, bridges did not benefit from the Gothic period of the twelfth to fourteenth century. They remained Romanesque in style, heavy and massive, until the Enlightenment. Whereas ribbed vaults and flying buttresses allowed cathedrals to stretch towards the sky, the horizontal bridges were left untouched by the revolution initiated in 1140 by the Abbott Suger at the Abbey of Saint-Denis. Although during the Renaissance bridges were refined by gradually flattening their arches (i.e. by moving from a semi-circular to a segmental design, as in Florence), this period's return to classical antiquity was not really conducive to technical progress.

The famous old bridges still standing are those of Rome (62 BCE), Zhaozhou (605), Regensburg (1146), Avignon (1188), Florence (1345), Cahors (1308-1350) and Prague (1347-1402). Most are used by pedestrians and attract millions of visitors today.

Starting in 1760 the great French engineer Jean-Rodolphe Perronet showed that one could simultaneously build all stone arches, which allowed the horizontal thrust of the bridge to be carried through successive spans to the abutments, while transmitting only vertical loads to the piers, which could thus become thinner. This second major technical progress was well illustrated in the Pont de la Concorde in Paris (1791). The nineteenth century then saw the appearance of metal: first cast iron, weak in tension, and then laminated or wrought iron, used for the chains of the Szechenyi Bridge in Budapest (1849) and for the triangulated arcs of Gustave Eiffel, applied in the Maria Pia and Dom Luis bridges in Porto (1877 and 1886). Finally the emergence of steel gave birth to suspension bridges, whose decks are supported by cables (such as the Brooklyn Bridge, built between 1869 and 1883), and permitted the construction of new arch bridges (such as the Pont Alexandre III, inaugurated in 1900). In 1960 free-standing cable-stayed bridges were first erected, and these continue to be widely used today to cross large stretches of water. The viaduct of Millau and the Vasco de Gama Bridge in Lisbon, and recent Shanghai bridges, illustrate this trend. This was the third major achievement enabled by new materials. Steel also led to the invention of reinforced concrete, and pre-stressed concrete by Eugene Freyssinet in the 1930s. This material became dominant for short-span bridges in the 1950s, and was essential for the realization of lightweight decks over box-girders, by linking and pre-stressing sections of large hollow concrete components (known as voussoirs).

Bridges are often classified according to type (vaulted arch, beam, suspension, cable-stayed), or by the main material they are made of (wood, stone, steel, reinforced and pre-stressed concrete). Arch bridges include both the viaduct of Garabit (lattice) and the Alexandre III bridge (cast steel).

Of course, progress has not been linear and accidents have happened. On 16 April 1850 in Angers a suspension bridge came into resonance during the passage of an artillery regiment and collapsed. Its frequency of vibration coincided with the pace of the soldiers. A similar disaster struck the Tacoma suspension bridge in the United States, which fell in 1940 when it came into resonance with vibrations caused by the wind. There should have been greater rigidity in its stiffening trusses, an imperative that designers of large suspension bridges had understood since the innovations of John Roebling. Recently engineers have been able to make positive use of the wind by designing aerodynamic deck profiles, which look like inverted airplane wings. The wind then produces a stabilizing force from top to bottom with a pressure above the deck and depression below. This lightens decks and stabilizes them at the same time.

Thirty years before the Tacoma collapse and on the opposite side of the same continent, on 29 August 1907, the Quebec Bridge over the Saint Lawrence River collapsed during construction, killing 76 workers, mostly Amerindians. The design of this cantilever bridge was defective, due to a miscalculation of mass and efforts. Once the design had been corrected, the installation of the 500-metre central span on 11 September 1916 resulted in the death of another 13 workers. Opened in 1917, and inaugurated in 1919, the Quebec Bridge remains the longest cantilever bridge in the world. Indeed, during the 1920s suspension bridges finally prevailed over cantilever bridges.

Accidents have continued to mar the history of bridge-building. In January 1975, a bridge in Hobart, Tasmania, collapsed under the impact of a barge, killing 12 people. The enormous socio-economic consequences of the communication breakdown between the two parts of the city is still remembered in Australia. In August 2007, a Minneapolis bridge collapsed for no apparent reason, forty years after its commissioning. Following inspection, it turned out that 74,000 bridges in the United States present technical deficiencies. The venerable Parisian Pont-Neuf itself partially sank in 1885!

As this list illustrates, the construction of urban bridges has known two periods of glory: the last third of the nineteenth century (a general phase of expansion) and the 1930s (the years of the Great Depression). This means that the construction of such infrastructure can be justified both in periods of economic growth, when bridges are required to meet increasing production needs, and in times of crisis, when bridges can contribute to stimulating consumption and employment.

In the selection presented in this book, eight bridges are ancient stone constructions (the ninth stone bridge being that of Constantine), eight are metal bridges of the last third of the nineteenth century (including Budapest Chain bridge, which is a little older), four are metal bridges of the 1930s, and three are recent bridges (1952, 1973, 1991) that have been chosen for their symbolic value (Hiroshima) or their strategic importance (Istanbul, Shanghai).

St. Petersburg, Peter-the-Great Bridge (1911) ©ki-boka/Shutterstock

All the main engineering techniques detailed above are, therefore, represented in this sample. Metal arch bridges in Porto and Sydney did not permit very large spans; Scottish cantilevers almost died in Quebec a hundred years ago; traditional suspension bridges have been put into question following the collapse of the Tacoma Narrows bridge in 1940. Over the second half of the twentieth century "scientific" (aerodynamic) suspension bridges have, therefore, occupied centrestage, especially in Japan. They are still popular in Asia and, fortunately, do not crumble anymore.

Tokyo, Rainbow Bridge (1993)
©MC_PP/Shutterstock

Cable-stayed bridges, which emerged during the 1980s, have demonstrated remarkable performance, for instance, in the Pont de Normandie (1994) and the beautiful Millau Viaduct (2004). These are also suspended bridges, but are self-supporting and oftentimes impressive. While cable-stayed bridges are not typically urban, we can admire the Vidyasagar Setu in Kolkata (1992), the Nanpu and Yangpu Da Qiao in Shanghai (1991 and 1993), or the small masterpieces of Santiago Calatrava and his followers.

In urban settings, pre-stressed concrete highway viaducts that penetrate the urban fabric have become popular, sometimes comprising several layers, such as in Bangkok. While suspension bridges are retained for their very large spans, tunnels are increasingly being dug to preserve land around urban structures. This marks a return to the 1927 debate between "tunnel supporters" and "bridge fans" as a means of crossing the Hudson in New York. This remains a key point of recurrent discussions on the possible options for crossing not only rivers but also the Strait of Gibraltar between Africa and Europe (obviously very expensive), and on futuristic projects across the Bering Strait between Asia and America.

A Personal Note on Cities, Bridges and Solidarity

Like the philosopher Michel Serres, author of *The Art of Bridges, Homo Pontifex*, I was born on the banks of the Garonne (he in Agen, I in Toulouse). I, like him, was born close to a stone bridge ("the Garonne ran a few yards away from my mother, she still burns in my arteries. I owe to that good fortune my passion for bridges. I love them from birth, genetically, incestuously", writes Serres). Toulouse is famous for its Pont-Neuf of 1632, Agen for its canal-bridge (a canal which flows on the bridge, while the Garonne River flows perpendicularly under its arches).

1. Pont du Gard ©Elena Eliseeva/Shutterstock

2. Pont d'Avignon

3. Pont Valentré, Cahors
©rudiuk/Shutterstock

5. Canal-bridge, Agen
©Charles de Coquereaumont

4. Pont-Neuf, Toulouse

6. Millau Viaduct ©PHB.cz (Richard Semik)/Shutterstock

SIX OCCITAN BRIDGES

Southern France (Occitania) has hundreds of remarkable masonry bridges, from the small medieval marvels of Belcastel, Estaing and Espalion in Aveyron to the monumental works on the Garonne in Toulouse and Bordeaux, and the old bridges of Albi, Béziers, Carcassonne and Montauban. Six of these bridges have been selected here because they have marked the history of bridge-building and their reputation transcends national borders.

1. The **Pont du Gard**, which allows the aqueduct of Nîmes (50 kilometers, 17 meters of difference in elevation between its two ends) to cross the Gardon valley, is one of the most wonderful vestiges of Roman antiquity. There are three levels of arches: the lowest level displays the largest arches, which are 22 meters high and span 142 meters. These support a second level of 19.5-metre arches, spanning 242 meters. Finally, on top of these lie the smallest arches (measuring 7.4 meters), which span 275 meters. Jean-Jacques Rousseau was duly impressed: "I walked along this beautiful three-storey building with a respect which almost kept me from advancing further."

2. The **Pont Saint-Bénezet** on the Rhone (named after the promoter of the bridge and the founder of the medieval Bridge Brotherhood) is more commonly known as the Pont d'Avignon – on which, according to the popular children's song, the aristocracy of the town gathered to dance. The bridge was built between 1177 and 1187, repaired repeatedly and abandoned to floods in 1669, and finally shortened to four arches. Saint Benezet, the patron saint of bridge builders (together with his colleague of Bohemia, Saint John of Nepomuk) has his chapel on the bridge.

3. The **Pont Valentré** in Cahors is probably the finest fortified bridge in France (and perhaps in the world). It is 138 meters long, with a hump-backed deck and three square towers. It was built from 1308 to 1380 on the Lot river to defend the Quercy province from an English invasion which never took place.

4. The **Pont-Neuf** in Toulouse, built between 1542 and 1632, has seven arches designed as basket handles. The harmony between stones and bricks is reinforced by open spandrels in each pier. Monumental and balanced, this old bridge, which is 220 meters long, is the symbol of the pink city. Its lighting at night over the Garonne is spectacular.

5. The **canal-bridge in Agen** (1849) allows the Canal Lateral to the Garonne (Toulouse-Bordeaux) to stretch perpendicularly over the river. It is 539 meters long and 12.5 meters wide, and rests on 22 piers. This is a slightly over-sized aqueduct on which riverboats can peacefully sail. Other beautiful canal bridges in the region include those of Beziers and Moissac.

6. The cable-stayed **Millau Viaduct** was opened in 2004 after less than three years of construction. Like the Pont du Gard, is not an urban bridge but an "infrastructural" crossing that carries cars across the Tarn valley, at 300 meters above the river. Its aesthetics is its major attribute, thanks to the spectacular design by Norman Foster and Michel Virlogeux.

From the Roman aqueduct carrying water to the modern motorway viaduct carrying cars, a loop of two millennia has closed, always with the same elegance and engineering genius.

The two neighboring cities share a love of rugby, a game of human bridges called scrums. Occitania (the South of France) is one of the richest regions in Europe as far as bridges are concerned: they are present in villages and small towns, as well as in large cities, firmly anchored in history (see box).

Though he claims to abhor cities, which he decries as "immodest architecture that despots deploy to crush human beings", the rural and marine philosopher Michel Serres loves the bridges that made him forget urban violence. For him bridges are realized hyphens between banks that would otherwise maintain few relations ("the bridge over the Bosphorus creates a short-circuit between Europe and Asia"). He admires civil engineers whom he equates with pontiffs, noting that "the pontiff links the human to the divine, earth to heaven, the immanent to the transcendent," and that "life functions as a multiplicity of bridges crossing a thousand symmetries, involving many scales and rhythms". Not a pontificating philosopher, Serres knows how to communicate his enthusiasm, which I hope will also be reflected in this book.

Downtown Toulouse,
Thirty-six Bridges St.

My contribution to the history of bridges has developed gradually in conjunction with stimulating years spent working at the City Agency of the United Nations, which has its headquarters in Kenya, a country with beautiful landscapes but only tiny bridges.

Having had the opportunity to work with colleagues and friends in many cities, across all regions of the world, I wish to pay tribute to a solidarity that went beyond borders and ignored nationalism, a unanimous thirst for peace and progress in all countries, despite a number of war-like or uncommitted leaders. I have been part of multinational teams in which professionals of several nationalities, including some from countries at war, delivered and succeeded. They gradually became elements of working communities, not without internal tensions, but respectful of differences. I learned that bridges between human beings can always be created as long as we share common goals. These transnational ties cannot be woven in the abstract; they must have a purpose, as do bridges. Some of my colleagues, urban planners at the UN who were part of such multicultural teams, have been willing to share their feelings about their changing cities. I thank them for their friendship and for the time they spent.

As a specialist in urban planning and city management, I have advised many cities in all latitudes. I have analyzed their multiple problems of inequality, poverty, pollution, and congestion. I have experienced the darker side of urban development rather than its bright side, the difficulties rather than the successes. But I have also dreamed of the ideal city and tried to help cities, rich and poor, to move towards this ideal. I saw beautiful cities, and fascinating neighborhoods in ordinary cities, attractive areas in mundane cities marked by international uniformity, fractions or pieces of my ideal city. In this book I will not speak of what I have devoted my career to (urban management and, more specifically, the management of urban deficiencies), but will focus on the most significant fragments of urban success, presented through different but complementary angles. This is, therefore, a cathartic book, a ray of sunshine to recall the optimism of a student who hoped for a better tomorrow, of *Architecture for the poor* (Hassan Fathy), of phalansteries (Charles Fourier), of the *Right to the City* (Henri Lefebvre), of urban composition and harmony, of public spaces for all, of social integration instead of spatial segregation, and of fraternal urban communities.

BRIDGES IN ART, LITERATURE AND COMMUNICATION

Bridges had a religious significance before having an artistic one: they were places of symbolic passage to the afterlife. In the Middle Ages, the construction of bridges was encouraged by the church, often in the form of toll bridges that provided revenue for the running of associated hospitals. The Charter of Tours, issued in 1031, mentions that bridges are "pleasing to God". Passage to the other side, into the unknown, was also endowed with mysticism in ancient Japan.

In the history of art, bridges frequently appear in the works of the Impressionists (the first "urban" painters) from Turner to Monet, Renoir and Van Gogh (see the chapter on Paris). Bridges animate rural landscapes, and mirror waterways and the environment in more urban settings. Seen from above, urban bridges are an essential piece of the animation and life of the city.

Bridges also feature in many books, particularly in American literature. Some even appear in the titles (Birth of a Bridge, the Three Arches Bridge, The Bridge on the Drina, The Bridges of Madison County). In multiple novels the Brooklyn Bridge provides a leitmotif or a backdrop to the story. Bridges have attracted many poets, from Alexander Pushkin to Hart Crane, Guillaume Apollinaire and Vladimir Mayakovski. Arthur Rimbaud dedicated one of his prose poems to bridges, "all so long and light that the banks charged with domes lower and shrink" (in Illuminations). Filmmakers too have used bridges, gradually evolving from an era of social realism (where the action takes place under the bridge or on docks), to using these gigantic structures to induce terror in viewers or to invoke sentimental romanticism (first or farewell kisses on bridges and aboard barges) and, more recently, to showcase post-modern aesthetics, marked by elegant aerial shots along rivers and their bridges.

Philosophy, on the other hand, has not fully exploited the evocative potential of the bridge. Nonetheless in Thus Spoke Zarathustra Friedrich Nietzsche observed in 1883 that, "What is great in man is that he is a bridge and not a goal. Man is a rope stretched between the animal and the superhuman, a rope over an abyss". Nietzsche often returned to the theme of crossing, the desire to reach the other side, asserting for example that, "it is above the smallest abyss that it is most difficult to lay a bridge". The Mostar Bridge could illustrate this maxim.

Philately and numismatics appreciate bridges because of their expressiveness and their synthetic value. Thus on the first euro banknotes, issued in 2002, appear the images of seven bridges symbolically launched across European borders, stylized by the Austrian artist Robert Kalina. The first five represent masonry bridges (5 €: Roman aqueduct, € 10: Roman, € 20: Gothic, € 50: Renaissance, 100 €: Baroque and Rococo). The 200 euro note represents a steel bridge (art nouveau), and the 500 euro note a modern bridge – possibly a cable-stayed combination of the future Millau Viaduct (opened in 2004) and of Santiago Calatrava's Alamillo Bridge (inaugurated in 1992 in Seville).

In the field of information technology and communication, an invisible virtual bridge connects billions of men and women as through a spider's web. The internet, the network of networks, can be likened to a multidimensional bridge still under construction, whose aesthetic remains debatable. The intangible weaves of this wireless bridge are less strong but as mysterious as the spider's threads. Humanity has indeed entered a networking and bridging phase. As put by Paul Valéry, "words are boards laid over an abyss". This sentence could be paraphrased and somewhat cynically updated, as the words that populate our emails are often bridges over our solitude.

Finally, the question of a bridge's eroticism cannot be ignored. Is the city a corsage tightly laced with bridges? Do the arches of a bridge evoke a woman lasciviously lying on the edge of an invisible sofa? Is the bridge a bow which could shoot arrows into the sky? The city widening its banks, the river flowing in its bed, ships sinking voluptuously under an endless bridge, how to avoid the illusion and allusion? The question has inspired artists, and some philosophers like Michel Serres, who does not hesitate to talk of "the erection of the deck whose stiffness advances, risky, daring, above the slot to fill ..."

Anecdotally, it is known that geographical names make abundant use of bridges in all languages. One of the world's most famous universities was born in the thirteenth century on the east bank of the River Cam, where a bridge was built and gave the city its name: Cambridge. Mostar (literally, "keeper of the bridge"), the symbolic town which inspired this book, provides another telling example.

Finally, bridges appear in many popular sayings and hundreds of songs in many languages. They are used to communicate simple messages, usually of strength and solidarity, but also of desire, longing and separation. Their image lends itself to multiple uses in all fields of culture and in all latitudes.

"The air of the city makes you free", academics used to say in Chicago around 1925, referring to an old German proverb while they were inventing urban sociology. This book, I hope, will bear testimony to this refreshing air and illustrate the relationship between *The Bridge and the City*. By associating bridges with freedom and social progress, at a time when access to urban living is increasingly being recognized as a universal human right, this book's ambition is to explore and report on a global love story, a centennial history of communication and exchange.

Time Goes By Like This Running Water...

(Fragments of a daydream)

Guillaume Apollinaire (1880-1918), a keen observer of the Seine, has captured the river's ambiguity and its magic, the inexorable flow of time that its bridges punctuate. His "Pont Mirabeau" is a hymn to the currents of love, which never turn back despite their most desperate efforts to ignore the passage of time. Apollinaire and other great poets around the world help us to perceive the poetry of the relationship between the city, the river and their subtle and unchanging hyphens. Imagine...

You walk into an unknown city in the spring, aimlessly, guided only by your emotions, attracted by a detail, a facade, a curve, a color. Without noticing it, you inevitably approach the river, that clear thread of an urbanity that brings nature into culture, carries water into stone, blends liquid with solid, the organic with the inorganic, and mixes movement with stability. The river introduces complex fluid mechanics into simple solid hyper-statics, it injects a perpetual motion between the banks, displaying their centuries of architecture, it adds an element of eternity to the powerful humanity that the bridge symbolizes with its quays, its banks, its fishermen, and its lovers – who watch the current that is so weary of being watched, and embrace each other without any assurance of brighter tomorrows.

In this dense city, the river attracts you like a magnet, like a seducer, even when you cannot reach it. You may imagine the Tiber, the Grand Canal, the Seine, the Thames, the East River, the Neva, the Danube, the Nile, the Bosphorus, these immortal souls that have shaped their cities since the dawn of civilization. Above the river-soul, you scan the bridges between the shores. Rather than choking that liquid avenue with their presence, they magnify the river as gracious orthogonal crossings.

From the top of the bridge, you glance at the river and the city that surrounds it and that is reflected in its waters. An impossible wide angle. The river is the image of the city: you dream of a clean river in a sustainable city, a natural threat tamed within a gilded prison that is open to the world, and where the cell's bars have been replaced by bridges. Your mind takes off and flies from the bridge down into the river' spirits, in search of the lost time in a Stendhal-type ecstasy. And your loves flow past like this running water, while a rainbow gently fades and, one by one, the city lights flicker to life.

It is time to cross the bridge, to close your dream-like parenthesis and to meet an unsuspecting human maelstrom. Welcome to the opposite bank, you can now continue your random journey through streets, squares and buildings. The river and its bridges will still be there tomorrow, accessible, conducive to new contacts and to more imaginary escapes.

ROME AND ITS
PONTE SANT'ANGELO

The history of Italy, the cradle of European urbanization, began with the Etruscans who inhabited an area between Florence and Rome. They founded the first cities in Europe 600 years before our era, based on meticulous planning, with houses built around a courtyard, and with cemeteries. They organized oligarchic republics and transformed a group of villages in an unhealthy and flood-prone area into a city, Rome, where they invented the first sewerage systems. But "federal" Etruria weakened slowly, and was conquered by the Romans in the third century BCE. Romans then built the first stone masonry bridges on the Tiber.

ROME AND ITS PONTE SANT'ANGELO

According to legend, Rome was founded in 753 BCE by Romulus, after he killed his twin brother Remus. Following the reign of seven kings (including Etruscans), it became a republic in 509 BCE and remained so for five centuries. Rome really took off around 300 BCE, gradually controlling the whole of Italy, and eventually destroying Carthage. By the second century BCE it had a population of 150,000.

Despite several civil wars and multiple conspiracies, Rome's growth continued unabated. Julius Caesar, Emperor-Pontiff, effortlessly conquered (Great) Britain in 54 BCE and Gaul in 52 BCE. He had built beforehand, in 55 BCE, a sturdy wooden bridge over the Rhine, near Cologne, to attack the Germans. After his assassination on 15 March 44 BCE, the struggle for power continued, and the Empire was born with Octave, who proclaimed himself emperor (Augustus) in 27 BCE. However, conflicts continued with Caligula, Britannicus, Agrippina, Nero and other future heroes of classical Roman tragedy (remember Camille's imprecations in Corneille's Horace: "Rome, the sole object of my resentment.") Only Vespasian stands out (during his reign, from 69 to 79 CE, the Coliseum was built) from the long list of whimsical and sometimes incompetent emperors of the first century.

In fact, the heyday of Rome lies in the second century, with three great emperors: Trajan (98-117), Hadrian (117-138) and Antoninus (138-161). The first two were born in Spain. They were fantastic builders, and like Antoninus, good administrators. Trajan's official architect was Apollodorus of Damascus, regarded as the first engineer of the Roman world (he built a 1135-metre long bridge over the Danube). Then, under Marcus Aurelius, the Barbarians (Germans) launched their first attack on the Danube in 166 CE, heralding the beginning of the decline of a gigantic empire which was becoming unmanageable. Trajan promoted urbanization and public works, but stretched too far beyond the borders of the empire, up to the Persian Gulf. Rome reached its zenith under Trajan and Hadrian, the time of Trajan's column, Hadrian's Wall on the borders of Scotland, his mausoleum and his bridge, aqueducts, baths, amphitheaters, temples and basilicas.

The town of Rome had been created by the Etruscans, who were master-builders, on the southern border of Etruria. Rome is the city with the oldest bridges, the "Eternal City" of the Supreme Pontiffs (titles of emperors and later of popes, who had to create bridges... between God and men).

The beautiful Ponte Sant'Angelo (formerly Aelius), was erected in the second century CE (in 134), when the city reached its peak and its troops took Jerusalem. Then it had almost one million inhabitants (it would only attain that number again in the twentieth century, under Mussolini!). Emperor Hadrian (Aelius Hadrianus) was to build a large mausoleum on the right bank of the Tiber, while the city laid on the left bank, hence the need for a new bridge (although the bridge of Nero was close). Neighboring the Vatican, the mausoleum would be transformed into a castle by the Popes in the eleventh century. It is called, since the change in its function, Castel Sant'Angelo.

The bridge was strengthened several times but four piers and three central arches are original. The same Hadrian built a large wall to separate his empire from the Barbarians: bridges and walls could sometimes co-exist together. Rome remained inside the Aurelian Wall (271) until the sixteenth century. The mausoleum was a bastion of the wall before becoming the residence of the popes, a fortress and a prison. Today the castle is a museum of fifty-eight rooms. It has a beautiful terrace where one can feel the memories of desperate Tosca, who jumps into the Tiber in the last act of Puccini's opera.

Sant'Angelo Castle at night
©Tkemot/Shutterstock

The Sant'Angelo Bridge is built on unstable ground. The Romans were able to solve the problem of foundations under five meters of water by setting up formworks of sealed oak piles (cofferdam) and by using the first pozzolanic mortar (named after the town of Pozzuoli near Mount Vesuvius, famous for its volcanic ash), and to build thick piers[1]. The piers were linked to each other by semi-circular stone arches. Vitruvius, the most famous Roman architect, has provided a detailed description of these techniques.

The Romans did not invent the arch design (they inherited it from the Etruscans), but they invented the masonry arches, which remained the most dominant technique until the eighteenth century. They were heavily influenced by Greek architecture and classicism. Over the centuries the bridges gradually evolved from semi-circular arches to segmented arches and lower decks.

Originally Rome was not really a river town; it was a city born out of the villages which existed on its seven hills. The Tiber Island, the mythical foundation of the city, never constituted its center, unlike the île de la Cité in Paris. A little aside, the small island received a hospital from the year 291. Thus the two oldest bridges in the city, joining the

---

1 A cofferdam is a watertight enclosure allowing underwater foundations to be built in the dry. It is made of sheet piles driven deep in the riverbed and connected together.

Sant' Angelo Bridge and Castle, upstream view ©stocker1970/ Shutterstock

Tiber Island to both banks, have been preserved. The small Fabricius Bridge (from the left bank, 62 BCE) is the oldest urban bridge still in use in the world. The famous Ponte Milvio in the north of Rome is older (115 BCE) but was rebuilt periodically. The first wooden bridge of Rome, Pons Sublicius, which is downstream, was built around 600 BCE, before the beginning of the Republic, when Rome was trying to become a town. This bridge was also rebuilt several times. The object of many superstitions and rituals, it offered the only access to the city across the Tiber, the sacred river, to those who came from the north. For the ancient Romans a bridge of wood or stone was seen as a victory of human intelligence over archaic fears and primitive beliefs, over the spirits of the river.

During the third century instability and anarchy grew in Italy. Vandals, Goths, Alamans and other Germanic tribes started to harass the Roman troops. With Diocletian (284-305) and his successor Constantine the Great (312-337) the empire tried to revive itself for a last time. The historical Battle of Ponte Milvio on the Tiber, on 28 October 312, saw the Western Augustus, Constantine confronting the seditious Maxentius. The victory of the man who would become Emperor Constantine the Great marked the beginning of a new era for the whole empire. Christianity started expanding because Constantine, having seen a cross in the sky announcing his victory, decided to tolerate the new religion. He then converted to Christianity, as did all his subjects. Ponte Milvio has recently become the receptacle of thousands of padlocks, symbolizing the permanence of love, just like the Pont des Arts in Paris.

Tiber Island

My friend Pietro Garau, a professor at the University of Rome and former director at UN-Habitat, is familiar with the place. He observes: "Curiously, the term 'span' applies in English both to the length of a bridge and to a time period. It's entirely possible that Rome may be the city in the world with the highest age difference, or time span, between its oldest and newest bridge. Today, within a mile or so you can find, arching over the Tiber, the ancient Ponte Milvio, built in 115 BCE by consul marcus Aemilius Scaurus, and the brand-new Ponte della Musica, completed in May 2011. The Ponte Milvio, still standing after many restorations, was built as the gateway to the city from the north at the intersection of the consular roads Cassia and Flaminia. Today, it is a pedestrian passage and a favorite meeting point for romantic couples who introduced the habit of securing a padlock on the bridge as a symbol of their love. The Ponte della Musica, just south of the Ponte Milvio, is an ultramodern span (for pedestrians, cyclists and light public transport only) serving the more modest purpose of providing a conclusion to the new urban axis marked by Renzo Piano's Auditorium and Zaha Hadid's new National Museum of Twenty-first Century Art (MAXXI). It would not be surprising if Ponte Milvio watched the arrival of its new colleague, not entirely void of elegance, with the indulgent indifference that typifies the Eternal City's attitude towards new little events in its history."

Constantine built Saint Peter's cathedral in Rome and founded a new capital in the East, Constantinople, in 324-330. He created a powerful new empire, the Byzantine Empire, "by fragmenting the West and unifying the East" (Catherine Brice) and returning to Greece. The western part of the empire finally fell in 476 under pressure from the Vandals, Saxons, Sueves, Franks, Alamans, Alans, Visigoths and other Germanic peoples. In 540 the emperor of the eastern part, Justinian, took back Italy but Rome by then was only a thing of the past. The western empire would reemerge in the year 800 with Charlemagne and last a long time as a loose federation, up to the period of the Habsburgs. But Italy would no longer be the center of Europe and its cities would benefit from being away from the imperial power to acquire larger autonomy (see box).

Rome, the papal city, would then be managed by popes who returned after a long gap (1309-1420). De-populated (17,000 inhabitants), rural and miserable in the early Quattrocento, it would re-vive with Martin V from the 1420s. This pope brought back a physical planning agenda; his successors, Nicolas V and Sixtus IV, then embarked on a plan to beautify the city between 1447 and 1484 when Rome regained its prestige. Sixtus IV was an enlightened planner and a great builder. In ten years he opened paths and passages, rebuilding forty churches, connecting the Vatican to the city, and moving the central market. He built the first modern bridge over the Tiber, which was later given his name, Ponte Sisto (1475). This bridge facilitated access to the Vatican and the Trastevere.

Vittorio Emanuele Bridge (1911) with the Vatican in the background ©Antoine Beyeler/ Shutterstock

THE THREE GLORIOUS ERAS OF ITALIAN CITIES

Three bridges and three cities in Italy are included in our sample of the finest bridges and most beautiful cities in the world. Although the United States has far more bridges than Italy – at least a few hundred thousand – Italy has the advantage of history; it is where permanent bridges first appeared, and Rome, the capital of a powerful empire, could be considered the mother of all bridges, the matrix of all crossings.

Italian cities have influenced the patterns of urbanization in the West, and were a reference point throughout Europe at the beginning of our era and between the late Middle Ages and the seventeenth century. From the tenth century the history of Italy, a stateless country, became the history of its cities. These cities would be managed as aristocratic communes, with elected councils, from the twelfth century. In 1165 they established the first association of cities in the world, the Lombard League, which included all the cities of northern Italy and which defeated Barbarossa. The Tuscan League followed in 1197.

The thirteenth century was a time of builders and of early Gothic art. The oligarchic republics of Genoa, Venice and Florence began to prosper. A new era started, which would reach its climax in the Quattrocento (fifteenth century), that of the Rinascita (Renaissance), the second period of Italian glory after the Roman Empire. This glory relied on the strength of several rival cities, namely, Milan, Rome, Florence, Venice, Genoa and Naples, which in turn dominated the Mediterranean world for two centuries, roughly from 1400 to 1600, and built architectural wonders.

Trevi Fountain in the center of Rome, Nicolas Salvi (1762)

Competition between Venice and Genoa vis-à-vis the Byzantine Empire lasted for several centuries, with peaks marked by several military conflicts between the thirteenth and the fifteenth centuries. An important Genoese colony settled in Constantinople, creating the Galata district in 1261 and introducing high customs duties. These two Italian cities controlled the sea trade between East and West until the advent of the Ottoman Empire. Then a Genoese discovered America, symbolizing the alliance of Spain with his city, and a new trade route opened across the Atlantic.

Naples on her part was autonomous from the thirteenth to the nineteenth century, and the capital of a powerful kingdom coveted in turn by the kings of France and Spain. In the seventeenth century it had become the largest city in the western Mediterranean, and an essential element of the Spanish Empire until 1714.

Italy's enlightenment was not very bright (her lights would dim) but her cities would continue to grow. The population of Naples increased from 215,000 to 426,000 between 1700 and 1800, while Rome had 163,000 inhabitants in 1800. Venice and Florence saw the stagnation and decline of their industries, but their cultural life was still very active. Antonio Canal aka Canaletto (1697-1768) accurately reproduced in his panoramic paintings (the vedute) the setting of a Venice that was falling into a slow decline. Neoclassicism took over, simple and "harmonious", and replaced Baroque exuberance. The French army occupied the country in 1799, and in response, a sense of nationhood began to emerge: Austrian rule was marked by hostility and rebellion; Cavour created "Il Risorgimento" in 1848; Venice and Florence revolted against the Habsburgs; Garibaldi took Palermo and liberated Sicily. Italy as a nation-state was born through pain. Rome became capital in 1870 (Florence was temporarily the capital from 1864 to 1870). Popes had to backtrack and Rome, with only 240,000 inhabitants, changed and became secularized.

However, this was the beginning of the hard part: one had to wait for the defeat of fascism (and the end of Mussolini's destructive megalomania) to see the country revive and enter vigorously into modernity and development. The second half of the twentieth century would be the third glorious era of Italian history, after the second and fifteenth centuries. This contemporary period is well known, but one often forgets that it is rooted in a unique past, in beautiful, strong and proud cities, sometimes competing and divided, jealous of their autonomy and their selective democracy, the many features that characterize the global cities of the twenty-first century, including those of the Italian peninsula.

It could be argued that the Ponte Vecchio in Florence heralded the birth of the Renaissance in 1345 (it was immediately delayed by 60 years because of the plague), the Ponte Sisto in Rome represented its heyday in 1475 and the Ponte di Rialto in Venice marked its conclusion in 1590. Florence, Rome and Venice are the three stars of urban Italy, but we should not forget Genoa, Naples, Milan, Bologna, Turin and other vibrant agglomerations. Italy is a country of cities full of sun, energy, social struggles, culture and especially history. Rome, the "eternal city", is now home to 3.4 million inhabitants, while Milan has long been the economic capital of Italy, as evidenced by its stock exchange, its airport, its fashion designers and its industry.

The new development was interrupted by the looting of the city by the mercenaries of Charles V in 1527. If the Castel Sant'Angelo resisted the general pillage, the emperor (who had been elected in 1519 as head of the Holy Roman Empire), captured Italy which then became Spanish. But the Renaissance did not end; the great artists Michelangelo and Palladio lived until 1564 and 1580, respectively, and continued to produce beautiful works throughout their lives. The plan of Domenico Fontana enacted by Sixtus V (1585-1590) led to the opening of several avenues linking churches and basilicas. The modernization of the city took on a new momentum.

The seventeenth century was marked by the Counter-Reformation (against Protestantism and Calvinism) and its artistic expression, the Baroque. Rome took back its position as the center of Catholicism and went through many physical and aesthetic transformations. In 1668 the architect and sculptor Gianlorenzo Bernini, the great master of Italian Baroque, author of Saint-Peter's Square, added ten beautiful statues on St. Angelo bridge, statues which inspired both German and Czech sculptors in Prague. These guardian angels, with those of Saint-Peter's Basilica, were meant to protect the bridge and the city.

The Ponte Sant'Angelo has long been a vital, if not unique, link between the city and the Vatican. It is now reserved for pedestrians. It is a symbolic synthesis of the emperors of the ancient city and the popes of the revitalized city, associating the power of Hadrian and the elegance of the Baroque ornament. It summarizes to some extent the history of Rome, combining in a single monument its two periods of glory.

Vittorio Emanuele Bridge and St. Peter Basilica ©Anthon Jackson/ Shutterstock

The past is omnipresent in the planning of Rome, which reveals the successive layers of a long story, so often chaotic, sometimes unexpected but often seductive. In his famous encyclopedic book, *The City in History,* Lewis Mumford has not been kind to Rome: "For more than two thousand years, Rome has continued to present a unique example of urban confusion, controlled in turn by premeditation, chance and caprice, reason, nobility and vulgarity. As in London today, the most contradictory tastes found their way in."

BERNINI, SCULPTOR AND ARCHITECT, THE "POPE" OF BAROQUE ART

Gian Lorenzo Bernini (1598-1680) was the complete artist who best symbolized the Baroque era. His work lent Rome a considerable part of its magic and influenced many other European countries. He was born in Naples on 7 December 1598 to Angelica Galante and Pietro Bernini, a mannerist sculptor of Florentine origin. The couple migrated to Rome in 1605. The young Bernini benefitted very early from the experience of his father, in particular in the organization of collective work on site and in merging architectural, pictorial and sculptural works in ensembles of polychrome marble.

Rome of the early seventeenth century was a city that witnessed a phenomenal artistic renewal, in particular with the naturalistic painting revolution introduced by Caravaggio and the Baroque influence initiated by Rubens in Flanders; it was a city where talent was recognized. Four works of art that occupied Bernini for five years made him famous. These are three mythological subjects and a biblical sculpture responding to the interests of their sponsor, Cardinal Scipione Borghese: Aeneas, Anchises and Ascanius (1619), The Rape of Proserpine (1622), David (1624) and Apollo and Daphne (1625).

Bernini (young), self-portrait

With David, Bernini, aged just 25 attempted to measure himself with the unsurpassed icon of Italian Renaissance, Michelangelo. Both artists epitomized the art of their time. The work of Michelangelo is dignified, classy and elegant, while Bernini's (as represented in his David, who is launching a sling shot, with torso turned and face grimacing) brings all elements of the Baroque: energy, movement, dynamism. Baroque art is a theatrical style, celebrating the splendor of monarchical and divine power. It is staged to impress doubters. It is a symbol of Rome's Counter-Reformation, of a Church ready to face its opponents, while Michelangelo represented with perfection the Renaissance in Florence, a city jealous of its independence.

St. Peter colonnade ©sokolovsky/Shutterstock

Bernini's talent was exploited by seven successive popes and many cardinals. Pope Urban VIII entrusted him with the construction of the facade of the church of Santa Bibiana in Rome (1624-1626), as well as the flamboyant canopy overlooking the high altar of St. Peter (1624-33) where he became Chief Architect in 1629. Bernini built several monumental fountains, including the Fontana del Tritone, completed in 1643, the first of a long series of "street furniture" and the beautiful Fountain of the Four Rivers in Piazza Navona (1647-1652).

Considered an equal of Michelangelo, Bernini sculpted the bust of Cardinal Scipione Borghese (1632), the monumental tomb of Pope Urban VIII (1628-1647) and that of Alexander VII, and the Throne of St. Peter (1657 -1666). Between 1647 and 1652, he worked on his masterpiece, the Ecstasy of St. Teresa, in the chapel of Santa Maria della Vittoria. The latter composition fully reflects the unique ability of the artist to combine marble, bronze and stucco in the same elevation movement.

Bernini spent five months in Versailles (the city and the Baroque chateau par excellence) in 1665, at the request of Louis XIV. The Hall of Mirrors as several staircases within German palaces constituted ideal settings for royal ceremonies but Bernini was not personally involved in these works.

Alexander VII, the humanist Pope and urban planner, elected in 1655, commissioned Bernini's colonnade of St. Peter's Square. Bernini crafted an elegant symbolic urban piece by designing a colonnade which deviates from the basilica like two arms that welcome a crowd. This elliptical plan was typical of Baroque architecture. The assistant of Bernini, Francesco Borromini, would also become a great architect, and later on his competitor, as would Pietro da Cortona, the third man of the Roman Baroque.

From 1658 to 1678, the sculptor-architect built the church of St. Andrew of Quirinal, which has an oval plan and which would serve as a model for many other Baroque churches. Bernini, who contributed greatly to the embellishment or finishing of existing buildings but constructed very few in their entirety, considered this church as his architectural masterpiece. The interior is made of dark marble, illuminated by a white marble dome decorated with gilding.

Under Clement IX, Bernini achieved the parapet and the series of angels of Ponte Sant'Angelo. In this series, only one statue was produced by the artist, who was then 69 years old. It is now preserved in the church of Sant'Andrea delle Fratte. The other nine were produced by students or assistants. Bernini also organized the bridgehead to create a link between the Vatican and Rome. In this regard it should be noted that there is no real "Baroque bridge", but only existing bridges reconditioned in Baroque style. One can also note the surprising Baroque contrast between an extravagant architecture and a rigorous, mathematical and uniform urban planning with broad prospects, alignments of buildings and star-like street-plans (as in Washington D.C.), which facilitated space control and culminated in the nineteenth century.

Bernini died in Rome in 1680 and was buried in the Basilica of Santa Maria Maggiore. He transformed the image of Rome and influenced the whole of seventeenth century Europe. He offered the Baroque to the Popes and in turn could claim the title of "Pope of the Baroque." He dominated Baroque sculpture just as Michelangelo had dominated Renaissance sculpture.

Bernini's marble statue on the Sant'Angelo Bridge
©NaughtyNut/Shutterstock

The Baroque era continued until the 1770s and came to a close with the Rococo and the end of the absolute monarchy. It reached its apotheosis in St. Petersburg in the middle of the eighteenth century with the fantastic works of Bartolomeo Rastrelli, including the Winter Palace, the Catherine Palace and the Smolny Cathedral.

The Tiber embankments,
seen from Sant'Angelo Castle
©ShopArtGallery/Shutterstock

Rome is a city of squares, not of streets. These squares (Navona, Farnese, di Spagna, del Quirinale, della Cancelaria, among many others) seem to have been dispersed in the urban fabric by papal fantasy, upsetting the existing buildings, without overall organization. The city has repeatedly been stitched into a poetic patchwork, dysfunctional but ultimately quite harmonious. It remains resistant to any serious planning. To make things worse, its network of public transport is frequently faced with impromptu archaeological excavations that disrupt its development and operation. The management of an Eternal City by mere mortals has certainly proved to be a daunting challenge.

FLORENCE AND ITS PONTE VECCHIO

While the Roman Empire was a confederation of largely autonomous cities, urban life declined in Italy with the invasion of the Barbarians in the third century and stagnated until the tenth century. During this long hiatus that lasted almost eight centuries permanent bridges were no longer being built. Then the towns of central and northern Italy awoke. In Tuscany competition for hegemony was intense from the twelfth to the fifteenth centuries between Pisa, Lucca, Siena and Florence. Hungry for freedom, Florentines systematically rejected the German imperial tutelage. They built a bridge-town and took over rival cities. They launched a cultural revolution, the Renaissance, which spread all over Europe.

FLORENCE AND ITS PONTE VECCHIO

The Arno flowing from east to west constitutes an obstacle that all north-south roads must cross. In Florence the river is narrow and navigable. Caesar founded a colony on the north shore in 59 BCE. In 123 a bridge replaced the original ferry; an aqueduct was then built to supply the 10,000 inhabitants of the city. Florence hardly changed for seven centuries (third to ninth) until the birth of strategic monasteries. In the eleventh century reformist Florence hosted a Concil and became one of the spiritual centers of Christianity, while remaining hostile to the emperor.

Since the eleventh century, Florence has built its prosperity around wool and a global banking sector. It created one of the first European currencies, the florin, and was able to establish financial relations with the whole of Europe. Florentines set up a complex system of governance in the twelfth century, with a municipal parliament and consuls. Long-distance trade in textiles grew rapidly; they were dyed in Florence and sold worldwide. At the end of the twelfth century the city had 25,000 inhabitants and a first stone bridge. Its suburb of Oltrarno developed on the left (south) bank, hosting workshops and warehouses. Yves Renouard emphasizes that economic takeoff really began at that time (circa 1180): "Florence was now a bridge-town straddling the river, whose corporations were particularly dynamic".

In 1218 a second bridge, the Ponte Nuovo (now Ponte alla Carraia), was built downstream from the first, which became Ponte Vecchio. Then a third bridge was opened upstream in 1237, the current Ponte alle Grazie. Convents and hospitals followed – the thirteenth century, as we know, was a century of builders. Florence quickly became the financial capital of the western world. A fourth bridge, the Ponte Santa Trinita, was built downstream in 1252. The city then had four bridges, which were renovated periodically till 1950.

After a difficult fourteenth century marked by the final reconstruction of the Ponte Vecchio (destroyed by a flood in 1333) and hampered by the plague that struck Europe in 1348, which affected half the city's population (the plague was not eradicated until 1417), Florence took off with the Medici family, especially Cosimo - "simple merchant and clever politician" - who ran the city from 1434 to 1464, and who was succeeded by Lorenzo the Magnificent, a refined patron in power from 1469 to 1492.

The business people, the popolo grasso, then dominated city management, skillfully combining commerce, finance and industry. Culture soon followed. At the turn of the fourteenth and fifteenth centuries (1380-1420) humanism emerged as a doctrine that would be the basis for the revival of the West. Florence triumphed economically and culturally, and took over Pisa in 1405. The Medici symbolized the success of a Florentine bourgeoisie whose funds became indispensable to the European aristocracy. The city reached its zenith, with private palaces growing like mushrooms. The euphoria continued until 1530 when the emperor (Charles V) and the pope jointly took over the city.

Italy then came under Spanish control. Florence and Tuscany experienced a revival between 1539 and 1559 but their true brilliance lay in the fifteenth century. The decline of Florence and other Italian cities began at the end of the sixteenth century, despite spectacular alliances, such as the successive marriages of Catherine and Marie de Medici to the French kings Henri II and Henri IV, respectively.

Flooding of the Arno frequently destroyed the bridges of Florence in the Middle Ages. That is why in the fourteenth century the Florentines decided to launch an ambitious program of containment and to (re)-build a stronger bridge. The city had just completed its sixth enclosure, of 8.5 kilometers and 63 towers encircling an area of 6.3 km². Taddeo Gaddi and Neri di Fioravante designed a new Ponte Vecchio with three low segmented arches. It was a decisive break (already tested in China in the seventh century) from the Roman semicircular arches. Work began in 1345. The bays are, respectively, 27, 30 and 27 meters long, while the piers are 6 meters thick.

Ponte Vecchio, a three-arched bridge ©Dan Breckwoldt/ Shutterstock

Florence at that time initiated a new historical era, the Renaissance. It took the lead in a huge cultural shift that would affect all of Europe. It, in fact, gave birth to the modern world, its art, its architecture, its aesthetics, its paintings, its humanism. It was not simply a re-birth (renaissance) of an older era but the creation of a whole new way of being. Florence, Venice, Genoa and Milan then had about 100,000 inhabitants each, while Rome was home to barely 50,000 people.

Brunelleschi, the father of Renaissance architecture, re-invented ancient columns in 1421 at the Hospital of the Innocents. He then built San Lorenzo and, without scaffolding, the fantastic and huge dome of the cathedral Santa Maria del Fiore (43 meters in diameter), which broke all records. Regularity, symmetry and geometric proportions were the keywords of the Renaissance, inspired by ancient Rome. Gothic was rejected as fanciful and barbaric. Paintings culminated in Venice in the sixteenth century while the architecture of the Renaissance, born in Florence towards 1420, would move to Venice and vanish after Palladio's death 160 years later.

MICHELANGELO, AN ICON OF THE ITALIAN RENAISSANCE

David, a mythical artwork, in the center of Florence ©Vichie81/Shutterstock

A native of Tuscany, the young Michelangelo arrived in Rome in 1496. He returned to Florence to carve his superb "David" in 1501, moved back to Rome to paint the ceiling of the Sistine Chapel (1508-1512), and returned to Florence in 1519 at the request of the Medici for whom he sculpted tombs. In 1534 he returned permanently to Rome where he spent the last 30 years of his life; he became the chief architect of St. Peter's Basilica in 1546. He died in Rome, but his tomb is located in Florence. Although influenced by antiquity, his powerful, very modern style could be called "athletico-erotic" (it is strangely considered "the last of the Gothic" by Auguste Rodin!). This style has been copied by generations of sculptors, including Baroque artists. Its fops (e.g. Apollo) are sometimes very effeminate, perhaps reflecting the artist's sexual orientation.

Michelangelo appears to many critics as the brilliant and versatile artist who epitomized all the virtues of the Renaissance. This reputation seems somewhat exaggerated although he authored some architectural masterpieces (such as the Capitol Square, the dome of St. Peter's in Rome and the Laurentian Library in Florence). Michelangelo was primarily a fantastic sculptor who created synergies, or artistic bridges, between Rome and Florence, between the popes and the Medici.

The biography of Michelangelo by Anthony Hughes sheds light on the character of this great artist while highlighting his weaknesses. The British professor uses and discusses biographies of the sixteenth century, particularly the one published in 1553 by Ascanio Condivi.

At the beginning of his career, Michelangelo was supported by Lorenzo de Medici, the Magnificent. At the age of 21, the artist went to Rome, which was then a small town ruled by the Pope, at the invitation of Cardinal Riario for whom he carved an androgynous Bacchus. However, his first major work was the "Pietà", an emotive sculpture of a young Mother Mary holding the lifeless body of her son Jesus, which was commissioned by the French cardinal Jean de Lagraulas in 1498. It is a remarkable and powerful piece of art. His second masterpiece was the famous and immense (517 cm) "David", commissioned by the Florence Cathedral in 1501 and delivered in 1504. Some biographers believe that Michelangelo's depiction of David – a perfect athletic body and an intense and defiant facial expression – reflect the artist's own rebelliousness against the Medici. Michelangelo's David is believed to be one of the most reproduced sculptures in the world. Michelangelo then took advantage of his fame to accept multiple contracts that he found difficult to fulfill. "The number of projects abandoned before their term exceeds that of those completed" (A. Hughes). The list of delays and dropouts was long, punctuated by endless disputes.

A great draftsman, Michelangelo moved to painting the Holy Family in 1504, a somewhat convoluted technical perfection in the style of Leonardo da Vinci (1452-1519, Mona Lisa dates from the same years). He returned to sculpting with the Madonna of Bruges in 1506: an always austere and sad mother holding a plump and chubby baby. Then he went back to Rome, where Pope Julius II commissioned a monumental tomb that he would be unable to produce and that would cause him a lot of trouble. Paranoid, he fled to Florence and went to Constantinople in May 1506 in response to "the attractive promise of Sultan Bajazet to design a bridge between Constantinople and Pera" (a mysterious episode organized by Franciscans). The Pope forgave him for escaping and summoned him to Rome to coordinate the paintings on the ceiling of the Sistine Chapel, which would become his most admired masterpiece. Painted by his team between 1508 and 1512, the fresco was actually a first for the artist. "It is not my job," he wrote to his father in 1509! This was probably why the comparison with the Scuola Grande di San Rocco of Tintoretto is not favorable to the Sistine Chapel. Its ceiling is certainly monumental and spectacular but too bushy, its allegorical reading almost incomprehensible, even for specialists. As for the colors, when compared to the brightness and sparks of Titian, Tintoretto and Veronese, they may seem naive or bland. That said, the Sistine Chapel's ceiling remains one of the iconic works of Roman Renaissance and the main pictorial work of Michelangelo.

Passignano, Michelangelo presenting his model of St. Peter to Pope Paul IV ©Photo Scala

Michelangelo's rise as an architect began in Florence with the façade of the Basilica of San Lorenzo, the Medici sacristy (interesting for its tombs, Dawn constitutes an erotic ideal of the Renaissance) and the adjoining library (1520-1534), with classic symmetries and stairs, but incomplete. When Rome was attacked by the Lutheran armies of Charles V in 1527, the Republic was proclaimed in Florence. Three years later Pope Clement VII and Charles V reconciled and the Medici returned to power with their support. This was a turbulent period that brought an end to Florentine grandeur. The Reformation was also gaining ground, trying to make the church simpler and less ostentatious.

The Laurentian Library was a success, but had to be completed in 1559 by Bartolomeo Ammanati. However the small and cutesy statue of Apollo (1530) does not express the strength that is usually associated with this god. Michelangelo finally left Florence for Rome in September 1534, abandoning the Medici Chapel. In 1535 he was appointed by Pope Paul III (Alessandro Farnese) as supreme architect, sculptor and painter of the papal palace. He painted the "Last Judgment" in the Sistine Chapel between 1536 and 1541, with a huge Christ at its center, which was supposed to arouse salutary fear among sinners; it is a large fresco (12x14 meters) on a blue background, which may appear dull and uninteresting to the layman. He concluded his work as a sculptor in 1545 with three statues for the tomb of Julius II, including the fascinating Moses. In 1555 he started to produce another Pietà, but left it unfinished. In 1547 he became the architect of St. Peter's Basilica and of Palazzo Farnese. He was 72 years old and would devote his last years to architecture (most architects of the Renaissance were initially sculptors). The dome of St. Peter's, after the Laurentian Library, represents his second major project in the field of architecture. His achievement as an urban planner was the Campidoglio on top of Capitol Hill. This symbolic trapezoidal square is a marvel of urban composition. It does not fully comply with the canons of the Renaissance, which perhaps explains its elegance. The precise role of Michelangelo in this project has not yet been clarified by historians.

Michelangelo passed away on 18 February 1564 in Rome. He was buried with great pomp in Florence on 11 March in the church of Santa Croce. You could say that the Florentine Renaissance was buried along with him that evening. After his death, Florentine works of art became the preserve of prominent members of the Accademia del Disegno, while Tintoretto was starting his Scuola Grande in Venice.

Michelangelo was a great sculptor and an outstanding draftsman. Admittedly, his treatment of colors and pictorial sobriety do not match those of the great Venetian painters. Even his unfinished sculptures are captivating while his celebration of the muscular male body contradicts the asceticism of his paintings. He was an exceptional genius who produced five outstanding statues: "Pietà", "David", "Victory", "Dawn" and "Moses", plus a library, a dome and a square. A great sculptor who sometimes tried to overdo it but who delivered some masterpieces that have yet to be surpassed in the art world.

On the Ponte Vecchio, which is 32 meters wide, two rows of houses were built on two levels (the first level in the fifteenth century, the second in the sixteenth). The first settlers were blacksmiths, butchers and tanners, whose work was noisy and smelly. At the end of the fifteenth century jewelers, who were more urban, became predominant. At the center of the bridge the statue of Benvenuto Cellini (1500-1571), sculptor and king of jewelers, pays tribute to this profession. Above is the Vasari Corridor, an art gallery designed by the architect Vasari (1560), linking the Uffizi gallery to the Boboli Gardens. Initially (in the middle of the sixteenth century) the gallery allowed the Duke of Medici to cross the Arno to go from his office (Uffizi) to his palace (Palazzo Pitti). The second level apartments and the second row stalls were gradually added between 1565 and 1800.

The huge central arch has survived all floods ©nhtg/ Shutterstock

Arriving in Florence in 1817, Stendhal staggered onto the sublime beauty of Florentine paintings: "I was in a kind of ecstasy. I had reached that point of emotion where the heavenly sensations provided by the fine arts and by passionate feelings meet. Leaving Santa Croce, I had a heartbeat, the life went out of me, I walked with the fear of falling." The "Stendhal syndrome" (a psychosomatic discomfort resulting from the contemplation of exceptional works of art) was born. Having regained consciousness, the writer had the opportunity to observe the city ("one of the most elegant of the universe") and to be impressed by the Palazzo Vecchio. He noted: "Florence has on the Arno four beautiful bridges, located at approximately equal distances, and which, together with the docks and the southern hill, filled with cypress drawing on the sky, constitute an admirable panorama. The second bridge in Florence (i.e. Ponte Vecchio), down the Arno, supports jewelry shops (...). This city, by the layout of its streets resembles Paris; it is located on the Arno as Paris on the Seine."

Cathedral and Palazzo Vecchio ©David Ionut/Shutterstock

In the nineteenth century Florence remained one of the cultural centers of Europe and was briefly the political capital of the new Italy from 1865 to 1870. It modernized its urban fabric and experienced rapid population growth. Today the city has about 700,000 inhabitants and remains, with its many museums and well preserved heritage, an important artistic capital of Europe.

Inhabited Bridges, A Concept To Be Revisited

Imagine financing contemporary bridges by building houses, restaurants and shops on their aprons, which would be rented to the highest bidders. It would be a welcome return to both the Italy of the Renaissance, the Old London Bridge and the old Pont Notre-Dame, a forgotten masterpiece, the last "living" bridge of Paris. These bridges were not only organic links between river banks but also supported multi-purpose buildings (residential, commercial, religious, defensive, productive etc.). They ensured a continuity of the built environment, creating a street above the water. More than a hundred of such bridges have been built between the thirteenth and the seventeenth centuries in Western Europe.

These toll bridges were, unfortunately, banned by the hygienists of the Enlightenment and removed from the urban landscape because they produced solid and liquid wastes. The houses and shops of the Old London Bridge were demolished in 1756. Inhabited bridges only remain in Florence, Venice, Erfurt and Bath. The Pulteney Bridge in Bath, derived from a project by Palladio for the Rialto, was the last one built, in 1770.

A superb and mainly residential bridge can be admired in Chenonceau in the Loire Valley. Here stands the most original French Renaissance chateau, built in the sixteenth century initially for Diane de Poitiers and then modified by Catherine de Medici, respectively mistress and wife of King Henri II. The large gallery over the river was reserved for receptions, dances and festivals. Much later it served as a hospital during the First World War and as a passageway to the free zone during the occupation of France by the Nazis. Today it receives millions of visitors. The Chateau of Chenonceau, which gently reflects in the tranquil waters of the River Cher, is undoubtedly the most exquisite palace of the Loire valley. A must-see among the inhabited or inhabitable bridges, older than the Pont-Neuf in Paris. We can also classify the Pont Valentré in Cahors (fourteenth century) in this category of inhabited bridges; soldiers occupied its three fortified towers, supposedly to stop English attacks during the Hundred Years War.

The castle-bridge of Chenonceau, across the Cher River, France

In 1996 the book Living Bridges and an exhibition at the Royal Academy of Arts in London show-cased inhabited bridges. A contest that year to design a bridge of this type on the Thames between Waterloo Bridge and Blackfriars Bridge generated seven proposals from well-known architects. The very interesting concept submitted by French architect Antoine Grumbach of a suspended "Garden Bridge", with an inhabited tower, a nod to Tower Bridge (pseudo-inhabitable), would deserve to be further explored. The Mayor of London, Boris Johnson, recently claimed that he wishes to re-activate this initiative. A new competition was held in 2009 to mark the 800th anniversary of the inauguration of Old London Bridge; it received 73 proposals.

Many other projects have been designed by famous architects (including Le Corbusier and Kenzo Tange) in the twentieth century, without more success. Jean Dethier of Centre Georges Pompidou recorded them on the occasion of the 1996 exhibition. Most of these projects were technically complex but financially viable, just as they were in the Middle Ages. In fact, these bridges could easily accommodate shopping malls, restaurants and hotels, with high profitability. As in Venice and Florence, they could also offer beautiful views of the river and its banks. Huge inhabited bridges were imagined in the years 1925 for New York (on the Hudson) and the San Francisco Bay. At a time when the concept of floating cities no longer seems completely wacky, it might be wise to revisit these megalomaniac projects.

Dubai might adopt the idea, and it could be more successful than its artificial islands. A proposal from Mario Bellini for the Pearl Bridge (1996) between Deira and Bur Dubai, including a conference center, was, unfortunately, dropped. The magnificent and habitable Khaju Bridge in Isfahan, formerly home to teahouses, could serve as an inspiration in this region.

A fine example of a living bridge can be admired in Yangzhou in Jiangsu province (west of Shanghai). This is the bridge of five pavilions, or Wuting, built in 1757 on a branch of the beautiful slender lake. China has hundreds of covered bridges of stone and wood, which served as resting places, a relay for men and cattle. Several Chinese provinces have recently erected new bridges supporting restaurants (e.g. in Chengdu), recalling the expertise of the Dong ethnic group in the south-west of the country which built many covered bridges that protected their users from wind and rain. The best known of these works, the Chengyang Bridge (Sanjiang, Guangxi), built in 1912-24 by the Dong, is part of the national heritage. The United States also has many covered bridges in rural areas (the six bridges of Madison County, now classified, stars of the seventh art, date from the 1880s).

A twenty-first century challenge would be to create new inhabited bridges in the heart of pedestrian cities. These would have several benefits: ecologically they would optimize the use of space; socially they would create new places of exchange; economically they would be an additional source of municipal finance and the site of business enterprises; and aesthetically they would give the urban landscape a new and interesting dimension. These bridges would become elements of an urban complexity that could replace the monotonous functionalism of the past century.

Ponte Vecchio, an inhabited bridge ©Andre Goncalves/Shutterstock

The Ponte Vecchio was repeatedly reinforced during its 670 years of existence It is the only bridge in Florence that survived the Second World War (despite the Nazi bombardment of 3 August 1944 that destroyed the Trinity Bridge, a masterpiece dating from the sixteenth century, which would be well reconstructed after the war). The high flood of 1966 ravaged the stalls but the Ponte stood firm. It holds a silver medal in longevity after the bridges of Rome, the untouchable Dean. It divides the city into two contrasting districts, the historic center and the Oltrarno, and elegantly connects the two banks of the river. The Ponte Vecchio is probably one of the few bridges in the world which has been continuously inhabited for six centuries. Tourists jostle here with enthusiasm and traders who occupy the monument pay their property taxes without complaining. The Ponte Vecchio was a great project, a work of art in the strictest sense and a highly profitable venture, an example to follow.

Florence is twinned with several cities, including Budapest, Isfahan, Istanbul and Sydney, other bridge-cities that we will discover with the same pleasure in the following chapters.

Bernardo Bellotto, View of Ponte Vecchio over the Arno, oil on canvas (1742), Foundation Alfred Beit, Russborough

The Ponte Vecchio today ©Baloncici/Shutterstock

PRAGUE AND ITS
KARLŮV MOST

In March 1935, André Breton travelled to Prague where he delivered a speech before the association of painters and artists. He spoke of "the magical city of old Europe", thus activating an image of postcards and mass tourism, which is still associated with the Czech capital. Albert Camus also undertook a trip to Prague in the summer of 1936. During a night in a hotel he felt suffocated by sadness, "the nausea of existence"; he discovered the absurd, which became the trademark of his novels. Both writers had to travel to Prague to review their perspectives and contextualize their work. Because one feels in this city, in its streets, squares, monuments and bridges, the full imposing force of European history.

◄The Vltava River
in the city center
©Courtyardpix/
Shutterstock

Charles Bridge seen from the
Old Town Tower (right bank)
©Jiri Foltyn/Shutterstock

PRAGUE AND ITS KARLŮV MOST

The heyday of Prague corresponds to the fourteenth century, when Charles IV became king of Bohemia. Crowned in 1347 at the age of 31, he established the capital of Central Europe in Prague, on the banks of the Vltava (Moldau in German). Prague would soon compete with Paris and Rome as a cultural capital. It then comprised two autonomous fortified old towns, one on the right bank (the Old Town or Stare Mesto), the other on the left bank, itself divided into a "Little Quarter" between the castle and the river (Mala Strana) and a newer "town" above the castle (Hradcany). In 1348 the king founded a new neighborhood considered to be the fourth town of Prague (Nove Mesto) on the right bank that was surrounded by walls. At that time Prague became one of the large cities of Europe (with 50,000 inhabitants), after Constantinople, Paris and Granada. The town would not be institutionally unified until 1784. It would be controlled from Vienna by the Habsburg dynasty from 1526 to 1918.

Educated in Paris, Charles IV, an enlightened monarch, rebuilt the castle and the cathedral of Prague, recruiting brilliant architects (such as Matthieu of Arras and Peter Parler, one of the geniuses in the history of architecture; the Parler were a family of builders present in Cologne and Strasbourg) and commissioning many churches. The Gothic style would dominate until the sixteenth century. An artistic explosion occurred during a period that coincided with the Hundred Years War (1337-1453), during which the two superpowers of the time, France and England, were weakening. This partly explains the dynamism of Prague, which was also spared from the plague of 1348-1350, which had ravaged many other European cities.

In 1355 Charles became Emperor of the Holy Roman Empire. This empire, founded in 962, was primarily Germanic (it covered the territory of present-day Germany and the Czech Republic, Slovakia and Austria). The Emperor, with limited powers, was elected by a panel of three archbishops and four princes (including the King of Bohemia). After the death of Charles in 1378, his son Wenceslas IV continued to promote arts and Prague reached its zenith. The only "collateral damage" was the assassination of John of Nepomuk (see below).

Charles Bridge (Karlův Most) was built from 1357 to replace the Judith Bridge that was damaged by a flood in 1342. The Romanesque Judith Bridge, dating from the twelfth century (1158-1172), had replaced a wooden bridge that was destroyed in 1118. Located at the same spot, between the Old Town and the Castle, it was lower and shorter than the Charles Bridge. It wore the name of the first wife of Vladislav and was inspired by the oldest bridge in Central Europe, which crosses the Danube in Regensburg, north of Munich (1135-1146).

The first stone of the new bridge was laid, according to legend, on 9 July 1357 at 5h31 (corresponding to the magical and symmetrical number 1357.9.7.5.31, a palindrome). Construction required more than forty years and was completed in 1402. The bridge is 515 meters long and 9.5 meters wide and has sixteen arches ranging in size from 16 to 23 meters. It is not straight but slightly curved. Its huge piers, designed to withstand ice blocks, are between 8.5 and 11 meters thick. This is not the oldest bridge in the Czech Republic (the Stone Bridge in Pisek dates from the twelfth century) but it is the most famous symbol of Prague and its golden age. Thirty Baroque statues, or groups of statues, of saints were added in the eighteenth century, giving it a family resemblance to the Ponte Sant'Angelo in Rome, and granting it a very romantic feel in harmony with the unique style of the old town. The Karlův Most was the only bridge in Prague until 1841.

The two towers that flank the bridge, especially on the right bank the so-called "Old Town Bridge Tower", are among the most beautiful Gothic towers in Europe. They are loaded with symbols. The third tower, the smallest, is also the oldest. Romanesque in style, it is a contemporary of the Judith Bridge. Of course, there is no symmetry between the two ends of the bridge. The bridge is asymmetrical longitudinally and transversely, reflecting the Gothic style that was scorned upon by the Renaissance. The magnificent tower of 47 meters above the apron coincides with the first span on the right bank, behind which the sun rises. It reflects the genius of Peter Parler, the prime designer of the bridge. It deserves to be visited and admired in particular for its eastern facade (the western facade was destroyed by Swedish troops in 1648). There are six arches on the left bank, over 200 meters, where the sun sets. The two unequal towers of the left bank, connected by an arch and a gate (1411) are quite far from the Vltava. The largest of these two towers dates back to 1464. This tower is a less decorated copy of the right bank tower. It houses a small museum on the history of the bridge. Towers on the left bank were renovated between 1875 and 1880. One can admire a beautiful panorama of the bridge in its environment at the Museum of the City of Prague (52, Na Poříčí).

French stamp ©Musée de la Poste

A famous anecdote is worth telling. On 20 March 1393, Vicar-General John of Nepomuk (born in 1340 in Nepomuk) was thrown over the bridge on the order of Wenceslas IV. According to legend he was the confessor of Queen Jeanne, who was suspected of adultery, and refused to betray the secrets of her confessions. He drowned in the cold waters of the Vltava and later became, after his canonization in 1729, at the height of the Counter-Reformation, the patron saint of Bohemia. He certainly remains the most popular saint of Prague. He is also the patron saint of bridge-builders (with his alter ego Saint Benezet of Avignon; interestingly Matthieu d'Arras had first worked for the Pope in Avignon). His bronze statue is the oldest of the thirty statues; it dates back to 1683 and was created by Jan Brokoff. It was produced in Nuremberg, the second artistic center of Bohemia after Prague.

Lesser Town Bridge Towers (left bank) ©JuliaSha/ Shutterstock

Peter Parler, Brilliant Architect Of The Gothic Era

Gothic art is etymologically Barbarian, the art of the Goths. It is anarchic but in many cathedrals it expresses God's greatness through imagery of a God soaring upwards towards heaven. Prague combines Bohemian Gothic and Baroque styles – it skipped the Renaissance period. Charles Bridge is Gothic in its towers and Baroque in the Brokoff's statues. Four centuries later the neo-Gothic Tower Bridge in London would further glorify Gothic towers by immersing them in the Thames.

Gothic architecture was born in Saint-Denis, near Paris, between 1140 and 1144 on the initiative of Abbot Suger (1081-1151), a childhood friend and advisor to Louis VI, and regent from 1147 to 1149 when Louis VII went on his crusade. According to Erwin Panofsky, Suger was "hard working and sociable, full of good sense, vain, witty and animated by an irresistible dynamism". He loved ornaments, stained glass and light. The new choir of the Benedictine Church of Saint-Denis combines all the elements of Gothic style and techniques: pointed arches; ribbed vaults above rose windows starting almost from the ground that create exceptional brightness; weightlessness; slender columns; light walls supported by flying buttresses; windows replacing the walls; richly carved facades; gables, pinnacles; and hooks on the walls. Between 1180 and 1270 eighty Gothic cathedrals were built in France, consolidating the power of the bishops and of the monarchy and contributing greatly to urban renewal.

Born in France, Gothic architecture expanded throughout Europe, starting with England (Canterbury, 1174) and Spain (Burgos 1221, Toledo 1222, León 1255) and the Germanic countries (Lausanne 1170, Cologne 1219, Trier 1230). In Germany it survived until the sixteenth century. Cathedrals of Sens and Senlis, and Notre-Dame de Paris (1163-1258), a large basilica with five naves, Soissons (1190-1280) and Chartres (1194-1260), the most

The Old Town Tower above the bridge apron ©Miroslav Krob

monumental, are prototypes of the Gothic of Ile-de-France, followed by Reims (1211-1290), Amiens (1220-1270) and many others. Its light style culminated in the Sainte Chapelle (1240-1246) built for King Louis IX (Saint Louis) in the heart of the royal palace, and in the reconstruction of the abbey of Saint-Denis which began in 1231.

The death of Saint Louis in 1270 was followed by the Late Gothic period, which was more academic. From this date architectural innovations came from England (Westminster consecrated in 1269, York 1291, Bristol 1298, Wells 1290, Exeter 1316, Ely 1321, Gloucester 1337, Winchester 1360 and the magnificent chapels of King's College in Cambridge, 1466-1515, and of Henry VII in Westminster, 1502 - 1509, the highlight of English Gothic and its conclusion), as well as from Germanic countries.

"While Gothic has not experienced a rapid spread in Central Europe, once adopted it became second nature, a natural part of the German cultural heritage," says Pablo de la Riestra, "now shared by ten European countries", from the Alps to the Baltic. Bohemia (Czech Republic today) with Charles IV became the center of this Germanic area, and Prague its capital in the middle of the fourteenth century. The Gothic of Central Europe began on the Baltic Sea in Lübeck, the flagship city of the Hanseatic League, with a town hall and a beautiful brick church (Marienkirche) built between 1277 and 1361. It continued to Nuremberg and Prague around 1350 on the initiative of Charles IV and under the artistic leadership of the Parler family. The Holy Cross Church of Gmünd in Swabia (south-west of Bavaria) is the seminal work of Heinrich Parler and his son Peter, from 1351. It served as their testing ground, with a church-hall plan instead of basilica design. Nuremberg, the second city of Charles IV, and its Frauenkirche are also marked by the interventions of young Parler, who would then take over from Matthieu d'Arras in Prague.

Gothic architecture was always considered a technical feat. This is why the names of the great master-builders often appear in the documents of the time. William de Sens conceived Canterbury Cathedral, Henri de Reims built Westminster Abbey, Matthieu d'Arras constructed St. Vitus Cathedral in Prague (1344-1352), which was later completed by Peter Parler (1352-1399). These masters, well paid and recognized, travelled a lot to learn from each other. The two builders of St. Vitus Cathedral are buried in the middle of the cathedral's chancel in tombs adorned with their effigies while their busts are on the walls of the triforium alongside Emperor Charles IV. The architectural profession did not exist then, yet these master builders were not just great architects, but amazing artists, organizers and designers, able to modify and adapt their projects according to the funds available.

Pablo de la Riestra states: "From 1352, Peter Parler gives the St. Vitus Cathedral a breath of modernism that we feel almost physically. Taking a traditional Gothic church, he turned it into an aesthetic ideal by showing an amazing inventiveness."

St. Vitus Cathedral and Charles Bridge in winter ©Kajano/Shutterstock

Heinrich and Michael Parler also conceived the great church of Ulm. They were also original sculptors. Parlerian influence spread to the late Gothic period until the middle of the fifteenth century. As in England, the Reformation blocked the development of religious architecture and terminated the Germanic Gothic. The Gothic town, both royal and episcopal, place of exchange thwarted by the aristocracy, would give way to the autonomous city of the Renaissance, a trade paradise and home of the merchant classes.

Gothic architecture, which is overwhelmingly religious, could be viewed as the architecture of cathedrals; it is sometimes described as embodying divine perfection as opposed to earthly mediocrity. But it was also the architecture of markets and textile halls (especially in Flanders) and town halls (Bruges, Prague). Trade diffused these architectural styles to Venice where the arches of the Doge's Palace (1309-1424) marked a pinnacle of civil and flamboyant Gothic. And, of course, the towers of Charles Bridge are part of this secularization, thanks to the genius of Peter Parler who knew how to add a Gothic touch (the tower of the right bank) to the Bridge, a nod to St. Vitus Cathedral that he built on the opposite bank of the Moldau.

Nearly four centuries later another family of architects, the Dientzenhofer, would create the Prague Baroque, in the early eighteenth century, without ignoring the Gothic heritage. Saint-Nicholas of Mala Strana is one of the best examples of their particular style.

St. John of Nepomuk,
patron-saint of Bohemia
and of bridges

In fact, most historians believe that John of Nepomuk was tortured and eliminated due to a conflict between the Church and the King about the status of the abbeys of Prague. The King wanted to prohibit monks from electing their abbots and was trying to place his favorites. It is, of course, not clear how John of Nepomuk could have been pushed from the top of a bridge that was then unfinished...

It seems that the bridge had been used from the 1380s, and then consolidated. In any event, John of Nepomuk would later become "the" holy fetish of Czech Baroque. His statue (there are actually hundreds of others in Prague and throughout Central Europe, and on the bridge of Chemilly over Durgeon, dating 1753, in Haute Saône, France) and his canonization symbolized a period of two centuries marked by the triumph of an architectural, sculptural and musical style that remains strong in twenty-first century Prague and contributes fundamentally to its charm. Facades of Nerudova Street, which leads from Charles Bridge to Prague Castle, are remarkable in this regard.

In the nineteenth century the architectural heritage of the city was spared by the Habsburgs who ran the empire from Vienna and ignored Prague. But it was seriously threatened at the end of the nineteenth century by attempts to modernize the city, inspired by the French Baron Haussmann. An Urban Renewal Law of 1893 authorized the destruction of many buildings and entire neighborhoods (including the Jewish Quarter) for hygienic reasons. Popular mobilization prevented any interference with the Little Quarter and saved the Old Town Square. In 1905 the first law to protect historical monuments ended this movement that was referred to as "municipal vandalism" by many intellectuals. Meanwhile, Prague saw the emergence of Art Nouveau buildings, which can be admired in the Municipal House and the facades of the Street of Paris.

Charles Bridge, so aptly named in 1870, witnessed many historical events, including the fierce battle against the invading Swedish army at the end of the Thirty Years War in 1648. In 1890 two of its arches were swept away by an ice-flood of the Vltava River. This impressed the young Kafka, but the bridge was quickly repaired. At the age of twenty, Franz Kafka wrote these verses:

Old bilingual stamp
of Bohemia-Moravia
©Route66/Shutterstock

"People who walk over obscure bridges

Passing in front of saints

With frosted lanterns

Clouds moving in a gray sky

Before churches

Whose towers bath in twilight

Someone is leaning against the parapet

Contemplating the evening water

Hands on the old stones."

(Letter to Oskar Pollak, 1903, translated from German).

Baroque statue, eighteenth century ©Capture Light/ Shutterstock

Later the great writer evokes "the exciting statues of saints on Charles Bridge and the strange evening light in summertime, when the bridge becomes desert." One of the inventors of modern literature kept alive in his mind a deep romance, steeped in the atmosphere of the streets of his old town.

"Walking over the bridge at midnight is magic," says the *Financial Times* (17 November 2007). But what is this undeniable magic that can be found on the banks of the Seine, on the heights of Pera, on the Grand Canal or on First Avenue? It seems that the air in some cities contains unknown particles that reach the nostrils of visitors and make them fuzzy. A surrealist phenomenon, André Breton might say.

"The exciting statues of saints" (F. Kafka) ©Alex Norkin/Shutterstock

The tourist capital of Central Europe, Prague now has a population of 1.3 million. It has an excellent network of public transport combining metro, trams and buses. The city has been able to reorient its economy, attract investors, and is hosting many foreign residents.

Prague is not only a historic and romantic city, with a fantastic Gothic and Baroque heritage; it is a modern city that bustles with economic and cultural life. It may also be a city of the future; it is of reasonable size, with a service economy, a cosmopolitan aura, a preserved environment, convivial public spaces and relaxed social relations. Prague, which experienced all the ups and downs, successes and conflicts, of European history could be viewed as a bridge between the past and the future, between the time of Charles IV and the modernity of the European Union.

Nothing is more beautiful than Prague's Spring ... especially when you cross the Charles Bridge at dawn.

Charles Bridge seen from the Cathedral

GERMANIC BRIDGES

Central and Eastern European countries, primarily Germany, have many bridges of interest. Prague was deeply influenced by German culture and is home to the prestigious Charles Bridge. The old Bavarian rival of Prague, Nuremberg, also has several pretty little bridges over river Pegnitz, including the Henkersteg, a covered crossing called "the hangman bridge."

The cities of Regensburg and Würzburg are known for their ancient bridges. The city of Erfurt has more than one hundred crossings, including the Krämerbrücke, a bridge built in 1325 that is inhabited by thirty-six three-story houses. Erfurt is the most bridged German city. Berlin has also its share of more recent bridges, which are loaded with history.

TWO HISTORICAL STONE BRIDGES

Steinerne Brücke (Regensburg)

This stone bridge over the Danube was built in the twelfth century (1135-1146). Already in 792 Charlemagne had built in the same place a pontoon of boats linked to each other. The Steinerne Brücke was for 800 years the only crossing in the city. With a length of 309 meters, based on sixteen piers, it was famous in its time and inspired many other European cities, including Prague. Recently, for safety reasons, its use has been limited to pedestrians. It is one of the oldest bridges in Europe, older than the Avignon Bridge.

Regensburg, Steinerne Brücke ©Scirocco340/Shutterstock

Alte Mainbrücke (Würzburg)

This bridge was the only crossing until 1886 over the Main in Würzburg. It connects the old city center on the right bank to the Marienberg fortress on the left bank. A first stone bridge was built at this location in 1120. The construction of the current bridge began in 1476 with the establishment of foundations, followed by temporary solutions of wood and stone for the superstructure, which was not completed (due to financial constraints) until 1703. The building is flanked by beautiful Baroque statues in sandstone, with a height of 4.5 meters.

FOUR BRIDGES IN BERLIN

In 1875 there were 55 bridges across the Spree River in Berlin, and many mills. Most were destroyed or converted during the late nineteenth century and the early twentieth century to improve traffic conditions in the city. The destruction of shops and mills, and the priority given to services on the Spree River, plus the lowering of the water level, led to a reorganization of the city center and the construction of many new bridges. This is why most of the bridges that exist today date from the years 1880-1910.

The Bösebrücke, a metal bridge inaugurated in 1916, was renamed in 1948 after a German resistant who was executed in 1944. On the night of 9 November 1989, at around 10.30, under pressure from protesters gathered in the East, the German Democratic Republic border guards opened here for the first time the passage between the two Berlins. East Berliners rushed to the Bornholmer Strasse and crossed the Bösebrücke to reach West Berlin. Crossing this bridge was the first step in the reunification of Germany. The Berlin Wall, the antithesis of the bridge, could then be destroyed.

The oldest bridge in Berlin, on the Spree, is the Schlossbrücke. An old wooden bridge at this location that Napoleon crossed to capture the city in 1806 was replaced between 1821 and 1824 by a stone bridge designed by Karl Friedrich Schinkel. Eight groups of larger-than-life statues, placed on the piers and connected by cast iron elements, majestically adorn the bridge.

Berlin, Oberbaumbrücke ©Jan Kramendonk/Shutterstock

In the eighteenth century a first wooden bridge was built on the Spree near the site of the current Oberbaumbrücke. The old bridge consisted of bascule spans in the center that allowed boats to pass through the opening and a walkway flanked by a large gate. Between 1894 and 1896 this bridge was rebuilt in neo-Gothic style, combining bricks and reinforced concrete, with a double deck, allowing both the passage of pedestrians and automobiles (bottom) and metro (top), recalling gates of the past. At the time of the Berlin Wall the bridge marked the border between the Russian and U.S. zones, and only controlled pedestrian crossing was permitted.

Another famous bridge is the Glienicker Brücke, the "Bridge of Spies" and detective movies. This bridge over the Havel River connects the ancient royal city of Potsdam with Berlin-Wannsee, the last battle zone of the city in 1945, where the famous "House of the Wannsee Conference" is located. On that bridge, which was divided by the border between the two Germanys until 1989, a number of spies (38) and opponents were exchanged during the Cold War.

MODERN BRIDGES

The destruction and bombing of Germany during the Second World War had a disastrous impact on all its bridges, especially those in cities. Therefore, most of the bridges in use today date from the period 1948-1962, during which many temporary bridges were repaired or replaced, using new reinforced or pre-stressed concrete techniques. This mass production aimed to meet huge needs in a very short time, and was influenced by financial constraints and new means of urban transport. This partly explains why artistic considerations were not a major concern during the reconstruction period.

New bridges were functional structures, often unadorned, whose special features lay in their shape and sometimes in the detailed techniques applied. For instance, the first cable-stayed bridges in the world were built in Dusseldorf on the Rhine in the late 1950s.

Later on, some newer bridges marked the urban landscape of Germany, such as the Hamburg Köhlbrandbrücke, which was built in 1974. This bridge across an arm of the Elbe is an example of modern cable-stayed construction. With its length (3,618 meters), it is the second longest bridge in the country. Given the growing size of vessels and, therefore, the heights of decks required, there are rumors that this bridge may have to be demolished within the next twenty years...

Hohenzollern Bridge in Cologne, built in 1911, destroyed in 1945, rebuilt in 1948-1959, with the cathedral in the background ©Abel Tumik/Shutterstock

Mostar And Its
Stari Most

On 9 November 1993, after 24 hours of artillery bombardment from the Croatian Defense Council, the Old Bridge in Mostar, Bosnia-Herzegovina, collapsed into the Neretva. This bridge, the Stari Most, was 427 years old, 28 meters wide and 21 meters high; in a single arch, it was rightly regarded as one of the treasures of Ottoman engineering. Ten years later its reconstruction marked the end of the Balkan war.

MOSTAR AND ITS STARI MOST

November 1993, Stari
Most in rubbles

Designed in the mid-sixteenth century by architect-engineer Mimar Hajrudin in honor of Suleiman the Magnificent (it was then called the Stone Crescent), the Stari Most was one of the oldest bridges in urban Europe since it was inaugurated in 1566, forty years before the Pont-Neuf in Paris. Besides the bridges of Rome, only the Ponte Vecchio in Florence and the Charles Bridge in Prague, both built in the fourteenth century, can claim greater age among the bridges in our selection. Note that Bosnia and Herzegovina (Mostar is in Herzegovina) were part of the Ottoman Empire for four centuries, from 1463 to 1878 (Serbia, for its part, became Ottoman from 1459). In 1878 Bosnia-Herzegovina was annexed by the Austro-Hungarian Empire, while Mostar started looking towards Western Europe.

The town of Mostar was born before the Ottoman conquest. It is located halfway between Sarajevo (135 km) and Dubrovnik (145 km). The village's name is mentioned in documents from the fifteenth century. It was then a hamlet where two towers flanked a wooden bridge, a toll bridge that allowed residents of the left (eastern) bank to work in the plain, west of the tumultuous Neretva.

At the end of the fifteenth century, Turks islamized the region and developed a small town on the mountainside, on the left bank. Mostar became the center of Herzegovina; the Mufti moved there. In 1558 a first stone bridge was built on the Radobolja, a tributary of the Neretva River on the right bank. This little hump-backed bridge is actually the prototype and neighbor of the Stari Most. Eight years later, Hajrudin, a former student of Sinan, built the new bridge, a very bold move to replace the wooden bridge over the Neretva. Sinan then designed another bridge in Bosnia, on the Drina, with his assistants. This bridge between Bosnia and Serbia was built in Visegrad between 1571 and 1577. It is featured in Nobel laureate Ivo Andrić's masterpiece *The Bridge on the Drina* (see box). This "magnificent building of incomparable beauty", based on eleven arches, was commissioned by Grand Vizier Mehmet Pasha, who was born in the region. Then at its peak, the Ottoman Empire equipped the Balkans with sustainable infrastructure, and Sinan led and managed all the Ottoman builders.

Confluence of Radobolja and Neretva Rivers

From that time onwards Mostar would expand on the vast and fertile right bank. An Orthodox bishop moved there in the eighteenth century and a Catholic bishop in the nineteenth. Croatians and Serbians mingled with Bosnians but remained on the right bank. The ethnic mix was evident only within a narrow strip of two hundred meters, close to the river.

Mostar survived the First World War and was strengthened during the Yugoslav era. In 1993 the Bulevar parallel to the Neretva became the dividing line between Bosnian and Croatian communities. After failing to push out the Muslims on the left bank, the Croatian army destroyed the Stari Most, a symbol of old Islamic architecture. The bridge had little strategic importance (there were several bridges in Mostar since the beginning of the twentieth century) but it symbolized the coexistence between communities and allowed the Muslims to maintain direct access to the right bank. The area between the Bulevar and the Neretva River became a wasteland, an uninhabitable and dangerous no man's land.

SINAN, GIANT ARCHITECT-ENGINEER OF THE SIXTEENTH CENTURY

Mimar Sinan worked for three Ottoman Sultans: Suleiman the Magnificent (1520-1566), Selim II (1566-74) and Murad III (1574-1595). His major mosques (Shehzade, Suleymaniye and Selimiye) should overshadow neither the Visegrad bridge which the Stari Most preceded by ten years (these two bridges in Bosnia and Herzegovina are listed as World Heritage sites by UNESCO), nor the aqueducts of Istanbul.

Sinan was working on the Shehzade when Michelangelo was working on St. Peter's in Rome (1547). He designed the Selimiye in Edirne when Palladio was designing San Giorgio Maggiore in Venice (1568). The Italian Renaissance therefore had an Ottoman counterpart with similar ambition and scope. In fact, Italians were rediscovering antiquity while Ottomans were rediscovering the Byzantine domes of Hagia Sophia. This is not really a coincidence because the relationship between Venice and Constantinople was always intense and cross-fertilizing. In both countries the domes would be one of the fundamental elements of the new architecture.

Mimar Koca Sinan (the great architect Sinan), an autodidact and seasoned traveller, would be Mimarbasi (Chief Imperial Architect) from 1538 until his death in 1588. Born in Cappadocia around 1490 (between 1489 and 1499, depending on the source) he was recruited in 1512 in the devchirme (imperial body of non-Muslim children trained for the army and civil service), and then assigned to the military as engineer of roads and bridges. He participated in several campaigns of the Ottoman army (Belgrade 1521, Rhodes 1526, Vienna 1529, Tabriz 1532). He was appointed Officer (or Chief Engineer) in 1526 after having built several bridges, including one on the Prut River (in thirteen days) in Serbia and one in Svilengrad, Bulgaria. Before becoming an architect, he mastered the calculation of structures. His first work as an architect is probably the Husrev Pasha Mosque (or Al Khosrowiya) in Aleppo (1536-1537). Upon his appointment by Suleiman the Magnificent as Mimarbasi, he built the small Haseki Sultan mosque for the Sultan's wife, Roxelana (1539), then the Mihrimah Sultan mosque in Üsküdar (on the Anatolian side of Istanbul) for the daughter of the Sultan (1540-1548).

His first major work was the exquisite Shehzade Mehmet (Prince Mehmet) mosque built between 1544 and 1548 in memory of the favorite son of the Sultan. Sinan adopted the classic square plan with a central dome on four piers, supported by four semi-domes. It was a bold plan, although not quite suited for prayer (a large central hall, no transept). It has an elegant façade and simple interior.

Sinan then moved to his great work in Istanbul, the Suleymaniye, in honor of Suleiman the Magnificent. Built between 1550 and 1557, it is considered one of the most beautiful mosques of Istanbul for its sheer size (inside dimensions 70x61 meters, dome 27.5 meters in diameter and 47.75 meters at the key), pyramid proportions, lighting (138 windows), its four minarets of 4 meters in diameter, 76 and 56 meters high and its location overlooking the Golden Horn. Its style is directly inspired by Hagia Sophia, the mother of Ottoman religious architecture. It is less innovative than its small neighbor, the Shehzade, but much more impressive. Especially since it is part of a complex (külliye) which includes huge Koranic schools, theological colleges, a hospital, hammams, shops, shrines (including later that of Sinan himself). The rectangle is 216 meters long and 144 meters wide. The Suleymaniye, the largest square-based semi-domed mosque built by Sinan, is twice as large as the Shehzade. If the dome is slightly smaller than that of the Hagia Sophia (whose diameter is 32 meters and height 56 meters), the interior illumination is much more uniform. With this mosque Suleiman wanted to mark his reign just as Justinian had marked his with Hagia Sophia a millennium earlier (532-37). He celebrated the rebirth of Constantinople and the transformation of the Byzantine Empire into the Ottoman Empire. Istanbul was then the largest city in Europe with 600,000 inhabitants, at par with Beijing.

Sinan's first mosque, the Khosrowiya in Aleppo, Syria

Sinan in front of his masterpiece, the Selimiye in Edirne, Turkey

As in Italy, a giant model of the mosque was made to enlighten the population and was paraded in processions. Sinan then passed to hexagon-based and octagon-based domes, for aesthetic reasons and to increase interior space. The Iznik ceramics and calligraphy adorning the walls of some mosques are simply fantastic. New designs are found in particular in the Rustem Pasha (a gem for the Croatian Grand Vizier, 1561), Mihrimah (1560), Kara Ahmed Pasha (for the Prime Minister, 1558-1565), Sokollu Mehmet Pasha Kadirga (for the Bosnian Grand Vizier, 1572), Atik Valide in Üsküdar (for the Venetian mother of Murad III, 1570-1579) and, of course, in the Selimiye Mosque. The latter was considered by Sinan himself as his masterpiece. It was built between 1569 and 1574 for Sultan Selim II in Edirne, the former capital of the Ottomans which already hosted three beautiful mosques of the fifteenth century. Its dimensions reached (finally!) those of Hagia Sophia. Octagon-based (eight pillars), its dome has a diameter of 31 meters and a height of 42 meters and its four dizzying minarets rise to 71 meters and are only 3.5 meters in diameter. The Selimiye is the culmination of Ottoman design and one of the pinnacles of Islamic architecture. The proportions are perfect, the building's silhouette is more slender, and the interior is bright and beautifully decorated. Selim II died a few months after the inauguration of his mosque. Sinan had still fourteen years to live under Murad III. And he went on with his research and operations. His last mosque was the Nisanci Mehmet Pasha (1584-1588) with a very beautiful interior. Throughout his life he was helped by many colleagues that he coached and who continued his work, notably in the famous Blue Mosque (Sultan Ahmet) built by Mehmet Agha (1609) close to Hagia Sophia, one of the most visited tourist sites in Istanbul.

His biographers claim that Sinan could have designed, constructed or renovated 477 buildings in his lifetime, including 84 major mosques and 12 bridges. In a career spanning fifty years this is not impossible. But the legacy of Sinan is not about numbers, it is the constant search for beauty, for an architecture that elevates human beings to perfection.

It would be vain or absurd to compare Sinan and Palladio from an aesthetic point of view, but I believe that the impact of Sinan on the vast Ottoman Empire, and later the entire Islamic world, has been greater than the impact of any Renaissance architect on the art and culture of Western Europe. Indeed, it would be interesting to compare the masterpieces of these two architects, namely San Giorgio Maggiore and Selimiye, which are absolute contemporaries since work began in 1566 for the first and in 1568 for the second. San Giorgio Basilica was completed in 1610 while the Selimiye Mosque was completed in seven years. San Giorgio is the most perfect example of a central plan at the end of the nave, a cross plan with a dome over the crossing, the archetype of the Basilica of the Italian Renaissance. The Selimiye is as bright as San Giorgio but much larger. Its four minarets are a little higher (85 meters from their base, 71 meters above the base) than the campanile (63 meters) but their momentum is comparable. The analogies between these two masterpieces are tempting. Could their total harmony, yet in very different cultural contexts, be a mere coincidence? One should superimpose their plans to solve this puzzle.

Professor Jean-Paul Roux, Director of Research at the French CNRS (National Scientific Research Centre) and specialist in Islamic art, brings us his perspective: "The church stands out for its mass, the mosque for its lightness, one clings to the soil, the other wants to detach. The Ottoman mosque is both a cosmic mountain and an image of the universe. The dome represents the sky and minarets evoke the four pillars that interconnect the two areas of the cosmos. It is not intended that believers look towards Mecca but direct their eyes towards heaven."

The Stari Most was built in white limestone, tightened by iron clamps and filled with molten lead. In fact it was the first bridge using metal clamps (iron wall ties were used in Mesopotamia during antiquity, but not for bridges and reinforced concrete appeared only in the early twentieth century).

For four centuries Mostar and its bridge have been perhaps an overrated symbol of cohabitation between Muslim Bosnians, Orthodox Serbs and Catholic Croats, and a commercial crossroad. Mostar was known as a city of culture, libraries, museums and theatres. The war that followed the breakup of Yugoslavia, which lasted from 1992 to 1995, was particularly destructive in Bosnian towns and cities, such as Sarajevo, Mostar, Banja Luka and Tuzla. Through a particularly murderous ethnic cleansing, cities were divided into homogeneous territories, hostile to each other.

In Mostar Croats tried to push the Muslims to the east of the Neretva, and to retain the right bank (west) as a whole. But they failed and the separation line, the "Bulevar" parallel to the Neretva, remained on the right bank. A strip of a few hundred meters between the river and the Bulevar was specifically targeted. In November 1993 the city buried thousands of its dead and lost its heart, its stone crescent, its colorful rainbow. Mosques and churches became places of hatred, minarets and steeples looked like guns pointed at the sky. The Neretva, "genuine mirror of history," only reflected ruins, not only those of the bridge but also of the Orthodox Cathedral (1873) and of many other historical buildings.

Stari Most seen from the top of a neighboring minaret

Mostar today has 120,000 inhabitants (all called Bosnians) who are trying to rebuild their lives. But the mafias have not completely disappeared and the city is still divided into two administrations. Despite the efforts of the United Nations, the path to a truly unified city is paved with pitfalls. Tourism recovered quickly (with 500,000 visitors in 2005) and the aluminum plant works pretty well. But the economy remains fragile and unemployment still needs to be addressed. In 2006 Mostar had a population made of 50% Croats, 40% Muslims and 10% Serbs. Croats control 70% of the total income of the city. They build huge churches, but in small numbers, while Muslims build dozens of small mosques – different strategies that reflect two conceptions of the relationship between religion and politics.

THE BRIDGE ON THE DRINA AND THE THREE-ARCHED BRIDGE

Two contemporary novels

Two contemporary novels tell the story of the construction of bridges in the Balkans at the time of the Stari Most, in the sixteenth century. The first one, The Bridge on the Drina (1944), is by Ivo Andrić, a Serbian author and winner of the Nobel Prize for Literature in 1961. The other, The Three-Arched Bridge (1981), is by the great Albanian writer, Ismail Kadare. Professor Claude Thomasset presented a detailed analysis of these two novels in his Sorbonne seminar devoted to medieval bridges.

Although the action of these two novels is not precisely dated, one understands that it takes place at the time of the Ottoman penetration in the Balkans, at the time of Suleiman the Magnificent and Sinan. In fact, the Bridge of Visegrad on the Drina, built between 1571 and 1577 to link Bosnia to Istanbul, was designed by Sinan himself and funded by the Prime Minister (Grand Vizier) Mehmed Pasha Sokolovic. The geopolitical context thus provides a common background to both works: the Ottomans arrived in the region and wanted to control territories through taxes and infrastructure. They reached Budapest and Vienna. Rural communities had a dim view of this invasion, which brought with it new ideas, technical progress and an eastern religion. The Turks acted with determination, quickly negotiating the submission of local lords without any qualms. The construction of numerous bridges at this time revealed the contradictions between autarkic and closed micro-societies and an expanding empire in which transportation and communication (roads and bridges) were of strategic importance.

Višegrad Bridge across the Drina River ©Patrisyu/Shutterstock

But the geopolitical aspects are secondary in these two works. Ancestral beliefs, myths and superstitions dominate much of the narrative. First, there is the struggle, thought to be impossible by farmers, against a river, a natural phenomenon that is to be respected and feared. The presumption of the builders seems outrageous. How could these intruders attempt to defy nature? It can only result in a disaster, and the devil himself is certainly watching.

Fortunately bridge-builders are aware of the risks and know how to secure their construction: they must offer a sacrifice to the spirits of the river. Traditionally, this sacrifice took the form of a person buried alive in the walled masonry. This violent death would also signify the violent birth of the bridge. The sacrifice is beautifully staged in the two novels, in different but equally mysterious forms.

Andrić's bridge is more social, friendlier, than Kadare's. In both cases, however, the bridge, completed after many vicissitudes, raises at first a little fear, followed by increasing admiration. The tragedy ends well. The effort was worthwhile. Progress outweighs obscurantism. Land takes precedence over water; ferries are defeated and must accept their announced decline.

What can we learn from these two stories with regard to the recent wars in the region? Balkan bridges have always been difficult to build and maintain. Unlike rivers, they are not natural elements. In 1993 was the old bridge of Mostar destroyed because it was a Turkish masterpiece (Turks being seen as spiritual ancestors of Bosnians) or because it did not respect the ritual sacrifice, or for geopolitical reasons?

I believe in the latter hypothesis. Stari Most was not the victim of river spirits. It was demolished by forces that wanted to return to the social fragmentation of the Middle Ages, who were confusedly looking for a lost identity, who wanted to bury both the Ottoman Empire and the Yugoslav Federation in the wreckage of the single arch. But again, builders won over the forces of the past, at the cost of thousands of lives.

On 23 July 2004 the new Stari Most, an exact replica of the original bridge, was inaugurated as a symbol of reconciliation between the communities of Bosnia and Herzegovina, and to mark the end of a decade of absurd massacres. Funding was provided by the World Bank (through a concessional loan of US$4 million), Italy (a grant of US$3 million), the Netherlands (US$2 million), Turkey (US$1 million), the Development Bank of the Council of Europe (US$1 million), Croatia (US$0.5 million) and the city itself (US$3 million). Retrieving techniques of the sixteenth century was not easy; it was a kind of archaeological challenge. The same limestone was used by the Italian, German and Turkish companies who worked on the project.

July 2004, Stari Most rebuilt ©Aleksandar Todorovic/Shutterstock

Historically teenagers used to show their bravery by diving from the bridge into the green waters of the Neretva. On 24 July 2004 they resumed the challenge and performed "angel jumps" which they had practiced by training on less prestigious bridges or on the temporary bridge. Those "angel jumps" inspired me to write this book.

National Geographic has produced an interesting film on the reconstruction of this beautiful dual symbol of war and reconciliation that the Stari Most has become. An International Conference of Ministers of Culture of South-East Europe was held in Mostar on 19 July 2004 with the support of Italy, UNESCO and the World Bank. Its title was: "Cultural heritage: a bridge towards a shared future." It aimed at symbolically rebuilding the bridges that existed between the peoples of Bosnia and Herzegovina. In the Mostar Declaration, ministers noted that "the opening of the Old Bridge of Mostar is a powerful and exemplary signal that symbolizes the ending of ethnic prejudice and highlights the normalization of inter-community relations".

On the day of the inauguration (23 July 2004) a wonderful book of reproductions of engravings and paintings covering the period 1848 to 2004 (256 illustrations on 368 pages!)

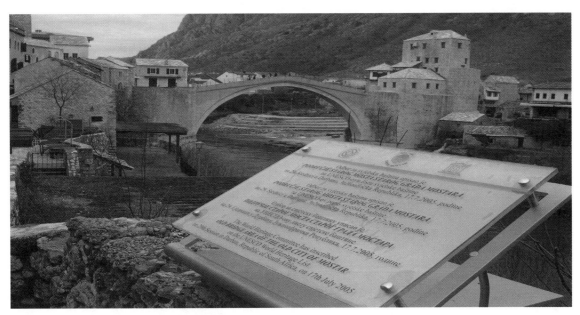

was issued. This superb compilation demonstrates the fascination that hundreds of artists hold for the bridge and the amazing diversity of their talents (see six reproductions on the next page).

Most-ar, Star-i-Most (most = bridge in Slavic, stari = old): the wooden bridge of the fourteenth century gave its name to the town. Mostar (plural Mostari) actually means "keeper of the bridge"; this was the safe place where people had to pay a toll (mostarina) to guards. Gods (Christian and Muslim) are blessed! The bridge was rebuilt and the stitched city was revived, leaving the terrible memories of the twentieth century behind it.

Bridges are no longer demolished in Mostar. The city and its Stari Most could be considered as the new mother of peaceful bridges in the world. Although Mostar is the smallest city in our selection, it is of special significance as it is a cultural melting pot, but also a place where deep divisions and warfare gave birth to symbols of unity and reconciliation. It represents a universal matrix of crossings, a symbol of social links, of outstretched hands. Once communitarian politicians allow it, the city and its bridge will certainly be able to regain their immense global significance.

July 2005, Old Bridge area inscribed on the UNESCO World Heritage List

Hope for a better world
©Alen/Shutterstock

Painting The Stari Most

Čermak František, 1850

Ćiril-Ćiro Raič, 1970

Ivan Ivica Bernadić, 1990

Painting The New Stari Most

Armin Hadžić, Almin Buljko (Illusion), 1993

Sead Vladivić-Guče, 2000

Đenad Bakamović, 2003

VENICE AND ITS
PONTE DI RIALTO

Unlike many cities in the Italian peninsula, Venice has no Roman roots. It was born in the fifth century (according to legend, on 25 March 421) when the Venetians, fleeing from the Barbarian invaders, took refuge on the islands of the lagoon. Its first doge (chief magistrate) was elected from one of the great local aristocratic families in 726. The city owed its prosperity to its location between the Carolingian kingdoms and the Byzantine Empire, and to the dynamism of its elites. Its development followed the pillaging of Constantinople in 1204, which considerably weakened the Byzantine Empire. Its great rival was then Genoa, which would later forge ties with Spain. The decline of the city-state began in the sixteenth century when merchant fleets decided to go to Asia through the Atlantic route, thus avoiding the Mediterranean. But the city managed to regain tourism from the eighteenth century. Apart from its canals and gondolas, Venice's charm revolved around two landmarks, the Piazza San Marco and the Rialto. The city eventually became Italian in 1866 after difficult years which followed the annihilation of the Venetian Republic by Napoleon in 1797.

VENICE AND ITS PONTE DI RIALTO

Venice was a thalassocracy that has for centuries controlled the West's trade with the East. Its most sumptuous era lasted half a century, during which it was the richest European city, and ended with the capture of Constantinople by the Turks and the fall of the Byzantine Empire in 1453. Venice lost territories but it bounced back through its shipbuilding and its banks, concentrated around the Rialto. The city paved its streets, built stone bridges and quays and multiplied its palaces. In 1500 it had more than 100,000 inhabitants. The Grand Canal, "the most beautiful avenue in the world", was surrounded by dozens of late Gothic palaces. The celebrations were magnificent, reflecting the wealth of the city.

The stagnation began in the late sixteenth century. The inauguration of the Rialto Bridge (1591), in fact, coincided with the end of the golden age of the late Renaissance. Until then Venice had lived off its laurels and had maintained some autonomy, but it lost its independence with the invasion of the Napoleonic troops and the sale of the city to the Austrians. It has only 270,000 inhabitants today, with only a quarter of the population located in the historic center, which is less than what it was in the fifteenth century.

Arriving in St. Mark's Square one immediately notices the Byzantine influence in the domes of the Basilica and the indoor mosaics. The reference to Constantinople is obvious. The Venetian Byzantine style dominated the twelfth and thirteenth centuries. The Gothic influence grew from the fourteenth century and is reflected on the facades of the Doge's

Palace and the Ca' d'Oro. In painting the Renaissance began with Giovanni Bellini (1432-1516) and his many Madonnas. It reached its peak from 1532 with an ambitious doge, Andrea Gritti, and a talented planner, Jacopo Sansovino, who was responsible for public buildings in the city as "protomaestro" (architect-in-chief) for forty years (1530-1570).

The great masters of Venetian painting, Titian (1490-1576), Veronese (Verona 1528-Venice 1588) and Tintoretto (1518-1594) painted enormous pieces, monumental compositions with bright colors. "Paradise" in the great hall of the doge's palace is 10 meters high and 24 meters wide, or 240 m²! The frescoes of Jacopo Robusti Tintoretto in the Scuola Grande di San Rocco make an ensemble that took more than twenty years to produce (1564-1587); it is one of the wonders of the art world, equaling and sometimes surpassing the power of Michelangelo's sculptures.

Tintoretto, The miracle of the slave (1548), oil on canvas, Gallerie dell'Accademia, Venice

The architect Antonio da Ponte was equally exceptional. He designed several beautiful rooms for the doge's palace (after the fire of 1577), including the Council Chamber, the palace prisons and the Rialto Bridge. His rival Palladio (1508-1580), the greatest representative of classicism, left a deep and lasting impression on Venice. He inserted his marble churches beautifully into the urban fabric. He was appointed protomaestro at the end of his life. His design for the Rialto Bridge was not accepted but a century later he influenced Andrea Tirali's design of the beautiful three-arched bridge at the mouth of Cannaregio (1688) and two centuries later that of the Pulteney Bridge in Bath (1770).

Tintoretto and Palladio, Two Faces Of The Venetian Renaissance

Venetian Renaissance saw a combination of very different, even opposing, talents. There is nothing in common between the "libertarian" Tintoretto, precursor of Baroque, and the hyper-classic Palladio, admirer of antiquity. These two artists, icons of the sixteenth century, represent two contrasting sides of the Renaissance: improvisation versus discipline, unexpected versus reassuring, revolutionary versus aristocratic.

Born in Venice in 1518, Jacopo Robusti Tintoretto owes his nickname to his father, Battista Robusti, who worked as a dyer. A student of Titian, he is deemed to have overtaken his mentor in the mastery of color and shadows and rendering the material, and is recognized as one of the greatest Venetian artists. The brilliant Tintoretto spent only a few months in Titian's workshop, but he became interested in the mannerist style of artists like Sansovino, Salviati and Schiavone and felt great admiration for the drawing skills of Michelangelo. Tintoretto had a passion for light effects: he made wax statues and experimented with the direction of different light sources before painting them. As a result, some faces reappear in different works from different angles and under different lighting.

Tintoretto disobeyed any convention in 1548 when he painted "The Miracle of Saint Marc Saving the Slave." He abolished gravity. He reversed the established order of reassuring beauty. He introduced excess and anxiety in his staging of sacred history.

He was recognized on 31 May 1564 when he unveiled his project for the Scuola Grande di San Rocco before the dumbfounded members of this brotherhood. Over 23 years he then created the most admired series of fifty paintings crowning the Italian Renaissance. In these works of impressive dimensions, Tintoretto elaborated compositions that were praised by critics as "dynamic and breathtaking spaces and exacerbated twists, dominated by a ghostly and dramatic chiaroscuro". An obsessive painter, he tortured forms, deepened colors and played with gravity. He illuminated Venice with its last fireworks before dusk. With his virtuosity and speed, he implicitly announced the decadence of his city.

A comparison of Tintoretto's "Last Supper" with that of Leonardo da Vinci's better-known rendition of the Last Supper (1498) reveals the evolution of artistic styles throughout the Renaissance. The treatment by da Vinci is very classical: the apostles are arranged around an almost perfect symmetry. In the hands of Tintoretto, the same event becomes dramatically tortured. The human figures are overwritten by the appearance of ghostly beings. The scene takes place in a dark popular tavern where saints' halos produce a strange light that highlights incongruous details. The tone is decidedly Baroque.

La Scuola Grande di San Rocco, ultimate masterpiece of Tintoretto

"In 1548, in Venice, under Tintoretto's brush, before practitioners, art lovers and wits, painting terrified itself. Then began a long evolution, which everywhere replaced the sacred with the profane: cold, sparkling, frosted, the various branches of human activity will arise one after another out of the sweet divine promiscuity. The art is affected: from layers of mist emerges a sumptuous disenchantment, painting." It is in these terms that Jean-Paul Sartre speaks of Tintoretto, the "Sequestered of Venice" in Situations IV. He evokes a piece that has become legendary, The Miracle of the Slave (see reproduction).

Tintoretto and Titian in painting, just as Palladio and Da Ponte in architecture, symbolize through their divergent styles the contradiction between symmetry and irregularity, between order and disorder, which would only be solved in the glowing late Venetian Renaissance, around 1594 (a worthwhile topic for an essay on art history). The artist died on 31 May 1594 in his beloved Venice.

Andrea di Pietro della Gondola, aka Palladio, is on his part the most famous architect of the Italian Renaissance. Born in Padua in 1508, ten years before Tintoretto, he owes his nickname to an angel in an epic poem ("Italy liberated from the Goths!") by his mentor Gian Giorgio Trissino. He made several trips to Rome between 1541 and 1554 and was impressed by the ancient ruins which inspired him throughout his career. He designed numerous villas in the Venetian countryside, with porticoes, columns, capitals and balustrades, always seeking the ideal proportions, symmetry and visual order. In his Four Books of Architecture (1570) he modernized Vitruvius, detailed his theories and presented his projects (including for the Rialto Bridge). A slayer of the Gothic (symbol of an unacceptable disorder), Palladio appears almost as an anti-Tintoretto. He died in 1580 after designing two magnificent churches in Venice, the San Giorgio Maggiore and the Rentore, urban monuments that place him at the pinnacle of the religious architecture of the sixteenth century.

His project for the Rialto was not accepted but it inspired the Poultney Bridge in Bath two centuries later. San Giorgio hosted the final version of "The Last Supper" by Tintoretto, an encounter between a rigorous architect and an unpredictable painter who jointly symbolized all the creative tensions of the Renaissance.

San Giorgio Maggiore, Palladio's masterpiece ©Radu Razvan/Shutterstock

Tintoretto's death in 1594 (he would have been able to cross the Rialto Bridge, unlike Veronese) marks the end of the Renaissance. The Baroque decline of Venice began, dominated by Baldassare Longhena's architecture, author of the magnificent Santa Maria della Salute (1631-1687). But the city remained classic: the Baroque would be mostly Roman. The last great century of Venice was that of Antonio Canal aka Canaletto (1697-1768), "vedudista" (panoramic painter) who painted the city in carefully drawn perspectives and views, using dense and saturated colors. As during the sixteenth century, Venice remained a magnet for painters and architects.

The Rialto ("high bank") remained the economic center of Venice, with the largest market for fish, vegetables and herbs (the Erberia) and many banks. The first bridge over the Grand Canal, a floating pontoon, dates back to the 1170s. In 1264 a wooden bridge was built with a tilting part that allowed the doge's boat to pass through. Throughout the fifteenth century the bridge had to be repaired or rebuilt many times. In 1525 it was decided to build a stone bridge. It took the Venetian Senate thirty years to prepare a tender, which, originally launched in 1554, aroused such opposition that three decades would pass before a decision was taken. The bridge competition has certainly been one of the most important and controversial tenders in the history of the city.

The winning project was designed by Antonio da Ponte (aptly named), who synthesized various proposals made by several architects (including Palladio) that had been rejected by the Senate and the population (divided between "pontisti" and "antipontisti"). A painting by Vittore Carpaccio (see reproduction) shows the

Vittore Carpaccio, The Healing of the Madman (1494), Tempera on canvas, Gallerie dell'Accademia, Venice

wooden bridge, which has the same hump-backed shape as the future stone bridge. In 1588 the Senate adopted the principle of a single arch, while an initial proposal by Vincenzo Scamozzi had included three arches. Da Ponte helped solve the contradiction between the supporters of a multiple-arched bridge, which would have been pedestrian-friendly but too low and too narrow for boats, and those who supported a single arch bridge, convenient for boats but too high for pedestrians if the semi-circular vault was adopted. Antonio da Ponte intelligently chose a relatively low single arch, leaving sufficient space for boats, while providing sloping access for pedestrians.

The Rialto Bridge is 23 meters wide. Its single arch is 29 meters long and rises 7.5 meters above the waters of the Grand Canal. It was built (on a drained terrain) starting from 1588, resting on 12,000 piles (6,000 on each side) and was inaugurated in July 1591, on the eve of an earthquake that left it intact.

The bridge, center of the city

Venice then had between 120,000 and 150,000 inhabitants. Until 1854, when the Bridge of the Academy was built, the Rialto was the only bridge across the Grand Canal. It played an important role in the development of local trade during the seventeenth century and remains one of the major landmarks of the city, the central place where a steady stream of hurried residents and an ever-increasing crowd of admiring visitors constantly converge and diverge.

Canaletto, Ponte di Rialto (1742), oil on canvas, Musée du Louvre

The arches of Rialto support two rows of stalls, twenty-four in total, and three pedestrian crossings (one between the stalls, two with views on the Grand Canal), which make the bridge a surprising urban building and an excellent observatory. The deck is in marble of Istria. The bridge is not huge, it is original, but with the stiffness and heaviness of the Renaissance. It symbolizes well the unity and uniqueness of Venice. Its triangular shape, regular and massive, and the gondolas and vaporetti sliding under its arch, are known worldwide. A century and a half after its construction, Canaletto painted several canvases depicting the Rialto Bridge, including at least two "capricci" reflecting the unsuccessful proposal by Palladio.

Canaletto, Palladio's project for the Rialto Bridge (1744), oil on canvas, The Royal Collection, Windsor Castle

Built a decade earlier, Ponte Delle Guglie, framed by four obelisks on the Cannaregio Canal, is a fine example of a Renaissance bridge with balusters. Venice, a city on water, has hundreds of bridges, some of which are hardly noticeable. The latest on the Grand Canal is signed by the famous sculptor of bridges, Santiago Calatrava. Some consider it too modern for the City of the Doges.

The great historian Fernand Braudel devoted an important research work to Venice, in which he describes the various stages of its evolution. He evokes with love the islands, palaces, canals and bridges (three hundred as in St. Petersburg, he claims) that structure the city. He even warns visitors: "It makes sense to get lost (in Venice), you find the Rialto when you wanted to go to Santa Maria Formosa (...) But you will not be irretrievably lost, a well-known advice saves the innocent :'Go with the flow,' they say, follow the crowd. Finally you will find yourself in front of the Rialto Bridge, maybe the most beautiful bridge in the world, with its three stairs and the double row of shops." At a conference in 1956 on economic life in Venice in the sixteenth century, Braudel stated: "The Renaissance's imprecise boundaries can be identified without much error, especially in Venice, with the sixteenth century as a whole. Its last decades are also its most brilliant fireworks. It is at that time the richest city in the world, the most luxurious."

Braudel's historical analysis is in sharp contrast to that of Georg Simmel, whose negative views of Venice portrayed the city as nothing but artificial decor. The psycho-geographer wrote in 1907: "Venice is the city of artifice. Even the bridge here loses its force. It usually manages to make indistinct what separates and what unites two points of space. This dual function here tends to fade, the streets slide without interruption on countless bridges. The monotony of all Venetian rhythms brings us close to a dream, in which we have only to deal with the appearance of things." According to Simmel, Venice suffers from the comparison with Rome, a city of unity and harmony in diversity, and with Florence, where art and nature go hand-in-hand.

The bridge, the night, the city…©Lele Orpo

Like Simmel, Michel Ragon, the architectural historian, emphasizes the artificiality and opera stage quality of this pedestrian city. For him, "Venice is the most authentic of all cities because it is the most artificial (...) It is a large ship moored to piles driven into the mud." A city that combines a medieval fabric with Byzantine influences, where the Renaissance has remained discreet, respecting a unique Gothic heritage. A city bridging two cultures, between East and West, a mixed and harmonious city like its big sister Istanbul.

The Grand Canal towards la Salute ©Tungtopgun/ Shutterstock

Philippe Sollers, on the other hand, is an educated fan of Venice. In his *Love Dictionary of Venice* he describes a city "protected by its mask, a chessboard, a web of paths that lead nowhere and are sufficient in themselves." The dandy writer finds in Venice an emotion, a spiritual breath, an enigma that only insiders (and certainly not "Japanese tourists furiously photographing paintings of Titian in order not to see them!") can pretend to solve. And he painstakingly analyzes the texts of dozens of writers who have not really understood the soul of the city, from Thomas Mann to Marcel Proust and Jean-Paul Sartre. In 1957 Sartre published in *Les Temps Modernes* an admiring article titled "The Sequestered of Venice" on Tintoretto, an artist who was rejected (in 1548) and worshiped (in 1564), ignoring conventions, obsessive and worried, talented, prolific and completely Venetian.

Venice floods periodically; in November 2008 water levels reached 156 centimeters on the Piazza San Marco, the lowest point of the city.

Acqua Alta over St Marc square ©Palmenpep/ Shutterstock

"Acqua alta" is a tradition that constantly threatens the city. The authorities have, therefore, decided to build removable and retractable gates and dykes to isolate the lagoon from the sea at high tide. This is the controversial and on-going mammoth project MOSE (Modulo Sperimentale Elettromeccanico) costing ten billion euro, which was probably necessary given that the city was slowly sinking into the lagoon. In addition, the city is also flooded by 22 million tourists every year (a world record of tourists per capita: 400/1). Its successive mayors are struggling to maintain the urban heritage and to contain the tourist tide.

My friend Marcello Balbo, Professor of Architecture at the University of Venice, expresses a sentiment shared by many Venetians: "By connecting the banks of the Grand Canal, which is the heart of Venice, the Rialto Bridge has always been with the Piazza San Marco, one of the two poles of the city. Despite the vendors selling masks and plastic gondolas and crowds of tourists who stop to take pictures, the Rialto Bridge

The Grand Canal in summer
©EMprize/Shutterstock

is a milestone of the city. With the market on one side and a square where people meet to share a Spriz, the typical Venetian aperitif, on the other, the bridge constitutes in the collective imagination one of the last Venetian defenses against the irresistible progress of mass tourism. On the deck local residents sometimes shout at those who do not understand that they must respect an absolutely amazing and unique urban environment."

Venice cannot be allowed to drown in sweet melancholy; it cannot vanish in a romantic haze and become a ghost town. Venice, the most original city in the world, must survive at any cost.

One of many contemporary paintings ©Studio37/Shutterstock

PARIS AND ITS PONT-NEUF

As a capital city, Paris was born during the reign of Philippe-Auguste (1180-1223) who had the main roads paved and who built a wall around the existing town, five kilometers in circumference, pierced with ten gates. Paris had 200,000 inhabitants in the thirteenth century and was the largest city in Europe. The city launched the Gothic style, built the Sainte-Chapelle (1243-1248) and (almost) completed the construction of Notre-Dame. It experienced a long depression due to the Hundred Years War (1337-1453), and then resumed its rise during the reign of Louis XI (1461-1483) around two axes crossing the Ile de la Cité (Petit-Pont to Pont Notre-Dame, Pont Saint-Michel to Pont au Change, all four inhabited bridges). The heart of continental Europe, Paris would remain the largest city of the continent for five centuries. It would be overtaken by London towards 1760; by then both cities had populations of around 600,000. With a stable population of 11 million for the agglomeration, Paris is now the largest city in Western Europe, before London. Both cities have been and remain the great rivals of old Europe.

PARIS AND ITS PONT-NEUF

The city of Paris was established like many others at the intersection of a road and a river. The city today hosts 36 bridges on the Seine (excluding those on the ring road). All these bridges are remarkable, functional and sober, well entrenched in an urban landscape that they embellish.

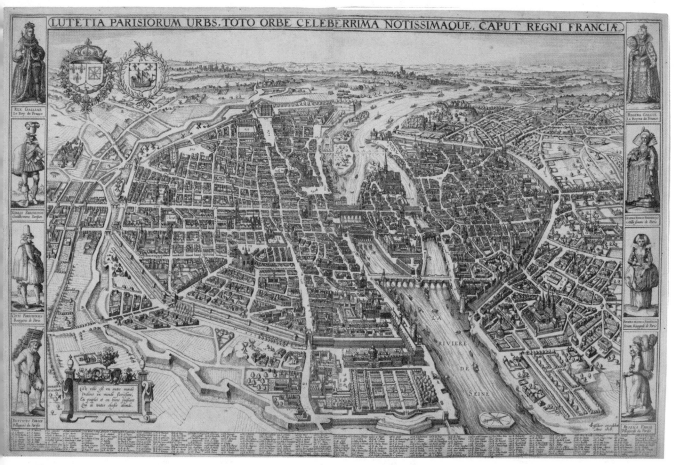

Claes Jansz Visscher, Map of Paris, engraving (1618) ©BHVP/Roger-Viollet

One must begin to discover Paris by the Pont-Neuf, powerful and open to the Seine and its quays, the oldest bridge in the city, which celebrated its four hundredth anniversary in 2007. Then continue with the Alexandre III Bridge, dedicated to Franco-Russian friendship, which is only a century old but whose allegorical decoration and impressive towers mark the urban space and attract many visitors. And between the two, stop at the Pont des Arts, as light as a feather, where you can admire the Louvre, the Institute, the Ile de la Cité and the Pont Royal. Further west, at the foot of the Eiffel Tower, the Bir Hakeim Bridge (1905), with its two floors, is an excellent spot for post-modern films and fashion photography. Poets have well perceived the intimate relationship between the Tower and the bridges, as Guillaume Apollinaire suggests in an evocative verse: "Shepherdess O Eiffel Tower the flock of bridges bleats this morning ..." This brings us to Porto, Portugal, where a piece of what would soon become the Eiffel Tower gave birth to the great Maria Pia and Dom Luis bridges over the Douro. And to Toulouse which also has, as head of the herd, a beautiful Pont-Neuf of the Renaissance (1632) across the Garonne, and next to which I had the luck to come into the world.

The first Parisian bridges were Roman. They were made of wooden decks on stone piers: two bridges linking the Ile de la Cité to the left bank (Petit-Pont) and right bank (Grand-Pont), the only Parisian bridges until the fourteenth century, which were repeatedly rebuilt. The first bridge made entirely of stone was the Pont Notre-Dame (on the site of the Grand-Pont and inaugurated in 1514), an inhabited bridge, simple but impressive, with 68 identical houses of 4x8 metres, with two or three floors, and luxury shops. A place of necessary crossing, the bridge was ideal for trade. It was richly decorated and sometimes was adorned with temporary ornaments, especially when kings like Henry II (1549) and Louis XIV (1660) were passing over it. The Pont Notre-Dame was the only monumental public space in Paris. It was taken as a model for the Pont Marie, Pont au Change and Pont Saint-Michel. But under pressure from the Encyclopedists (also hygienists), a royal decree in 1786 ordered the destruction of all houses on Parisian bridges. At the time of the French revolution there were only a few huts on the Pont Saint-Michel, which disappeared between 1807 and 1811. The owners were compensated, and the bridge lost its function as a place where people could live and work. In London the magnificent Old London Bridge suffered the same fate. The Pont Notre-Dame was rebuilt in 1853, without any particular charm.

The Pont des Arts (in the foreground) and the Pont-Neuf ©Elena Elisseeva/ Shutterstock

The Pont-Neuf, on the other hand, marked the end of the Middle Ages. Ordered by Henri III, designed by Baptiste Androuet du Cerceau and Pierre des Illes and built by François Petit and Guillaume Marchant, its first stone was laid by the king and his mother, Catherine de Medici (the Lady of Chenonceau), on 31 May 1578. Sealed silver coins of the year were placed under the stone for good luck. By royal decree, the bridge was funded by the Generalities of Paris, Champagne, Normandy and Picardy, and by the Treasury (through a tax on wine). The bridge was inaugurated by Henri IV in 1607 (its construction having been interrupted from 1589 to 1598 because of repeated conflicts between Catholics and Protestants). Coming to Paris in 1594 after the nightmare of the religious wars, including the massacre of Saint-Bartholomew from which the Seine had carted the corpses, the king wanted to "make the city beautiful,

Theodor Hoffbauer, Panoramic view of Paris in 1588 with the Pont-Neuf under construction (1890) ©Musée Carnavalet/ Roger-Viollet

calm and full of all possible conveniences and ornaments, complete the Pont-Neuf and restore public fountains and make a world of this city and a miracle of the world". He also hoped that "both sides of my good city of Paris, my capital, be treated as twin sisters." A contemporary of the Pont-Neuf, the most beautiful square in Paris, the Place Royale (now Place des Vosges), was designed by Henri IV and Sully with the same urban intention: to develop an area offered to the public to walk, stroll and socialize. Henri IV was assassinated in 1610 by a lunatic extremist, Ravaillac, but his wishes were fulfilled.

Located at the western (downstream) tip of the Ile de la Cité on which it rests, the bridge is "new" in that it hosts no houses. It is very wide and has sidewalks. An elegant building housing the Samaritan pump (1665) was later added. Its decor of carved masks, its parapet modeled as an overlooking path and its cornice all made this gazebo a favorite place to observe both those wandering on it and the surrounding city. Henry IV not only inaugurated the Pont-Neuf but he could also be credited with giving birth to the spectacular city of Paris. Decades behind Italy, Paris fully entered

the Renaissance era during his time. On this bridge, there was not a single house but wonderful perspectives. It is 239 meters long (it crosses the widest section of the Seine), with seven arches over the Grand Arm of the Seine, originally semicircular (modified in 1850 and replaced by basket handles) and five arches over the Small Arm, the Ile de la Cité splitting the deck into two parts. The arches have been restored many times and were completely renovated between 1990 and 2007.

The Pont-Neuf surrounding the Western end of the Cité Island ©Cardaf/Shutterstock

The success of the Pont-Neuf was immediate. Stalls were opened on its half-moons, jugglers and booksellers invaded its sidewalks. Place Dauphine was developed and the bronze statue of the Vert Galant (another name for Henri IV) was erected on the island after his death, near the center of the bridge and facing it. This was the first equestrian statue in Paris. Technically the Pont-Neuf does not innovate much (it is a very massive and majestic monument but with classic masonry arches). Socially it is a lively public space that heralded the start of a real urban policy for Paris. The capital by then had 400,000 inhabitants. The city was to resume its rise after the religious wars, and the Pont-Neuf quickly became a symbol of strength. This has given rise to commonly-used similes in the French language, such as "strong as the Pont-Neuf" or "solid as the Pont-Neuf". The wisdom of nations often refers to bridges (to burn bridges, finish under the bridge, make a bridge of gold, don't cross your bridges before you come to them ...) in different languages.

The Pont-Neuf across the small arm of the Seine

The Pont-Neuf with its Place Dauphine extension was the most popular and lively place in Paris, where provincials arriving in the capital were first brought by their hosts. Thieves and pickpockets, "officers of the Pont-Neuf" or "courtiers of the bronze horse," were there in large numbers.

In his novel Captain Fracasse published in 1863, Théophile Gautier devotes an entire chapter to the Pont-Neuf. The action takes place during the reign of Louis XIII in 1635. Sigognac (Fracasse) lives in a hotel on Rue Dauphine. Théophile Gautier writes: "The Pont-Neuf was to Paris what the Sacred Way is to Rome, the passing, appointments and peripatetic gallery of novelists, flycatchers, poets, swindlers, pickpockets, entertainers, courtesans, gentlemen, citizens, soldiers, and people of all status. Where passersby could enjoy one of the most beautiful sights of the universe because its panorama did not have then - and has not yet - any rival in the world." T. Gautier adds: "The Pont-Neuf did not host, as did the Pont au Change and the Pont Saint-Michel, two rows of tall houses. The great king (Henry IV) who had built it did not want stunted and gloomy buildings to hide the view of the magnificent palace where our kings reside."

Jean-Baptiste Raguenet, La joute des mariniers entre le Pont Notre-Dame et le Pont au Change, oil on canvas (1756) ©Musée Carnavalet/ Roger-Viollet

T. Gautier was inspired by Edouard Fournier, author of History of the Pont-Neuf in 1862. But he emphasizes that it is mostly "the infinite number of people, the influx of populace, the spectacle of the street" which impressed the provincial newcomer hurrying up to visit this mythical spot in the capital. And he carefully describes "the originals of the Pont-Neuf, extravagant and heterogeneous figures" that seem to be permanently living there. We find here, from the pen of a seasoned traveller (see his notes on Granada and Constantinople), a vivid description of the impact of the Pont-Neuf on seventeenth century Paris. Both an observatory and a public space, the Pont-Neuf then became the real center of the city.

The Pont-Neuf inspired many artists in the nineteenth century, starting with the pre-Impressionist William Turner who painted the bridge many times. "The Pont-Neuf and the Vert Galant" (1833) is perhaps one of his most remarkable pieces. The Impressionists and Post-Impressionists were passionate for bridges, Alfred Sisley for the "Footbridge in Argenteuil" (1872), Gustave Caillebotte for the "Bridge of Europe" near Gare Saint-Lazare (1876), Vincent Van Gogh for the "Langlois Bridge in Arles" (1888), Claude Monet for the "Waterloo Bridge" (1903). Auguste Renoir painted the bustling city beautifully in his superb back-lit "Pont-Neuf" (1872).

Camille Pissarro devoted one of his last paintings to "The Pont-Neuf on a winter morning" (1902) and the young Picasso produced a cubist "Pont-Neuf" (1911). Hundreds of paintings and thousands of photos, including a dreamy, misty one by Cartier-Bresson (1951), express this shared fascination for a public space with mysterious qualities.

The Pont-Neuf was not just the subject of many paintings, but itself became a piece of art in 1963 when the Greek artist Nonda built a Trojan horse under the bridge and settled there, then in 1985 when Christo wrapped it in a huge beige canvas and

"One of the most beautiful urban backlit views of all times", Auguste Renoir, Le Pont-Neuf (1872), oil on canvas, National Gallery of Art, Ailsa Mellon Bruce Collection, Washington D.C.

in 1994 when Kenzo covered it with begonias. Its 384 humorous carved stone masks attract the fleeting attention of riverboat passengers. Nearby the Place Dauphine forms a calm triangle in the Ile de la Cité, offering weary tourists a break, as does the Vert-Galant square. Downstream, the Pont des Arts (rebuilt in 1983) has recently become the privileged domain of lovers from all nationalities, who have been placing thousands of padlocks on its railings to "lock" their union.

The seventeenth century saw the construction or reconstruction of several stone bridges up to the Pont Royal (1689), which faces the Pont-Neuf and bounds, with the quays, an aquatic area worthy of ancient amphitheaters, which could host grandiose celebrations. The Pont-Neuf was partially reconstructed and consolidated in the nineteenth century under Napoleon III. It allowed the left bank, the area of universities, to catch up with the right bank, the area of production and trade.

The Pont des Arts with the Institute dome at the back ©Jozef Sedmak/Shutterstock

The bridge that could claim to challenge the Pont-Neuf as the most beautiful in Paris is not the Pont Marie (despite the opinion of Michel Serres), but rather the Alexandre III Bridge, opened in April 1900 as the jewel of the Universal Exposition. This bridge, the first stone of which was laid by Tsar Nicolas II four years earlier, sealed the alliance between France and Russia.

Alexander III Bridge with the Invalides Dome at the back
©ErickN/Shutterstock

It is the work of a brilliant civil engineer, Jean Résal. It is a technical feat owing to its flattened vault of 107 meters in cast steel (permitted by huge oblique foundations on each side), and an architectural success by the exuberance of its decoration. Festooned with lamp posts, railings, piers, cuffs, masks, garlands and four towers of 17 meters at its abutments, the bridge highlights the elegance of the single arch that supports the deck. The keystones found upstream represent the arms of Paris and the Seine nymphs, and those downstream illustrate the arms of Russia and the nymphs of the Neva. Forty meters wide, the bridge unifies the buildings on both sides of the Seine and creates a new axis between the Invalides and the Champs-Elysées, and between the Grand and Petit Palais. Criticized at the time by functionalists (Auguste Perret, predominantly) for its "superfluous" decoration and "hybrid" character, the Alexandre III Bridge, recently restored, is a marvel. Though it was inaugurated by the last tsar, it is, in fact, an ode to the triumph of the Republic. However, in the Parisian rating, it ranks second, after the Pont-Neuf, which has more history, and is more representative of life in the capital. Beauty is not just a matter of aesthetics; it is also made of history, a condensation of the past and of people's memories.

Other bridges in Paris are, of course, worth mentioning. Among these is the Pont de la Concorde designed by Jean-Rodolphe Perronet. This discreet but innovative bridge was a milestone in building techniques. It opened the era of scientific computing with lightweight structures. But it also marked the swan song of the masonry bridges while the metal was emerging in the U.K. (the Pont des Arts, partly metallic, would be inaugurated in 1802). The Concorde Bridge, completed in 1791, did not bear the name of Louis XV as envisioned before the French Revolution.

JEAN-RODOLPHE PERRONET, ENGINEER OF THE ENLIGHTENMENT

Jean-Rodolphe Perronet

The Corps des Ponts et Chaussées (Bridges and Roads Corps) was established by Colbert in the late seventeenth century under the authority of the Comptroller General of Finance to maintain the bridges, roads and other transport infrastructure of the kingdom. An engineer was assigned to every Generality. Fernand Braudel notes: "With the roads created in the eighteenth century by the admirable engineers of Ponts et Chaussées, there was an important increase in the French domestic market." In 1789 there would be 40,000 kilometers of roads and 1,000 kilometers of canals, which marked the beginning of a transport revolution and the unification of the French national territory.

J.R. Perronet was born in Suresnes, near Paris, on 25 October 1708. He studied with the Sieur de Beausire, the city architect of Paris, from 1725. In 1736 he was hired as an assistant engineer at the Generality of Alençon. His job was to survey, inspect and design local roads and to build a bridge over the Mesme, which he did successfully. His reliability and efficiency were noticed in the capital.

Daniel Charles Trudaine, Intendant of Finances, created an Office of Designers in 1744 to draw up all the plans of the country's roads, but also to train engineers. On 14 February 1747 (the date commonly cited as the date of birth of the Ecole des Ponts et Chaussées) Perronet was appointed Director of this Office and set up a training program on the basis of his practical experience in Alençon. Trudaine also created the Assembly of Ponts et Chaussées and appointed Perronet as the secretary of this new body. Starting in the late 1740s, engineering candidates flocked to the new school. They studied algebra, geometry, mechanics, hydraulics, and structures. The School of Bridges and Roads itself gradually expanded into the Marais (in Hotel Guénégaud) and was officially sanctioned by Jacques Turgot in 1775. In 1750 Perronet was appointed Inspector General of Bridges and Roads and in 1763 became the "First Engineer" (in charge of all public works) and made a nobleman. But he continued to fully run the school that accepted foreign students on recommendation from 1786. In 1791 the French Revolution endorsed the role of the School, which became national, and established a competitive selection process. The indefatigable Perronet directed the school until his death on 6 Ventôse An II (24 February 1794). He had by then trained hundreds of engineers.

Before Perronet's time, most bridges were designed by architects. Based on his experience, Perronet submitted two memoirs to the Academy of Sciences (in 1773 and 1777) regarding the arches of bridges. He introduced a theoretical revolution aimed at reducing the thickness of the piers and lowering the vaults. Perronet expressed some reluctance about the use of iron for the construction of arches, without formally rejecting the new material.

In fact Perronet, when he was appointed First Engineer at 55 years of age, had little practical experience in bridge building. In 1763 he modified the bridge of Mantes by reducing its arches and tested the simultaneous construction of arches to balance horizontal thrust. He then began his career as a builder. He designed the bridge of Nogent-sur-Seine and reconstructed the wooden bridge of Neuilly in 1768. This latter bridge revolutionized the ratio of thickness of piers to the opening of (five) arches, previously set to a fifth and here passing to a tenth (13 feet against 120). The piers were very thin and the deck could be flattened, thanks to low vaults designed as basket handles. The project was also part of a deliberate urban plan, linking Neuilly to the Champs-Elysees through to the future Place de l'Etoile. The delicate removal of the scaffolding began on 14 August 1772 and ended in great pomp, in the presence of King Louis XV, on 22 September. It was celebrated in a painting by Hubert Robert, and was much admired, despite some criticism from traditionalist members of the Corps des Ponts et Chaussées. It was opened to traffic on 24 October 1773.

Entrance of the Hotel de Fleury, where the National School of Ponts et Chaussées was located until 2008.

At that time Perronet started designing the Pont de la Concorde, also with five arches, from 78 to 96 feet wide. Construction began in 1787 after another controversy in the Assembly des Ponts et Chaussées on the thickness of the piers and on the opening and lowering of the central arch, which was deemed excessive. Enlarged between 1929 and 1931, the Pont de la Concorde is not particularly spectacular but it represents the apotheosis of the stone masonry technique. Perronet would monitor the construction process from the nearby Moreau pavilion where he resided, to the west of square Louis XV (d. 1774), the future Concorde Square. Built during the French Revolution, the bridge was inaugurated in November 1791.

Perronet also proposed a bridge across the Neva in Saint-Petersburg, with a central drawbridge, which could withstand the impact of ice blocks, but that project was unfortunately not realized. He built other modest bridges, developed the technique of foundation in cofferdams and continued his research on the art of bridge-building until the end of his life. In his will, he bequeathed his library and models to the students of his beloved Civil Engineering School.

In 1997, on the occasion of its 250th anniversary, the National School of Ponts et Chaussées began a partial move to Champs-sur-Marne, southeast of Paris. In 2008 it finally left the Hotel de Fleury (where it had been located since 1845) and the center of Paris altogether. It is considered by the American Society of Civil Engineers and by its own graduates as the oldest engineering school in the world. However, the design of roads and bridges now represents only a small component of its vast curriculum.

Another bridge worth mentioning is the bridge of Bir Hakeim, inaugurated in 1905 and combining a road crossing and a metro viaduct. This two-story structure designed by architect Formigé actually consists of two bridges linking the banks to the Ile des Cygnes (Island of Swans). The Art Nouveau columns supporting the upper deck and framing the central promenade provide the most striking effect, especially at sunset. The upper crossing for the metro, a functional ornament, doubles the lower deck with great elegance. The bridge is decorated with classic and impressive bronze nymphs placed at the forefront of its arches. The sudden entry into the Passy metro station, between two buildings with rotundas topped by domes, is always too quick, an emotional thrill, as inexplicable as it is repetitive, played out at the feet of Gustave Eiffel's shepherdess.

The Bir-Hakeim Bridge towards Passy.

Finally, we should mention the Pont Mirabeau, where Résal made his debuts between 1893 and 1896 before designing the Alexandre III Bridge, because this bridge has become the subject of one of the most beautiful poems of French literature. It is a metal structure of two articulated half-bridges, unfortunately now facing an architectural horror called Front de Seine. It could be compared with the contemporary Trinity Bridge built in 1897 by Batignolles in Saint-Petersburg. Under the Pont Mirabeau, as stated by G. Apollinaire, "the Seine still flows, together with our romances..."

In 2012 the great Parisian singer Juliette Greco paid tribute to her city's bridges in a disk titled "Ça se traverse et c'est beau" (going across something beautiful, an analogy between bridges and human life), deservedly praised by critics. The bridges of Paris, a source of inspiration for generations of artists, certainly have "a soul, which is attached to our soul and force it to love." They respond positively to the famous question that Alphonse de Lamartine asked about the possible soul of inanimate objects that somehow spread an inexplicable animism.

Paris today is still considered by its inhabitants, even those who have never travelled abroad, to be the most beautiful city in the world. Tourists confirm that point of view and have made Paris the most visited city of the planet. But downtown Paris (within its 32 kilometer peripheral ring road) represents only 20% of the greater Paris agglomeration, or 2.2 million people within an area of 105 km², a density higher than that of most Western capitals.

The Seine River, eastern view from Notre-Dame ©Crok Photograph/Shutterstock

Since the 1960s Paris has become gentrified, and a million people have migrated to the suburbs where land and housing are more affordable. The so-called unhealthy flats were eliminated and people were displaced by the direct effect of the real estate market. Museums and restaurants have experienced a new vitality and architectural heritage has been carefully restored and enhanced. Large projects have found their place in the urban space. According to the opinion of visitors, as well as residents, the most successful include the Centre Pompidou, the Louvre Pyramid, the Institute of the Arab World, the Grande Arche de la Défense, and the Orsay Museum. Opinions are more divided on other recent creations, such as the Bastille Opera, the Ministry of Finance or the Bibliothèque Nationale de France. While almost all tourists still begin their journey at the Eiffel Tower and Notre Dame, and stop at different metro stations of line 1 (including the Louvre), they are increasingly likely to venture into the streets of the Marais, Saint Germain and Montmartre, which carry a certain aroma of the old Paris, that of Doisneau and artists from around the world. This is a largely an artificial feeling since only the decor remains, but it suffices for the casual visitor.

Whereas the cultural prestige of the city faces international competition, its architectural cachet remains intact and its urban landscape, especially around the Seine and its quays and bridges, always amazes even the most jaded globetrotters. More prosaically Paris remains a benchmark for public transport, with the densest system of underground metro, regional express network (RER) and railways in the world. Foreigners are not really fond of the Paris airports but they appreciate being able to move easily in a homogeneous city of human scale, where streets and avenues logically structure the urban fabric, where public space is frequented by a cosmopolitan crowd and where everyone is free to move according to his or her interests, desires, relationships or simply by chance.

The Seine and Alexander III Bridge, seen from the Eiffel Tower ©Georgios Alexandris/ Shutterstock

The Parisian Bridges have been represented on many stamps. Among the finest, some celebrate conferences or events, such as the packing of the Pont-Neuf which caused some controversies in 1985
©L'Adresse, Musée de La Poste, Paris

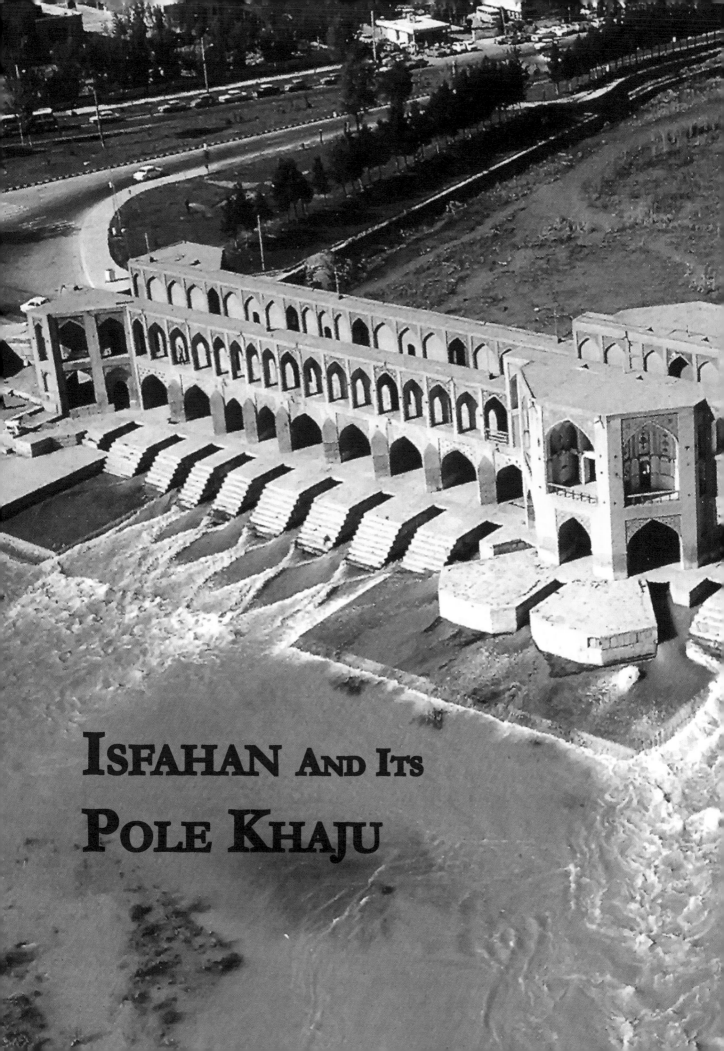

ISFAHAN AND ITS POLE KHAJU

Isfahan, the Pearl of Iran, had moments of glory and vicissitudes. The brilliant capital of Persia in the seventeenth century, the city possesses many wonderful jewels of Islamic architecture, including two bridges without equal in the world.

ISFAHAN AND ITS POLE KHAJU

In 1387 Tamerlane took Isfahan and cut off 70,000 heads. Coming from Samarkand, and a descendant of the Mongols, Tamerlane had no mercy for his co-religionists. In 1502 the Safavids (religious order founded in Ardabil around 1300) came to power in Iran and Ismail was crowned Shah (king) in Tabriz. The Safavids would reign for 250 years and impose Shiaism as the state religion. But in 1514, the Safavids were defeated by the Ottomans in Tchaldiran near Tabriz, and Suleiman the Magnificent took Baghdad in 1534. From the fourteenth to the sixteenth century, Persia was in trouble. Its interface position between East and West, between Central Asia and the Islamic world, certainly allowed her to absorb rich cultures and influences, but it presented obvious risks of aggression when the internal structure of the state was weak. Under pressure from the Ottomans, the Persian capital was transferred to Qazvin (north-west of Tehran) in 1548. Qazvin was a site of architectural and urban innovation foreshadowing Isfahan.

Khaju Bridge, morning
tranquility

With the support of the powerful governor of Mashhad (capital of Shia Muslims in the east of the country) the young prince Abbas overthrew his father in 1587. He was not yet seventeen. He would reign until 1629 and would be the greatest monarch of Persian history. He would reform the administration, advocate religious tolerance and transfer the capital to Isfahan, an oasis in the arid center of the Iranian plateau, 1600 meters above sea level. Around its new Meidan (Grand Place, now Imam square) the city became the "Pearl of Islam."

SHAH ABBAS THE GREAT, VISIONARY URBAN PLANNER

Throughout the sixteenth century Safavid power was threatened by the expanding Ottoman Empire. In 1585 Tabriz fell into Ottoman hands. The Eastern provinces reacted and de facto dismissed the weak Shah Muhammad Khudabanda. The governor of Mashhad appointed in his place young prince Abbas and entered Qazvin. The Shah did not resist and transmitted the reins of power to his son in October 1587.

Abbas the First was not yet 17 years old but he would quickly establish himself as an enlightened and effective monarch. In 1590 he concluded a truce with the Ottomans to gain time to rebuild his army. He then retrieved one by one the lost territories, including Khorasan (Herat), Azerbaijan, Bahrain, Armenia, Georgia, Kurdistan and Iraq. But his greatest successes would be obtained within his home country. After transferring the capital of the Safavid Empire to Isfahan, he made the city the "Pearl of Islam". He vigorously centralized the administration, neutralized influential groups (including Turkmen emirs), created an army on the model of the Ottoman Janissaries, and ensured the loyalty of the many Christians of Caucasian origin (70,000 Armenians, 100,000 Georgians). Isfahan became in a few years one of the largest cities in the world and, along with its rival Istanbul, the most beautiful of the Islamic cities. Shah Abbas attracted artisans and artists of all religions and gave them autonomy and protection. His royal factories exported to the West, Russia and India. He unified the currency, reformed taxation and property rights and improved the road network. He created a port (Bandar Abbas) on the Strait of Hormuz, after expelling the Portuguese in 1622, where he controlled the maritime trade in the Gulf. At the time of his death in 1629 Persia was a modern empire at its economic and political peak.

The heart of Isfahan, designed by Shah Abbas the Great

Shah Abbas moved the capital to Isfahan to make it more central and less exposed to external aggressions. During the eleventh and twelfth centuries the city had been the capital of the Seljuks (builders of the Friday Mosque in 1072). From an architectural standpoint Shah Abbas the Great is best known for having created the huge Royal Square, the Meidan, and the buildings that surround it. This beautiful rectangular square, known as the "pattern of the world" of eight hectares (512x160 meters) was built between 1590 and 1595, originally for ceremonial purposes. It was designed by Sheikh Bahai, a Syrian theologian and architect. In 1602 two floors of (180) shops were added, making the Meidan an extension of the bazaar and the shopping core of the city, a place of life and entertainment, convertible into a sports-pitch (polo) or parade field, when required, and illuminated at night by thousands of lanterns. Portals of entry consisting of four magnificent buildings overlook the square: in the north gate of the bazaar, an iwan (vaulted hall opening onto a courtyard or square) which connects the new town to the old; in the west Ali Qapu palace (or Ali's gate pavilion), an observatory with three levels (inspired by Qazvin) and an elevated terrace, which was also the gateway to the royal palace and its gardens; in the east the Sheikh Lutfallah mosque built between 1603 and 1619, a fabulous jewel by architect Muhammad Reza, whose dome is beautifully decorated with ceramics, floral arabesques and resplendent calligraphy, both outside and inside, a very original mosque without a minaret or courtyard; and finally in the south the great Shah or Imam mosque oriented at 45 degrees from the axis of the Meidan to face Mecca. This monumental mosque (150x130 meters) designed by architect Ali Akbar Isfahani, includes a rectangular inner courtyard with arcades on two levels and four imposing iwans with a central pool, two madrasas (Islamic schools), several side rooms for prayer and four minarets. Its entrance portal or pishtak is surmounted with niches containing complex stalactites decorated with magnificent mosaics. Its huge turquoise dome (comparable to the mausoleum of Tamerlane in Samarkand) is 38 meters (inner ceiling) and 52 meters high (outer surface, the dome is double-layered); it has long been the highest point of Isfahan. The Imam Mosque, Isfahan's symbolic building, was built between 1612 and 1630.

Indeed the action of Shah Abbas was not limited to providing his capital city with a new center and prestigious monuments. It consisted also in re-planning the city, for example, by moving some functions to the south, encouraging traders to relocate their activities by creating new roads and bridges, such as the north-south Chahar Bag avenue (two kilometers) and its gardens, and the Sio Seh Bridge. The monarch was in fact a real planner who re-modeled Isfahan and made it one of the most beautiful cities in the world. Four hundred years later his genius still marks the city that remains a jewel of Islamic architecture and the most attractive city in Iran. Shah Abbas who, according to historians (including Eskandar Monchi, author of a History of the Safavids) "enjoyed wine and the company of women" is without a doubt the founder of modern Iran.

Corridor of Lotfallah Mosque

But Shah Abbas the Great did not prepare his succession. His successor, his grandson Safi I (1629-1642), was a paranoid alcoholic whose weakness encouraged the Ottomans to re-capture Baghdad in 1638. They would keep the city until the First World War. Fortunately, Safi's son was of a very different caliber. Under the name of Shah Abbas II, he reigned from 1642 to 1666, fighting corruption, improving legislation, encouraging trade with India and the West, and annexing the Afghan province of Kandahar in 1648 at the expense of the Mughals, an error that would prove fatal 74 years later. At this time northern India enjoyed the prosperous period of the Mughals (from Akbar, 1542-1605) who tried to promote a tolerant co-existence between Islam and Hinduism. The relations between the two countries were strong: for example, in 1631 the Mughal emperor Shah Jahan called in Persian architects to build the Taj Mahal in Agra.

The Golden Age of Isfahan coincided with the seventeenth century. It was also, as we shall see, the golden age of Amsterdam. Armenian merchants connected the two cities. This golden age spanned over 124 years, from 1598 to 1722, with a gradual decline from 1660.

Khaju Bridge at dusk

It began with the selection of Isfahan as the capital of Iran and ended painfully during the siege of the city by Afghan tribes (April-October 1722).

The Safavid dynasty thus experienced two great kings, Shah Abbas the First and his great-grandson Shah Abbas II, who were both visionary builders. They first liberated Persia from the Arabs, Turks and Mongols, and planned a city for 300,000 inhabitants. The role and influence of Shah Abbas the Great are comparable to those of Peter the Great a century later in St. Petersburg: in both cases, the monarch decided to create a new capital and make it one of the most beautiful cities in the world, and participated directly in town planning and architectural design.

Morning meditation on
Sio-Seh Bridge

The great-grandson of Shah Abbas the Great restored several monuments and protected painters and artists. He permitted the Armenians to build the Vank cathedral in the new Jolfa, on the southern shore of Zayandeh-Rud. Isfahan became the first Armenian city in the world after the exodus of Armenians from Jolfa and other cities of Armenia in 1605. Armenians controlled the trade, under the Shah's protection.

The two kings ordered the building of beautiful bridges across the Zayandeh River, exceptional bridges aimed from the outset not only to facilitate the crossing of the river but also to boost economic and social life. A promoter of the Iranian Renaissance, Shah Abbas the Great built the largest bridge, the Sio-Seh Pole, between 1602 and 1608. This bridge, which is 295 meters long and 14 meters wide, is sometimes called Allahverdi Khan, after the Georgian general-architect, and adviser to the king, who planned it. It comprises 33 arches, thus its name Sio-Seh (33), with regular spans of 5.6 meters. It is a living bridge on two levels, with two passages surrounding a sheltered route for the crossing of caravans, and delicate arches. It is the true heart of the city because it prolongs the Chahar Bagh ("Four Gardens") Avenue and connects it to the new center south of the city (Royal Garden of Hezar Djerib or Thousand Acres). Regarding that bridge the Roman scholar and traveler Pietro Della Valle, who spent five years in Isfahan from 1617 to 1622, wrote: "On the river, a bridge was built in bricks, much wider than those of Rome, and three or four times longer than the longest of ours. It has an extraordinary form, with porticoes and very high galleries, instead of parapets. These galleries serve as walkways above and below, some are covered and others open (...) There is nothing more delicious in summer, because of the shadow,

Sio-Seh Pole, 33-arched
bridge (1608)

the freshness and the murmur of water, and in order to increase the sound and the
beauty, they made a bed of close-knit stones, with a little slope, which forms a waterfall
that charms both the sight and the ears."

The bridge-dam built downstream fifty years later, around 1650, by Shah Abbas
II is the Pole Khaju. It is shorter (133 meters) and more narrow (12 meters) but also
includes two levels of terraces on the river. If it closes its gates, which act as locks, it
becomes a dam capable of supplying the city with water and Zayandeh-Rud becomes
a lake, not far from the royal palace.

It is an imposing semi-habitable bridge having at its center a royal octagonal pavilion
joining two pentagons (the parlor of the Princes), a twenty-three arch bridge where,
until recently, one could have tea with friends and contemplate the world. Pole Khaju
allowed caravans to cross the river via the central path on the second floor. It has become

Khaju, both bridge and dam

a promenade, more touristic than the Sio-Seh but a bit less popular with the local population. The two bridges are, in fact, the real symbols of the city, of its past grandeur, and today of its revival. The Khaju is more sophisticated than its predecessor, the Sio-Seh Pole – its terraces extend the piers downstream and allow people to dominate the river. Pointed arches, such as those of Isfahan bridges, with angular points at the top, are known among architects as Persian arches. During the same period (1647) the Chehel Sotun palace was built with its columns, pool, frescoes and mirrors; it was here that Shah Abbas II received guests in solemn audience.

Pole Khaju, a social meeting place

Note that the city of Dezful ("Fortress Bridge") on the Dez in western Iran has a fourth-century Sassanid bridge, rebuilt by the Safavids and periodically renovated. This may be the oldest bridge in the world that is still used by vehicles (the Sant'Angelo is reserved to pedestrians). The oldest bridge in Isfahan, the Shahrestan, with massive pillars, dates meanwhile in its present state from the fourteenth century.

In 1655 a young Venetian en route to India, Niccolo Manucci, who was seventeen years of age, stopped in Isfahan. In his memoirs he writes: "The city of Isfahan is very large and located in a vast plain at the foot of some hills of modest height. Four channels flow in the center, the water of which is used to irrigate the gardens, which are fed by a river, Zindahrud, coming from Jolfah and spanned by four bridges. Two are particularly beautiful, the first one on the road to Jolfah (...), the second bridge, the most beautiful, is called Shiraz (Khaju, ed) because it goes towards this city. It has three floors, in addition to the middle. The king goes there sometimes with his harem and can go down to the water's edge without being seen. Water flows between stones which were set artificially high or low to create waves pleasing to the eye." The young Niccolo would be one of the greatest travellers and adventurers of his time. He spent sixty years in India, meeting powerful people as well as bandits, going from Delhi, Lahore and Agra to Dhaka, Goa and Madras. From his brief visit to Persia he would remember the beauty of the bridges of Isfahan and the hospitality of the court of Shah Abbas II and his prime minister. He would be followed by Jean-Baptiste Tavernier, who would be less appreciative of the city's beauty, complaining about the poor quality of roads and the low density of the city due to its many gardens (in his travelogue published in 1677).

ANCIENT CITIES OF THE MIDDLE EAST

The first cities in history were born in the Middle East, in Mesopotamia. Because they were built with mud bricks (adobe) for the most part, over time they disappeared in the sand, so there is little evidence of their existence. As stone has been used for a long time in the Near East (Syria, Jordan, Palestine), it has been easier to find archeological remains there.

Cities have always depended on access to water; therefore most were developed along rivers or streams. Urbanization began in the Fertile Crescent, the cradle of agriculture, and in the Jordan Valley where the first permanent settlements appeared some 10,000 years ago. Jericho is considered the first village, built near the Dead Sea in the Neolithic age, between 10,000 BCE and 6,000 BCE, with rectangular houses and an eight-meter high funeral tower. In Anatolia, Catal Huyuk was a small town of five thousand inhabitants with mural paintings. In Mesopotamia the first towns were born in Tell-Hassuna (near Mosul) and Samarra, around 6,000 BCE, while the first canals appeared in Eridu around 5,000 BCE.

The urban revolution began in earnest with the Sumerians in Uruk, south of present-day Iraq, on the Euphrates, towards 4,000 BCE. Uruk is generally considered the first city in history, the first center of political, commercial and religious power.

The Sumerians of Uruk built canals and barges, temples and ziggurats (pyramids). They raised cattle, grew all kinds of vegetables, and produced works of art, including two large temples. The city expanded over a long period, from 3,300 BCE, and reached its peak around 3,000 BCE. Other autonomous cities then appeared, including Nippur, Kish, Lagash and Umma, each with their own ruler. But Uruk remained the largest city until the arrival of the Akkadians (Semites) who founded the first great empire. Gilgamesh, the legendary king of Uruk (2,700 BCE), was celebrated in the first epic poem in history.

Several centuries later, in 2,350 BCE, Sargon established a new empire throughout Mesopotamia. He built roads and set up a cadaster. But this empire lasted only 150 years. Ur took over and developed trade, taxation and literature. This was the "Sumerian renaissance" until 2,000 BCE. Then began the struggle between rival states – Amorite, Hittite, Assyrian, Elamite and Kassite – each taking in turn advantage over its neighbors. This regional tribalism lasted until the birth of Hammurabi (Amorite) and the growth of his capital, Babylon (80 kilometers south of Baghdad). Hammurabi (1,792 to 1,750 BCE) created a lasting empire. His famous Code is considered an important step towards the rule of law. It dealt with construction problems and penalties for poor workmanship. It reads for instance: "A manufacturer having built a house of poor quality, which collapses and causes the death of its owner, will himself be executed." This was the first building regulation.

Uruk stylized

The Kassites ruled over Babylon from 1,570 BCE till 1,155 BCE and provided stability while the Hittites controlled Anatolia (Hattusha, their capital, had more than 10,000 inhabitants). Cities of the Levant, such as Aleppo and Damascus, developed at this time. In 1,275 BCE at Kadesh (near Homs) Ramses II confronted the Hittites unsuccessfully and signed with them a pact of non-aggression. Assyrians, around Mosul, coexisted with the Hittites and maintained contacts with Babylon whose king Nebuchadnezzar the First (1,124 to 1,103 BCE) defeated the rival state of Elam (in Iran). The Hittite state fell in 1,190 BCE and the Kassite state in 1,155 BCE.

Assyria dominated the Middle East from the ninth to the seventh century BCE, with seventy provinces and governors. A new empire was born. Its last capital, Nineveh, may have been the largest city in the world during that time. King Ashurnasirpal II (883 to 859 BCE) established his capital at Calah on the Tigris (replacing Assur). It was 360 hectares in size and surrounded by a wall of 7.5 kilometers. Sargon II (721 to 705 BCE) created a fortress (a new city, Dur-Sharrukin) and crushed the rebellions of Hama, Damascus and Israel. He resided in Babylon from 708 to 705 BCE.

Cities grew with their palaces, canals, temples, reservoirs and aqueducts. Ashurbanipal (668 to 627 BCE) reigned for 40 years and crowned his dynasty at Nineveh by creating the largest library in the world. Babylon's importance declined but the city would become more prominent after the death of Ashurbanipal and was probably the largest city in the world during the Neo-Babylonian dynasty. Nineveh fell to that dynasty in 612 BCE, Jerusalem in 586 BCE, and Nebuchadnezzar II (reigned 605-562 BCE) made Babylon a very prosperous city. It was then 8 square kilometers in size, located on the banks of the Euphrates, with its temples, libraries and hanging gardens (some historians believe that these gardens were actually located in Nineveh), and its walls that were 18 kilometers in circumference. It had 200,000 inhabitants before the ascent of the Persian king, Cyrus the Great, in 539 BCE, after which it entered a phase of slow decline.

The Persian Empire, founded by Cyrus the Great in 550 BCE, lasted only two centuries but dominated all of Mesopotamia, particularly during the reigns of Darius the First (522 to 486 BCE) and Xerxes the First (486 to 461 BCE) . Cyrus had his capital at Pasargadae where his tomb still stands. Darius extended the empire as far as Libya and India. He built a Royal Road from Susa (his capital, present-day Shush) to Anatolia (2,400 kilometers), a canal between the Nile and the Red Sea in Egypt, the palaces of Persepolis and other infrastructure. He created an efficient administration. His son Xerxes also built many monuments. He invaded Greece in 480 BCE but failed in his conquest (at the Battle of Salamis). Darius built a floating bridge on the Bosphorus that was 700 meters long in 513 BCE (for his war against the Scythians) at the location of the current Fahti Sultan Mehmet Bridge. Xerxes built another floating bridge that was 1.2 kilometers in length on the Hellespont (Dardanelles) in 480 BCE. These were the first major bridges in history, bridges for military use, bridges of war and not peace. Similar pontoons of assembled boats permitted passage across the Tigris and Euphrates rivers and the Royal Route. The failure of the war against Greece was a major moment in Western history, heralding the end of the Persian Empire and the rise of Athens and other Greek cities. The Macedonia of Alexander the Great would then defeat the last Persian Achaemenids in 330 BCE.

The Middle East's strength declined as Greece and Rome became more powerful (from the sixth century BCE). Alexander crossed the Hellespont with 50,000 men to invade Asia and defeated the Persian army at Granicus River in 334 BCE. He conquered Egypt and founded Alexandria during the winter of 331 BCE. Then he took Babylon and the Middle East, including Persia. He only stopped at the Indus when he lost his faithful horse and turned back, under pressure from his generals. He returned to Babylon, where he died on 13 June 323 BCE, probably due to alcoholism. He had founded 70 cities, and imposed Greek planning with theatres, citadels, forts and giant sculptures. His succession would be fought over between the Seleucids (in the Middle East, main town Antioch in Syria), the Ptolemies (based in Alexandria), the Parthians (capital Ctesiphon, near present-day Baghdad) and the Romans. The latter had an advantage over the Greeks and the Carthaginians in the second century BCE and then over the Ptolemies, Seleucids, Gauls (around 50 BCE, the time of Julius Caesar) and Parthians. Rome then replaced Alexandria as the largest city in the West and in the world. The time of permanent bridges was about to start.

After the Afghan troops of Mir Mahmud took over Isfahan in 1722, Persia sank again into anarchy. In the nineteenth century it became the victim of rivalry between England and Russia. The short interlude of the two Shahs can be physically represented by two bridges, the Sio-Seh and the Khaju, whose construction dates could be viewed as two brackets around the heyday of Isfahan. But Isfahan and its roses would inspire many poets, such as Guillaume Apollinaire, who exclaimed: "Isfahan, for the scent of your roses, I would make an even longer trip", while Pierre Loti evoked an Isfahan of "ruin and death, which is increasingly gloomy as the sun goes down". Despite these literary differences the city remains embedded in greenery, with its irrigated and well-maintained gardens, and its famous roses.

In 2014 Isfahan has 2 million inhabitants; it is the third largest city in Iran after Tehran and Mashhad. According to architects Darab Diba and Serge Santelli, it may be "engaged in a process of urban decay" associated with the modernization of the urban fabric, including the opening of large avenues and construction of some unsightly buildings. It seems that the municipal authorities are gradually becoming aware of this serious problem and are trying to restore the reputation of the Pearl of Iran.

My friend and former colleague at the United Nations Environment Programme, Hossein Fadaei, who was born in Isfahan, still bears the city in his heart. But he raises some current concerns: "Sio Seh Pol and Pol Khaju, historic buildings of prime value, are first and foremost hotspots for social contacts. This is where people take a break from their day's work, admire the river and relax peacefully. Thursday nights and Fridays are obviously the busiest times. We can then see an endless stream of young people joking or singing,

Social interactions inside
Khaju Bridge

boys and girls chatting and dating, families taking pictures under the arches. However the Zayandeh Rud, which symbolizes life and hope, has been drying up periodically in recent years due to the dry climate of the region and an inappropriate management of water upstream of Isfahan. We'll have to revitalize it. On the other hand, the new metro passes under the river near the Sio Seh Pol and its vibrations seem to affect the building. The metro has certainly improved the conditions of urban transport but its impact on the heritage should have been better taken into account."

Any historical city must live in the present, but it needs to respect its past to prepare for the future. Isfahan is no exception to the rule.

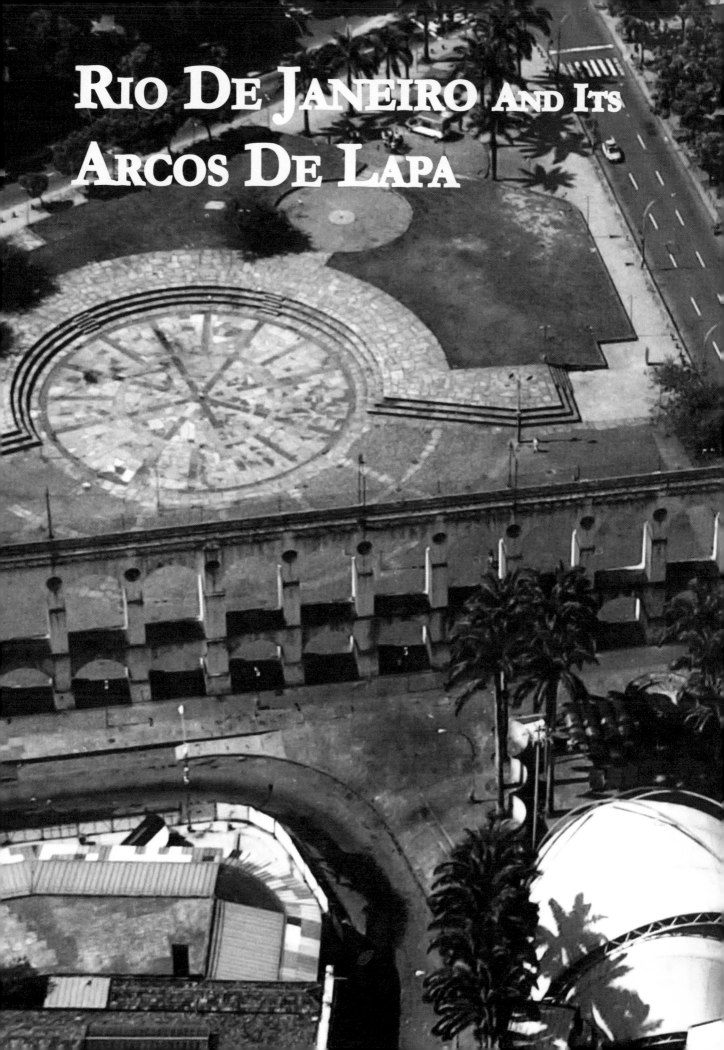

RIO DE JANEIRO AND ITS ARCOS DE LAPA

The city of Rio de Janeiro, Brazil's capital from 1763 to 1960, is undoubtedly the most beautiful agglomeration in South America, thanks to its fantastic location. It was erroneously named "River of January" by Portuguese explorers in 1502, when in fact it lies around a bay (an "arm of the sea" or Guanabara according to indigenous toponymy). The city (São Sebastião do Rio de Janeiro, the name of the King of Portugal, Dom Sebastião) was officially founded in March 1565 at the mouth (west) of this spectacular bay surrounded by steep hills. It did not need a bridge though a few aqueducts were necessary to feed a site that was sorely lacking fresh water. The largest of these aqueducts, built in 1750, became a bridge at the end of the nineteenth century.

RIO DE JANEIRO AND ITS ARCOS DE LAPA

In 1555 the French Admiral Villegagnon founded Fort Coligny on a small island in the bay around present-day Rio de Janeiro. But this attempt at colonization was immediately thwarted by the Portuguese. The first two centuries of Rio were difficult because the site was small and lacked drinking water, and was not immune to attacks by native tribes. For decades water was transported in barrels by Indians, often slaves, who took it from the orange valley (Laranjeiras).

Sugar cane farming, introduced in 1530, was based on the importation of African slaves, 15,000 per year in 1730, of which 3,000 landed in the port of Rio. They came mainly from Angola (the importation of slaves was prohibited in 1850, and the domestic slave trade stopped in 1885.) Former slaves would progressively become part of an elitist Portuguese society to create the rainbow nation of Brazil of today. Coffee for its part would only become an important cash crop in the nineteenth century.

The city of Rio de Janeiro deserves to be admired not only for its stunning site, but also for its palaces, mountains, parks, beaches, carnivals, and the ingenuity of its favelas (slums) that cling to its hillsides. However, the Arcos de Lapa, an aqueduct that is the largest colonial structure in Rio, is also worth noting.

Entrance to the bay of Rio de Janeiro ©ep_stock/ Shutterstock

In the mid-eighteenth century, agricultural commodities emanating from the country made King Joao V of Portugal the richest monarch in Europe. Rio took off for military reasons (to contain the Spanish based in Rio de la Plata) and to export gold from Minas Gerais. The Franciscans came to build a beautiful Baroque church, Sao Francisco da Penitencia (1737) next to the Convent of Sao Antonio. It was then decided to build the Carioca aqueduct (Aqueduto Carioca or Arcos da Carioca).

The Arcos in the eighteenth century

The silhouette of this elegant aqueduct is reminiscent of the Pont du Gard and of the Roman aqueduct of Segovia. It is directly inspired by the aqueduct das Aguas Livres in Lisbon (1744), which is higher, and which survived the earthquake of 1755. In 1783 it was adjoined by a public garden (Passeio Publico), which offers visitors a view of the bay, in the district of Gloria.

The aqueduct became a bridge in 1896 when the tram line that it now supports was installed to carry passengers from Lapa to Santa Teresa. The comings and goings of the little tram (or Bondji or bondinho, from the English word bond, or financial obligation) jolting down from Santa Teresa is a familiar image of the city.

The Bondji, historical tramway

Now the Arcos de Lapa and its Bondji are one of the four symbols of Rio, together with the Sugar Loaf Mountain, the Corcovado and the Copacabana beach's undulating pavement. Note that the bridge was shortened in the 1970s to give way to the avenue of Chile during a major renovation of the district. The Arcos de Lapa were rehabilitated between 2011 and 2013, in conjunction with the International Conference on Sustainable Development of June 2012 and in preparation for the Football World Cup of 2014.

AQUEDUCTS OR WATER-CARRIER BRIDGES

Aqueducts are upside-down bridges. Instead of trying to pass over or avoid water, they carry it in their bellies. These "bridges" are not built over waterways; they are built over land. They were once vital bridges because they carried water, which is essential to human life. Aqueducts captured, domesticated and distributed this essential commodity. Technically aqueducts are similar to bridges; they aim to overcome obstacles, but functionally they can be seen as raised pipelines, smoothly inclined earth-scrapers or horizontal sky-scrapers. The Romans invented them and the Ottomans adopted them, before the advent of hydraulic pumps and cast iron pipes.

The aqueducts of Lisbon and Rio de Janeiro were among the last water-carrier bridges in the world. In France the last aqueduct was inaugurated in 1772 in Montpellier. One can admire beautiful aqueducts in Southern Europe and the Mediterranean region, not only in the Gard and Istanbul but also in Spoleto, Italy, and in Segovia, Spain.

In the nineteenth century very special "aqueducts" were built to ensure that navigable canals could cross over rivers. They are the spectacular canal-bridges such as those of Briare and Agen in France. Recently (2003) the canal-bridge at Magdeburg on the Elbe, in Germany, broke the European record with a length of 918 meters.

Aqueducts were one of the best demonstrations of human intelligence and engineering techniques in the era preceding the industrial revolution.

The Aguas Libres Aqueduct in Lisbon (1744) ©Luis Santos/Shutterstock

The ancient aqueduct is located in a central area that attracts artists, it was built by slaves between 1744 and 1750. Some of the stones were, according to the journal of Louis-Léger Vauthier, imported from Portugal. Streams and rivers from surrounding mountains, especially Corcovado, had to be channeled to supply Rio, and had also to cross swamps, such as the unhealthy Lagoon Boqueirão. Two successive Portuguese General Governors played an essential role in achieving the Carioca Aqueduct. The first, Ayres Saldanha, channeled the river Carioca (Carioca means "House of Strangers" in Tupi language), which descends from the Tijuca Forest, and opened the first public fountain in 1723. The second, Gomes Freire de Andrade, who remained in Brazil for thirty years (1733-1763), completed and inaugurated the bridge in 1750. This aqueduct of stone, with two-levels (such as the Valens aqueduct in Istanbul, built in 378) and 42 superimposed arches, is 270 meters long and 17.60 meters high. It allowed the town to grow rapidly. A few years later, in 1763, Rio became the capital of the viceroyalty of Brazil, replacing Salvador de Bahia. The city then had about 30,000 inhabitants.

1750 was the year of the Treaty of Madrid that re-divided South America between Spain and Portugal, replacing the meridian of Tordesillas (adopted in 1494) by the rule of effective occupation of the territories and therefore extending the borders of Brazil to the west. In 1763 the Peace of Paris reconciled France and Spain with England, which increased the vulnerability of Portuguese territories and justified strengthening the role of Rio and the transfer of the capital to the center-south of the country. New neighborhoods appeared, Jesuits' properties were confiscated, scholarly societies were born, but the factories remained banned. Colonial rule began to be challenged by intellectuals inspired by the American Revolution. A separatist plot failed in 1789 and its leader, Tiradentes, was executed in 1792.

The ancient aqueduct renovated in 2012 ©Celso Pupo/Shutterstock

In March 1808 King Dom João VI of Portugal, fleeing Napoleon's armies, made Rio the capital of his declining empire and, on 7 September 1822, Brazil became independent, with Emperor Dom Pedro the First, son of Dom João VI, as its first ruler. Rio was then a true capital whose population doubled between 1810 (65,000 inhabitants) and 1838 (130,000 inhabitants, two-thirds of whom were African slaves). Despite an urban tax (decima urbana) established in 1808, its infrastructure left much to be desired. The first sewers did not appear until 1857. The Rio-Niterói Bridge, like running water and sanitation, belonged to a distant future. Epidemics (cholera, yellow fever) were recurrent throughout the nineteenth century.

Brazil would find an enlightened monarch with Pedro II (who ruled from 1841 to 1889, and died in Paris in 1891) and would become a Republic in 1889. The architecture of Rio would be strongly influenced by France (reflected in the Municipal Opera and do Ouvidor Street). The population of the city, which extended northward, reached one million around 1910. The Cortiços (hives) and overcrowded yards constituted the dominant form of low-income housing in the late nineteenth century. Residents faced frequent forced evictions. In 1899 demobilized soldiers were allowed to settle on the hill of Providence. They baptized this colony "favela" in memory of a typical plant of the sertao, which gave its name to a strategic hill during the crushing of the Canudos rebellion near Bahia. Thus the first favela was born. As demolitions increased, favelas would replace the 1,500 Cortiços surveyed in 1900.

Lapa area in 1912
©Augusto Malta

The "Baron Haussmann" of Rio was Francisco Pereira Passos. He studied in Paris at the Ecole des Ponts et Chaussées between 1857 and 1860. He restructured Rio from 1903, dividing the city into 23 districts, defining rules of sanitation, widening streets, drilling avenues (Avenida Central or Rio Branco), multiplying ways, scheduling prestigious buildings, demolishing Cortiços and, unfortunately, neglecting social housing. Carnivals and sambas were born in these years, and soon became the trademarks of Rio.

1758   1840

1906

The town planning agency IplanRio has produced six posters representing the evolution of Lapa between 1758 and 1991.

1958

1988

1991

BRAZILIAN CITIES, LATIN AMERICAN CITIES

In 2013 the Latin America and Caribbean region had a population of 610 million, including 490 million living in urban areas. Its urbanization level (80%) exceeds that of Europe and North America. It has 8 cities with more than 5 million inhabitants: Sao Paulo (21 million), Mexico City (21 million), Buenos Aires (13.2 million), Rio de Janeiro (12.2 million), Lima (9.3 million), Bogota (9 million), Santiago de Chile (6.1 million) and Belo Horizonte (6 million). These cities are growing more slowly than intermediate cities and towns which are now the locus of the urbanization process. It is estimated that the region has 2,000 cities with over 20,000 inhabitants; smaller cities often lack management capacities and financial resources.

Among the 18 Latin American cities with more than 3 million people, half are in Brazil. Among the 6 Brazilian cities with around 4 million inhabitants, 5 (Porto Alegre, Recife, Salvador, Fortaleza and Curitiba) are coastal cities, while Brasilia (which was planned in the 1950s as a capital city) is the only city in the interior. This reflects the exogenous mode of urbanization in South America, particularly the influence of colonization, with its export-oriented economy and its exploitation of the region's resources. In fact, Brazil and China share a common characteristic: in both countries urbanization is concentrated on an eastern coastal strip, with an intensification of socio-economic synergies within large urban multipolar areas.

A typical favela in Rio ©David Davis/Shutterstock

The major countries of Latin America are among the most urbanized. In 2013 Brazil had 170 million urban residents out of a total population of 200 million (85%), Mexico had 88 million urban residents out of a total population of 112 million (79%), Colombia had 36 million urban residents out of a total population of 47 million (76%), and Argentina had 37 million urban dwellers out of a total population of 41 million (93%). Yet these countries are major agricultural exporters because of the size and the industrial organization of rural properties (latifundios).

Latin American cities, the engines of the region's economic development, are still marked by poverty and social inequality. A quarter of the urban population in Brazil is considered by the World Bank to be living below the poverty line (two dollars per day). The same proportion lives in slums and under-serviced neighborhoods. Poverty has decreased over the past decade due to economic growth and the redistributive policies of President Lula. But inequalities remain widespread: the richest 10% of the population still get 40% of the national income. The informal sector, therefore, constitutes a lifeline for low-income communities, and represents between one-third and half of urban employment, which partly explains the dynamism of the Brazilian economy.

Poverty and inequality provide fertile ground for gangs, including drug traffickers. Violence seems to have been reduced in some cities (e.g. in Colombia) but has increased in others (north of Mexico), while the city of Rio de Janeiro has recently launched a program of peaceful re-conquest of the favelas that is yielding some results. The fact, however, remains that Latin American cities are still topping the list as the world's most dangerous cities, with urban violence affecting primarily the poor, the young and often women.

The cable-stayed bridge Octavio Frias de Oliveira across Pinheiros River has been inaugurated in 2008 in Sao Paulo ©Celso Diniz/Shutterstock

Most Latin American countries have since the 1980s adopted decentralization policies that put the future of cities into the hands of local governments. However, these policies tend to favor, despite governmental transfers, those municipalities that are already successful, rather than those that are disadvantaged. Civic participation is encouraged and often innovative (participatory budgeting was invented in Porto Alegre, Bogota introduced voluntary self-taxation and Brazil imposes penalties for exceeding zoning regulations). Water and sanitation utilities are generally quite effective and public transportation has made some progress, needed to address the de-densification of the urban fabric in many cities, which happens through infrastructure expansion. Although Latin American cities have developed interesting modes of public transport including well-designed tramways and lanes reserved for rapid buses, they are also becoming increasingly aware of the limitations and dangers of an excessive use of private cars. In Rio de Janeiro, less than 20% of daily trips are undertaken in private cars but this rate could increase dramatically as poverty levels decrease.

Gradually, the Latin American city has been evolving from a place of scarcity, individualism and strong contrasts towards a territory where collective claims to the right to housing and "the right to the city" are changing human relations. Social demands, once focused on basic services and infrastructure, now include demands for security, mobility, environmental protection and citizen participation in the affairs of the city, particularly to reduce inequalities. In most countries, including Brazil, the divided and dual city and the relational and friendly city now coexist. Duality is reflected in the social and spatial segregation while conviviality results from the ongoing transformation towards more connectivity, more competitiveness, more synergies and social networks. These two faces of the city are found in varying degrees throughout the region. The quality of the urban environment, of public spaces in particular, constitutes an indicator that allows assessing which of the two aspects predominate. This is particularly clear in the deeply segregated neighborhoods of Rio de Janeiro, which are ever diverse and changing, mostly friendly but sometimes hostile. Rio could certainly do with more fluid and flexible boundaries.

It may also be noted that Latin American cities have very few impressive bridges. This is certainly due to the size of their rivers, which are either too wide or too narrow, as in sub-Saharan Africa. But it is tempting to view this absence as a symbolic reflection of the lack of harmonious relations (or bridges) between the social classes, who tend to ignore each other, and sometimes clash, in a number of cities.

From 1919 to 1950, Brazil experienced a period of political instability marked by various attempts to enter modernity. After the populist upheavals of the 1950s, a dictatorship was gradually established from 1964 (the Garota de Ipanema, flagship song of the bossa nova, by Antonio Carlos Jobin and Vinicius de Moraes, was written in 1963). Meanwhile Rio lost its status as a capital on 21 April 1960 in favor of a city of cardboard, or rather an empty shell of reinforced concrete, called Brasilia. Rio was abandoned by the technocratic elite that wished to appear as modernist and functionalist, and who failed to tackle its biggest scourge – crime and inequality. Untamed, Rio became the "crime capital" of South America and host to hundreds of favelas. Though there were attempts to gradually improving the infrastructure in favelas (e.g. Rocinha) many of them remained the domain of gangs and religious sects. The new upper classes, meanwhile, moved to Barra de Tijuca on the Atlantic coast in the southwest of the city.

The Arcos in front of St. Sebastian Cathedral ©Celso Pupo/Shutterstock

The democratic transition of the 1980s culminated in a massive vote for Lula in Rio in December 1989, but the country preferred Collor and Lula had to wait till the twenty-first century (January 2003) to access the presidency. Rio became more provincial but remained the soul of Brazil and its mixed cultures.

Today the city has 12 million inhabitants (against 4.4 million in 1960) spread over 14 municipalities (Rio stricto sensu has seven million inhabitants) and tries to remain one of the cultural capitals of Brazil, in contrast to hyper-dynamic Sao Paulo ("energetic counterpoint to the hedonistic languor of Rio", according to Le Monde dated 4 February 2006), which has more than 20 million people and rivals New York and Mexico for the title of most populous city of the American continent. Rio's urban fabric is heterogeneous due to the highly contrasting topography of the location. There is nothing in common between Copacabana, Santa Teresa, Barra de Tijuca and the favelas that are themselves enclaves with diversified faces. Between the three adjacent neighborhoods of Gloria, Lapa and Santa Teresa, differences are clearly visible.

Separated by just a few meters, the opulence of the Central Business District (headquarters of BNDES, Banco do Brasil, Petrobras, near the National Library, Municipal Theatre, Museum of Fine Arts, etc. .) is in sharp contrast to the decay of Lapa, south of the aqueduct, and to the steep cobbled lanes of Santa Teresa. But nothing prevents one from taking a break at Bar do Gomes (1919) or at the beautiful Confeitaria Colombo (Art Nouveau, 1894) to savor the retro atmosphere of old Rio.

The Arcos at night ©Luiz Claudio Ribeiro/Shutterstock

Rio de Janeiro is a patchwork of neighborhoods, each with its own identity, its own atmosphere, its own lifestyle and its own history. Generally, the rich tend to live near the sea and the poor on the hill-slopes, where many have, as in Orfeu Negro, a breathtaking view of the bay. Climate change threatens the rich with floods and the poor with landslides. In April 2010 heavy rains and mudslides destroyed thousands of homes and killed more than a hundred people. But the city remains a prime venue for major international conferences and global sporting events.

A city without rivers, which is named after a river, solved its water problems by building a bridge. This was the paradox of Rio de Janeiro, the River of January! Bridges have helped the city solve its environmental problems and access natural resources, and facilitate urban transport, not only with the mini-tram of Lapa but also with the huge Niterói Bridge.

The Ponte Rio-Niterói was built between 1969 and 1974. It is 13 kilometers long and crosses the Bay of Guanabara (which had been mistaken for a river in 1502), between Rio and Niterói (Tupi name meaning "hidden water"). It links the federal highways Rio-Sao Paulo and Rio-Salvador. Its three largest spans are 200, 300 and 200 meters long. It is a pre-stressed concrete bridge using precast voussoirs (3,000 in total). The bridge is monumental, aesthetically uninteresting but well integrated into the site. Sometimes it is called Ponte Presidente Costa e Silva. Its construction was an ambitious undertaking, typical of large modern works. The impact of this bridge is primarily economic; it was designed to allow Rio to regain its past momentum. It has fulfilled its function so far as a link between the two sides of the bay.

The impressive Niteroi Bridge
©Gilliard Lach

The discovery in 2007 of giant oilfields off Rio has brightened the city's prospects. Important investments have been made by Petrobras in Niteroi, which are completely changing the local economy.

Paragliding over the bay

Note that one of the most beautiful bridges in Brazil can be found in Florianópolis. It is the largest suspension bridge in the country, named Hercilio Luz, and was built between 1922 and 1926 by David Steinman. But Florianópolis, in the south of Brazil, cannot compete with Rio. Also note also that gradually the entire periphery of the Guanabara Bay (over more than 100 kilometers) is urbanizing. The Rio-Niteroi metropolitan region will soon exceed a built-up area of 1000 km²; its population may well reach 30 million before 2050. The awakening of Guanabara is clearly underway.

Hercilio Luz Bridge connects Florianopolis to Santa Catarina Island. With 820 meters, and a central span of 340 meters, it is the longest suspended bridge in Brazil ©Gilliard Lach

My friend and Carioca colleague Alberto Paranhos, an urban planner who has repeatedly introduced me to Rio de Janeiro's life since 1996, reflects the spirit of his city: "Because the city was founded on a beach, its inhabitants always thought that the sea view was their most precious landscape. Rio is wedged between water and mountains and lies in valleys surrounding Tijuca Forest, whose hills represent a third of the municipal territory. The city became in 1808 the new capital of the United Kingdom of Portugal, Brazil and the Algarve, following the arrival of the Portuguese royal family who escaped Napoleon's army. Not content to occupy the best site of the Americas, Rio de Janeiro was for thirteen years the only American city that was the capital of a European kingdom. This event allowed the city to become a cultural capital, an attribute it retains today, even after the transfer in 1960 of the national political power to modernist Brasilia. This is without a doubt the 'beloved city' throughout Brazil, absolutely adored by its residents who believe they are blessed by heaven to enjoy such a privilege. Even with the violence due to drug trafficking and weapons, and often chaotic transport, the 'Cariocas' by birth or by choice consider it pointless to live elsewhere, and enjoy the opportunity of beaches near their offices, samba and caipirinha on weekends, carnival in February and rehearsals throughout the year. Tourists come back and try to stay there, or spend their lives wishing they were Carioca".

Arcos de Lapa, a symbol of Rio de Janeiro

BUDAPEST AND ITS SZECHENYI HID

The history of Budapest is one of a succession of invasions. The future emperor Hadrian, Roman legate then, settled there in the year 105. He built roads, aqueducts and baths. The city, called Aquincum, grew from 10,000 to 50,000 inhabitants during the second century. It would only attain that population again 1,600 years later. It was an important market which diminished in importance following the decline of the Roman Empire. The Huns invaded the place in the fifth century. Later Byzantines and Franks made it a border town between East and West. Buda and Pest would only be consolidated in 1873, after having built their magnificent Chain Bridge.

BUDAPEST AND ITS SZECHENYI HID

The Magyars occupied the site of present-day Budapest in the late ninth century. A medieval city then expanded in Pest, Buda (new name of Aquincum) and Óbuda, with monasteries, churches and aristocratic mansions. The Mongols of the Golden Horde invaded the town briefly between 1241 and 1242.

Buda became the capital of the Kingdom of Hungary and hosted a large German population. In 1310 the nobles elected a French king from Anjou, Charles Robert the First. Angevins were builders; they renovated and transformed castles and palaces. The Bohemian Gothic reached Buda with Sigismund, son of Charles IV. In 1400 Buda had 15,000 inhabitants, Pest 10,000 on the other bank of the Danube. Mathias, the last ruler of Hungary (1458-1490), was also a builder who spread the Renaissance style. After his death another long decline began.

Hungary came under Ottoman rule from 1526, following the defeat of Mohacs, and remained so until 1699, with Budapest falling in 1541. The first floating bridge of boats on the Danube seems to have been built under the Buda Castle around 1650. Other Ottoman legacies were renovated baths, croissants, cafés and sorbets. The Ottomans tried to take Vienna in 1683, without success. The imperial counter-offensive pushed back the Turkish troops and the Habsburg army seized Budapest in 1686. The city started growing and entered the Baroque era in the 1720s.

A university was founded and an engineering school opened its doors in 1782. Pest drove the economic revival, its fairs took off, textile manufacturers appeared.

The city had 26,000 inhabitants at the turn of the century and attracted many rural migrants. However, the floating bridge between Buda and Pest, renovated in 1767 and made of fifty boats connected with chains, had to be dismantled each winter because of the icy waters.

Hungary remained under Austrian rule until the Compromise of 1867 which transformed the Habsburg monarchy into the dualistic Austro-Hungarian Empire. A country wedged between rival empires, Hungary had to struggle to assert its identity and to gain independence. It became a republic in 1918.

Along with Prague, Budapest represents Central Europe in this book. This choice seemed obvious because neither Vienna nor Warsaw nor Krakow have been able to build structures as striking as the Chain Bridge that was the first permanent bridge over the Danube to connect the cities of Buda and Pest. These cities – with Obuda, the old Buda - would give birth to Budapest a few years later, in 1873. Until that time Buda and Pest clearly turned their backs to each other. On the hills of the right bank, Buda was historical, aristocratic, German, the city of power. Pest on the other side was modern, flat, wide, Hungarian, the city of economic and cultural dynamism.

The construction of the Chain Bridge was decided in 1836, before the great flood of 1838 that killed tens of thousands people and destroyed two-thirds of the houses in Pest.

The National Commission in charge of the project was headed by Count Istvan Széchenyi, one of the main leaders of the modernization movement that the country was experiencing. He founded the Society of Hungarian Scientists, the future Academy of Sciences, in 1831, and the Company of Budapest Bridge in 1832. He had visited bridges and railroads in England.

Snow on the city, February 2012 ©Botond Horvath

Count István Széchenyi, Modernizer Aristocrat

Barabas Miklós, Count István Széchenyi, 1848,
National Museum, Budapest

Count István Széchenyi, who was born in Vienna in September 1791 and died in Döbling in April 1860, was one of the greatest statesmen of Hungarian history, the modernizer of the country between 1825 and 1850, an enlightened aristocrat who gave Hungary a decisive impulse at a critical time. His father, Count Ferenc Széchenyi was Grand Chamberlain and founded the National Museum and the National Library.

Széchenyi was an officer of the Imperial Army until 1826 and then turned to politics and infrastructure development. He travelled extensively in Europe and established personal relationships in different countries. The rapid modernization of England fascinated him and strongly influenced his ideas. The Count quickly became aware of the gap between the industrial West and his own country and decided to make every effort to reduce this gap.

Széchenyi gained wide popularity in 1825 when he offered the annual income of his properties to finance the establishment of the Hungarian Academy of Sciences. This was the starting point of the reform movement. In 1827 he set up the National Casino, a club of young aristocrats, to encourage political dialogue as well as trade and industry, and to promote national production.

To reach a wider audience Széchenyi wrote three political books: Hitel (Credit, 1830), Világ (World, 1831) and Stadium (1833). He lambasted the conservative nobility and encouraged his peers to abandon their privileges (such as tax exemption) and become modernizing elite. These books aroused the enthusiasm of young nobles and intellectuals. Stadium became the bible of Hungarian reformists.

Széchenyi considered his program in the framework of the Habsburg Empire. Although a nationalist, he thought Hungary had to develop before gaining autonomy. Besides his broad political vision, his attention focused particularly on the development of transportation, a vital factor to boost economic growth. One component of this program was the regulation of the lower Danube between Pest and the Black Sea. He became the figurehead of this project in the early 1830s. At that time the river was dangerous and difficult to navigate. Széchenyi recognized its commercial potential for the region and mobilized support in Vienna. He was appointed High Commissioner and oversaw improvement works for many years.

In 1836 he took the initiative to promote before the Diet the first railway in the country, having travelled on the Manchester-Liverpool line. The first section of the railway (Pest-Vac) was inaugurated in 1846. Then he supported the construction of mills to expand the milling industry. The Pest milling company opened its doors in 1841, the starting point of a thriving industry. His theories on credit (his book of 1830) were the basis for the creation in 1840 of the Pest Savings Bank, which opened branches all over the country. Versatile and humanist, he even supported the introduction of horse-racing in Pest in 1827 and founded the breeding society in 1830, at a time when carriages and horse-cabs were a vital means of transportation.

A major ambition of Count Széchenyi was the development of the sister cities, Buda and Pest, as the political, economic and cultural center of Hungary. He played a major role in the construction of the first permanent bridge between Buda and Pest, a symbolic bridge that opened in 1849, and which paved the path for the unification of the twin cities and the birth of the Budapest agglomeration.

During the revolution of 1848 he accepted the post of Minister of Transport and Social Affairs. But the failure of the revolution against the Austrian forces plunged him into depression and he had to be admitted at Goergen Asylum in Döbling. He wrote his last book Ein Blick (A Look) on the problems of Hungary, but his depression persisted.

Subjected to continuous harassment by the Austrian police and affected by the death of a close friend, he committed suicide on the night of 8 April 1860. He left the world when the Austrian monarchy was about to finally recognize Hungarian identity. The entire country mourned this loss, including academics and intellectuals. His statue was unveiled in Budapest on 23 May 1880. And the Chain Bridge became the Széchenyi Hid in 1899.

Count Széchenyi was part of all progressive struggles until the spring of 1848. He was often the initiator of such movements. He successfully devoted his fortune, his time and his intelligence to the modernization of Hungary. He was for twenty-three years "the greatest of the Hungarians" as recognized by his rival Lajos Kossuth (*), and remains a huge figure in Hungarian history.

Barabas Miklós, Groundbreaking ceremony of the suspended bridge (1842), National Museum, Budapest

(*) The other national hero, a journalist born in 1802, leader of the Lower House and of the 1848 revolution, Chairman of the National Defense Committee who tried to loosen the Austrian grip, head of the short-lived Hungarian government from April to July 1949 before the counter-offensive and the return of the Habsburgs, then in exile until his death in 1894.

He appealed to G. Sina to mobilize the necessary funds (under the Chain Bridge Share Company) and selected the Scottish architect-engineer, born in Bristol, William Tierney Clark (1783-1852) for the design. The suspension bridge project was approved in September 1838. The bridge measures 380 meters and consists of three spans of 88.50 meters, 203 meters and 88.50 meters, respectively. It is 14.5 meters wide. Its metallic structure originally weighed 5,200 tons. W.T. Clark recruited his namesake Adam Clark to lead the project, which was carried out by dozens of English workers. The main difficulty was building the foundations of the two piers under the water of the Danube.

Right bank pier ©R. Nagy/ Shutterstock

This was achieved by driving thousands of stakes that created a waterproof casing within which the foundations could be built. The first stone, on the Pest side, was laid down by the independence leader Lajos Kossuth on 24 August 1842. Note that W.T. Clark had built between 1829 and 1832 the same type of bridge over the Thames at Marlow (see box).

MARLOW BRIDGE, PROTOTYPE OF THE CHAIN BRIDGE

The town of Marlow, Buckinghamshire, had a wooden bridge over the Thames from the thirteenth century. A new bridge had to be built to cope with a significant growth in traffic in the early nineteenth century. It was designed by engineer William Tierney Clarke, who also oversaw its construction from 1829 to 1832. It is a suspension bridge, or a chain bridge, whose central span is 72 meters long. Ten years later the same W. Tierney Clarke was recruited by Count István Széchenyi, who had visited England, to design the Chain Bridge in Budapest. The latter is three times longer than its British prototype but both have an undeniable family resemblance.

The Marlow Bridge was completely renovated in 1965 and "twinned" with the Széchenyi Bridge in 1996. It is open to vehicles of less than three tons and to pedestrians.

Marlow Bridge ©Margaret Smeaton/Shutterstock

William Rey, a Swiss employee of the Society of Navigation on the Danube, based in Vienna, wrote in 1848: "The last time I arrived (in Buda), we saw two dark masses rising from the bosom of the waters and covered with machines, beams and men, from which emanated the hurried wheeze of high pressure steam machines. Since then, these two marine castles have become the two piers of Pest suspension bridge, the boldest of the continent."

View from Pest on Buda castle ©David Berry/ Shutterstock

Laminated iron chains were forged in England. They were installed in 1848 at a time when the revolution broke out in Pest (15 March 1848, now a national holiday) and in other European cities, but the war of independence against the Habsburgs (1848-1849) slowed down the work process. The troops of the Austrian emperor crossed the Danube on an unfinished bridge to take Pest on 5 January 1849. The Hungarian army counter-attacked, Kossuth declared independence on 14 April and the Austrians retreated to Buda where they tried in vain to destroy the bridge. Finally, the Austrian imperial troops, backed by 200,000 Russian soldiers, defeated the Hungarian insurgents in August 1849. The bridge was officially opened by the occupiers and the first toll levied on 21 November 1849. The bridge quickly became profitable; the funds for its construction were repaid in less than 20 years. The four stone lions from Janos Marschalko were added in 1852. The horse-pulled omnibuses soon made full use of the crossing. Adam Clark then pierced a tunnel facing the bridge under the hill of Buda Castle, which opened in 1857.

In February 1867 the Austro-Hungarian Compromise, the Ausgleich, created an autonomous government. Budapest became the second capital of the Austro-Hungarian Empire, and the town was united administratively in 1873. It adopted a master plan and entered a phase of sustained economic and cultural growth, especially on the Pest side. Budapest's population grew to 730,000 in 1900, compared to 100,000 in 1840, and has a population of about 1.8 million today.

The economic and demographic boom in Budapest occurred between 1873 and 1900. Stations, a port, a tramway, factories, banks, a new master plan (1894), electrical networks, wide boulevards, a huge parliament building modeled on London's parliament houses,

The neo-gothic Parliament in Pest ©Ekaterina Shtern/ Shutterstock

a national opera inspired by Paris opera and several new bridges (Margit Bridge built in 1872-1876 by the Société des Batignolles, Liberty Bridge in 1894-1896, Erzsebet Bridge in 1899-1903) then reflected the great dynamism of the "Pearl of the Danube".

In 1899 it was decided that the Chain Bridge would be named after its visionary sponsor. The Chain Bridge (Lanchid) thus became the Széchenyi Hid. Between 1914 and 1915 all the metal structure, deemed unstable and insufficient, was replaced. The roadway had to be renovated. Automobile traffic on the bridge had increased considerably, resulting in excessive vibrations.

At the end of the Second World War the Nazis, threatened by advancing Soviet troops, destroyed all the bridges in Budapest - the Margit Bridge on 4 November 1944 and the Chain Bridge on 18 January 1945.

The bridge destroyed by the Nazis in January 1945

Reconstruction in 1949 ©Brendan Howard/ Shutterstock

Three temporary bridges were put into service by the Red Army, but they were too narrow and weak to withstand heavy traffic. A century after its birth the Széchenyi Bridge had to be rebuilt. Popular enthusiasm was immense for this reconstruction: a committee was formed, funds raised, parts were retrieved from the river (76% of the chains), modern methods of calculation were used and the bridge was re-opened to traffic on 20 November 1949, exactly 100 years after its first inauguration.

The bridge, renovated in 1973, is the symbol of the independence of Hungary and of the rebirth of Budapest. It is beautifully highlighted at night and connects in a big way the hill of Buda and its imposing palace, accessible by funicular, and the plain of Pest, with its restaurants, cafés and entertainment spots. As stated in several guidebooks, "the Hungarian capital is one of the most vibrant and liveliest cities of Central Europe". Bridges on the Danube are true works of art; their impact on the city can legitimately be compared to the impact of the East River bridges on New York City.

Liberty Bridge in winter
©Botond Horvath

But progress is still possible. My friend Ivan Tosics, Doctor in urban sociology and resident in Budapest, recommends reviewing the primary function of the bridge and its use: "The Chain Bridge is not only one of the most famous symbols of Budapest; it is also the main tourist link between the Castle Hill and downtown Pest. Foreign visitors pass through in large numbers, taking ceaselessly photos of each other with the bridge in the background. Other frequent users are local cyclists

Sidewalk or bike path?

who are not allowed to take the narrow roadway congested with vehicles and must share the sidewalks with tourists. Being myself a passionate cyclist, I experienced many times a dangerous rapprochement of these two, very different, types of bridge users. Cyclists are (unusually) very polite when crossing the Chain Bridge on the sidewalks and address the pedestrians automatically in English or German – the likelihood to meet domestic pedestrians being quite small. Thus the Chain Bridge brings tourists and cyclists close to each other – much closer than needed. The solution is obvious: the narrow roadway should be closed to motorized traffic, allowing bikers to occupy this part of the bridge, reserving the sidewalks for the tourists. Sustainability, tourists, bikers and the bridge would all benefit from this pedestrianization of the oldest bridge of Budapest." I can only support this idea, already implemented for the Magere Brug in Amsterdam, which would bring back to the Széchenyi Hid its initial character and improve the aesthetics of the city.

AMSTERDAM AND ITS
MAGERE BRUG

Among European cities, the great triad of canal-and-bridge cities includes Venice, St. Petersburg and Amsterdam. Each of these cities has hundreds of small bridges, some very discreet, others purely functional, and some bright as infra-sculptures that animate the urban fabric and contribute to imbuing it with a soul. With its canals and bridges, the historic center of Amsterdam is a beautiful example of urban planning on a human scale.

←The Magere Brug (1871), nine-arched bridge ©Eric Gevaert/ Shutterstock

AMSTERDAM AND ITS MAGERE BRUG

The rise of Amsterdam coincided with the struggle of the United Provinces against Spanish rule. The Netherlands, which became Spanish with the accession of Charles V to power in 1515, rebelled in 1568, both for religious freedom and against new taxes. After a period of wars and compromise, the seven Northern provinces formed the independent United Provinces in 1581, the ten southern provinces, the future Belgium, remaining Spanish. This gradual liberation attracted wealthy Jewish families, traders from Antwerp and French Huguenots to Amsterdam, the largest city in a loose federation without a reigning prince. The city became a place of refuge, a place of free thinking.

For several decades, until the Treaty of Westphalia (1648), relations with Spain remained tense; conflicts were frequent while the maritime trade and warehouses grew rapidly around the port of Amsterdam. Taking advantage of the weakening Mediterranean economy, Amsterdam became the commercial and financial capital of Europe throughout the seventeenth century. Its population grew from 50,000 in 1600 to 200,000 in 1700. It took over from Genoa, Antwerp and Venice to become the last imperial city, before being overtaken by territorial states, primarily by England. Holland and Amsterdam were the economic engines of the dense United Provinces, with 50% of the population living in urban areas, within a synergetic urban network.

Across Amstel River which gave its name to the city ©Gordon Bell/Shutterstock

Water and bridges have been of vital importance in the history of Amsterdam. The town developed along the Amstel River and has always depended on water for transportation of goods. On this river was once built a dam (dam on the Amstel: Amstel-dam), which also constituted the first bridge between the two banks. In the sixteenth century Amsterdam had already a hundred wooden girder bridges when three concentric canals were built around the city center. Their number doubled in the seventeenth century after the adoption in 1610 of the development plan of the city, in a star pattern. This was the Golden Age of the city symbolized by Rembrandt (1606-1669), King of Chiaroscuro, and Baruch Spinoza (1632-1677), a philosopher and political scientist, precursor of the Enlightenment, who was excommunicated in Amsterdam at the age of 24 years by the Jewish community, and whose ideas on individual freedom, creativity and institutions remain strangely modern.

Typical facades of old Amsterdam ©Devi/Shutterstock

Amsterdam then became one of the most powerful financial and maritime centers in the world. Its fortune and that of the United Provinces emanated from the Baltic and Spain. The Dutch fleet superseded and replaced the Portuguese in Asia with the creation of the VOC (East India Company) in 1602, and the founding of Batavia, the future Jakarta, in 1619. The city had about 120,000 inhabitants in 1650. Its per capita income was four times that of a Parisian in 1685, which explains the quantity and quality of real estate projects along the canals. Amsterdam was confirming and developing its tradition of a bourgeois, humanist and tolerant market town.

Amsterdam Canal District, Masterpiece Of Urban Planning

On 14 June 2010, Amsterdam's canals entered the UNESCO World Heritage list as "Area of concentric canals of the seventeenth century inside the Singelgracht." Amsterdam's canals have earned the city its nickname "Venice of the North". The city's canals extend to a total of more than one hundred kilometers, with hundreds of bridges, linking approximately ninety islands.

Overview of the canal area ©Aerophoto Schiphol

Historically the Singel (not to be confused with the Singelgracht) was the first canal that served as a medieval moat until 1585, when Amsterdam started its urban expansion. At the end of the sixteenth century the city was still confined inside this semi-circular canal, designed both for drainage, boat traffic and military defense. The Singel was transformed into an inland harbor between 1601 and 1603.

A comprehensive network of canals was designed to the west and south of the medieval village. It was accompanied by shifting inland the limits of the fortified city, which was closed by a new boundary canal, the Singelgracht. The idea was to expand the city by draining the swampland through concentric canals and backfilling the interspaces. These spaces allowed the development of an urban complex consisting of gabled houses and numerous monuments. This urban extension was the largest and most homogeneous of its time; it represented an example of large-scale urban planning which served as a reference throughout Europe until the nineteenth century, so much so that the stern Lewis Mumford could qualify Amsterdam as an "exemplary commercial city", recognizing that "by its size, its unity, the intelligible order of its facilities, the project of the three canals was a complete success".

Inhabited canal ©Luismonteiro/Shutterstock

One has indeed witnessed the creation of an entirely artificial port-city that was at the same time a masterpiece of hydraulic engineering and urban planning, and a rational program of construction and bourgeois architecture. The network of canals that form the urban fabric, complete with radial waterways and streets, was then fully established, with its embankments and historic façade alignments. The vast majority of the houses built in the seventeenth and eighteenth centuries are still standing today, and in a good state of preservation.

The area between the Singel and the Singelgracht offered the possibility of a new space but needed draining and backfilling. The project was designed by Hendrick Jacobszoon Staets, and focused on the construction of a new port and trading city, built along a network of three main canals that would allow commercial vessels to dock. A master plan was adopted in 1610. The new canals were dug beyond the Singel, reproducing its hydraulic morphology. They were undertaken simultaneously from the Ij, southbound. The first two tranches of work reached the radial Leidsegracht canal and launched backfills and constructions; the third phase joined the canals to the Amstel around 1620.

The three main canals built in the early seventeenth century were named Herengracht, Keizersgracht and Prinsengracht. The Herengracht ("Lord's Canal") is the first and shortest of the three canals. It extends to the east by the Nieuwe Herengracht and flows northwest into the Brouwersgracht. It is famous for its "golden bend" (Gouden Bocht) between the bridges of Leidsestraat and Vijzelstraat, the district of wealthy merchants. The Keizersgracht ("Emperor's Canal") is the second and widest canal from the center of town. It extends to the east by the Nieuwe Keizersgracht and flows northwest into the Brouwersgracht. The Prinsengracht ("Prince's Canal") was named in honor of the Prince of Orange. This is the longest of the three canals, being the outermost. It extends to the northwest by the Korte Prinsengracht and to the east by the Nieuwe Prinsengracht.

The Magere Brug crosses the Amstel between Keizersgracht and Prinsengracht. Note that different types of canals bear various names in Dutch language: gracht, sloot, vaart, vliet, tocht, among others.

The management of the canal district falls under the responsibility of the Central Borough of Amsterdam while its monitoring depends on a horizontal body, the World Heritage Bureau of Amsterdam, a city that is more than ever the financial, academic, artistic and historical capital of the Netherlands.

Canals junction ©Massimo Catarinella/Shutterstock

Amstel River and an affluent
©Gordon Bell/Shutterstock

The example of this city, enriched by its maritime trade, defended by its canals, dams and locks, which has never been flooded throughout its history, attracted the attention of all major European builders of the time. It directly influenced civil engineering and urban planning in England, Sweden and Russia, where Peter the Great hired directly its artisans and engineers to create St. Petersburg, which had a terrain similar to that of Amsterdam, marshy ground bordering a vast estuary.

The second generation of bridges that appeared during this golden age is that of vaulted masonry bridges with semicircular or elliptical arches. All major bridges of the seventeenth and eighteenth centuries, for example in the area of Keizersgracht, fall into this category. However, these bridges were no longer movable and had a limited height. The boats had to lower their masts to pass under them. This inconvenience led to the subsequent evolution towards bascule bridges with porticoes and lifting beams.

After a period of relative decline from the 1780s, during which London and England became hegemonic, the second great period of growth of the city began in 1860. New neighborhoods appeared, the center was renovated and canals were reorganized, sometimes filled. A new canal was dug to connect the port to the North Sea (1876) and bridges were demolished or "flattened" to allow trams to pass. Wooden bridges disappeared. In 1875 there were no more than 68 masonry bridges.

Canal and bridge, Amsterdam' signature
©Christopher Poe/ Shutterstock

The Magere Brug was built in 1871 on the Amstel to replace a narrow ("meager") bridge dating from 1691. It symbolized the new bridges of the time. A metal bridge with nine spans, the Magere Brug's central part is that of a double-bascule bridge, consistent with local traditions. It was restored in 1934 and renovated in 1969. It is a romantic bridge, used only by pedestrians and cyclists since 2003. Of modest dimensions, it is very well lit (1200 light bulbs) and must be visited when night falls.

Amstel River, its locks and "meager" bridge ©Frans Lemmens

Despite the size difference, the Magere Brug evokes a bit of the Tower Bridge, the famous bascule bridge to be built a few years later on the Thames. This difference

Inside the Magere Brug
©Devi/Shutterstock

is directly proportional not only to the respective width of the rivers, but also to the difference between the modest (but wealthy) Kingdom of the Netherlands and the more opulent and regal United Kingdom at the peak of its power.

Erasmus Bridge in Rotterdam (1996) ©J. Van der Wolf/ Shutterstock

Norwegian readers may compare the Magere Brug with a nice drawbridge, built in Trondheim in 1860 on the Nid River. Those of Provence (and the world) will find some resemblance with the Langlois Bridge at Arles that Van Gogh magnified in several paintings in 1888. And we must not forget that Rotterdam also has some beautiful crossings, though less romantic, such as the great cable-stayed Erasmus Bridge, opened in 1996.

A bridge worth of Van Gogh
©Tawann P. simmons/
Shutterstock

Indeed Amsterdam is a bourgeois city that has rarely been the official center of political power and where Protestant discretion is the rule, a self-satisfied city without ostentation, a city of merchants who have always concealed their fortunes, both a successful and austere city. In the twentieth century there would be a restoration of its classical stone bridges and the introduction of railings and iron sculptures, under the influence of architect Piet Kramer and the Amsterdam School of Architecture.

The city would regain its reputation as the Venice of the North and attract millions of tourists. By 2014, it had 1.1 million inhabitants. Far from the flamboyance of Venice or Saint Petersburg, other cities of canals and houses on stilts, Amsterdam is an intimate, relaxed, tolerant city which has always integrated external inputs and benefited from them.

Worldwide celebrity ©Igor
Golovniov/Shutterstock

This is an open city where individual freedom is a shared value that cannot be questioned. The Amsterdamers love freedom as much as finance. According to British writer Ian McEwan, Amsterdam appears as "a wonderfully calm and civilized city, a soothing tolerant, unprejudiced, adult place with its beautiful brick and woodcarving warehouses converted into tasteful apartments, and its small bridges coming out of a Van Gogh painting." Nice reputation.

Vincent Van Gogh, Le Pont de Langlois à Arles (April 1888), Oil on canvas, Paris, private collection

My friend Eric Verschuur, a native of Amsterdam, has travelled extensively throughout the world, but he always comes back to his city with great pleasure and admiration. He remarks: "Amsterdam is a concentration of humanity, the most cosmopolitan city in the world. It includes 180 nationalities and a third of its population has a foreign passport. This gives it a casual, relaxed atmosphere where cohabitation is indispensable and where ethnic tensions remain abated despite a recent surge of nationalist movements. Amsterdam is also a city which is flat, at sea level, which could lead to monotony, but became instead, thanks to its 165 canals and its thousand bridges, a greener city; it is the bicycle capital of the world. I think that it has as many bikes as people. This city known for its tolerance of the sale and consumption of certain substances is also multilingual. Most of its inhabitants can communicate easily in English and Dutch, often also in German and French. For all these reasons, Amsterdam is loved by its residents as well as by its numerous visitors."

Walter Süskind bascule
Bridge, near the Magere Brug
©Ivo Kendra

NEW YORK AND ITS
BROOKLYN BRIDGE

In 1626 the Dutch, at the height of their power, "bought" the island of Manhattan for sixty guilders from the Algonquins. New Amsterdam - so named because its river system was vaguely similar to that of Amstel - was born. It became a commercial warehouse, a small town which was seized by the English in 1664. King Charles II gifted the island to his brother, the Duke of York, the future James II. The town of 1,500 souls then became New York. The city would fully take off after the American civil war in the late nineteenth century when the Brooklyn Bridge that connected Manhattan Island to Brooklyn was inaugurated.

NEW YORK AND ITS BROOKLYN BRIDGE

For a few months between 1789 and 1790, New York would be the capital of the United States before this function was transferred to Philadelphia (briefly) and finally to Washington D.C. (permanently). Its population increased from 5,000 inhabitants in 1700 to 13,000 in 1750, 33,000 in 1790, 60,000 in 1800 and 123,000 in 1820.

Sunset over the East River

New York's famous orthogonal grid (12 Avenues, 152 streets) was established in 1811. This constituted a milestone in the history of urban planning, with street widths that seemed to have anticipated the age of the automobile and with an extremely simple plan (like the one which, twenty years earlier, Pierre-Charles L'Enfant had designed for Washington D.C.). It would inspire many other American cities.

By 1811, New York was already the largest city in the country, the center of import-export activities, and the starting point of the railway network. From the 1840s banks began to proliferate. Industrial units appeared in large numbers in Manhattan, Brooklyn and throughout the suburban belt. Urban transport (bus, tram, aerial metro) appeared. The city was growing due to immigration, while remaining fragmented into separate communities. A water supply network began to be installed from 1842, followed by sewer systems during the years 1860-1880. But the city was becoming increasingly congested.

Neighboring crossings: Manhattan Bridge (foreground) and Brooklyn Bridge (behind) ©iofoto/ Shutterstock

Starting in 1814, a ferry was established by the engineer Robert Fulton. It sailed every five minutes between Manhattan and Brooklyn. Tens of thousands of workers from Manhattan slept in Brooklyn on the other side of the East River. The master plan of Brooklyn was approved in 1838. The idea to build a bridge emerged, but it would have to wait for the end of the civil war (1861-1865) to take serious shape.

From the beginning, John Roebling, a visionary German engineer and a former student of Hegel in Berlin, was convinced that he was going to build a masterpiece. In 1867 he described his project as "not only the greatest bridge in the world but also the greatest engineering work of the American continent and our time." He conceived the two pierced towers as national monuments that would forever mark the face of New York. And he won his ambitious bet.

But he also wanted to connect two rival cities that previously communicated by ferry in difficult weather and traffic conditions, especially in winter. His socio-economic arguments facilitated the setting up of a public-private partnership that was the forerunner of many others (the bridge charged a toll until 1911).

GREAT AMERICAN ENGINEERS

John Roebling, designer of
the Brooklyn Bridge

As chairman of the Department of Engineering at Duke University, Henry Petrovski wrote a beautiful book about the great American civil engineers of the period 1870-1940. His opus, *Engineers of Dreams*, begins: *"Imagine a world without bridges. Imagine London, Paris and Rome without dry paths across the Thames, the Seine, and the Tiber. Imagine Manhattan as an island."*

New York has more than eighty major bridges, all metallic, including six across the East River and one over the Hudson. The United States has hundreds of thousands of bridges (some of which require better maintenance). Among the top bridge builders (who rightly deserve the title of Pontiffs) one must highlight Eads, Cooper, Lindenthal, Ammann, Steinman and, of course, Roebling. *Try and imagine a world without engineers...*

It all started with **John Roebling**, a German engineer born in 1806, a graduate of the Polytechnic Institute of Berlin (and amateur Hegelian philosopher), who emigrated to the USA in 1831 and invented the spinning of cables formed from steel wires bound in strands to support suspension bridges. He built the first railway suspension bridge over the Niagara in 1855 and from 1857 began lobbying for a bridge between Manhattan and Brooklyn. Ten years later he designed an emblematic bridge which would be the first suspension bridge using steel cables. But Roebling was wounded by a ferry accident in 1869 and died of gangrene. His son **Washington**, a young engineer of thirty-two years, took over and built the bridge in fourteen years. His dealings with the caissons are legendary. Washington's wife **Emily** played a leading role in completing the Brooklyn Bridge from 1872 as he was incapacitated (due to the dreaded decompression sickness) and had to supervise the work from his room at 111 Columbia Heights. The inauguration took place on 24 May 1883 amid great pomp and ceremony. A masterpiece of art and technology was born.

James Eads, born in 1820, built "his" bridge over the Mississippi at Saint-Louis. The crossing was opened on 4 July 1874 after five years of work, with a large fireworks display. A brilliant autodidact, Eads established the Illinois and Saint-Louis Bridge Company in 1868, and designed a great steel bridge with three arches of 150 meters each. During a trip to France he discovered the technique of building foundations in pneumatic caissons while visiting a site in Vichy. He adapted this technique to the conditions of Saint-Louis and work began in late 1869. He became chief engineer of the first steel arch bridge in the USA[1] without having obtained any university education! But caisson decompression sickness took its toll, leaving sixteen dead. And a controversy ensued with Roebling, from 1870, about the authorship of the caissons. Technically the bridge of Saint-Louis is based on the cantilever principle. Many young engineers worked on the design and construction of the bridge. Eads then became interested in the Isthmus of Panama (he advocated an alternative to the canal, the *ship railway*), before he died in 1887 in Nassau, Bahamas.

The longest cantilever in the world was to be built in Quebec on the Saint-Lawrence from 1905 under the supervision of **Theodore Cooper** (a respected engineer born in 1839, who participated in the project of Saint-Louis). On 27 August 1907 Cooper was informed of serious problems of torsion of the deck. He did not have time to stop the project (he was in New York) and two days later the bridge collapsed, causing the death of 75 workers. This accident prompted the engineers to review their calculations, for example for the Queensboro Bridge (1909). The Quebec Bridge was rebuilt in 1916 but the last span collapsed into the river, marking the end of cantilevers. It was, however, completed in 1917.

Gustav Lindenthal strongly criticized the design faults of the first Quebec Bridge. Born in 1850 in Brno (Moravia) he was the greatest engineer of the period 1885-1920. He built many bridges and dominated the profession for forty years. His masterpiece is the Hell Gate Bridge. Self-taught, he began working in Vienna before migrating to Philadelphia. He became an engineer in 1879 and moved to Pittsburgh where he built his first steel bridge (the Smithfield Street Bridge) in 1883, the year of the opening of the Brooklyn Bridge. He then devoted himself to mechanical theory and his great project of crossing the Hudson River in New York. He said: "If art to build bridges is ancient, science of bridge building is modern" – indeed, an art older than man, "because monkeys also build bridges". Two companies were competing for the bridge over the Hudson in 1890-1891. A suspension bridge was approved by the Corps of Army Engineers. Lindenthal began his work in 1895 but never got the contract. He was appointed Commissioner of Bridges in New York in 1902. His Williamsburg Bridge over the East River was built between 1895 and 1903 by L.L. Buck, and was a little longer than the Brooklyn Bridge (487.5 meters against 486 meters). His Manhattan Bridge followed between 1906 and 1909 while the Quebec Bridge collapsed and the cantilever Queensboro Bridge opened in 1909. No longer Commissioner, Lindenthal then undertook his great work, a viaduct from Long Island to Manhattan and the Bronx, with two young assistants, Othmar Ammann and David Steinman.

---

1 A few years later in Scotland, in 1890, the massive Firth of Forth Bridge, designed by Benjamin Baker, was inaugurated. It is composed of six giant cantilevers, with three piers and two 500-meter spans. At that time there was a serious competition between cantilevers and suspension bridges.

This was the Hell Gate (a railway bridge) whose metal arch of 310 meters, a gateway to New York Harbor, opened in 1917. Lindenthal then resumed his project on the Hudson, still without success. He passed away in 1935 in New Jersey.

Born in Switzerland in 1879, **Othmar Ammann** took over from his mentor. He became a civil engineer in 1902, went to America and began to dream of crossing the Hudson. He joined the Pennsylvania Steel Company, worked on the construction of the Queensboro Bridge and participated in the investigation on the Quebec Bridge. In 1912 he joined Lindenthal's company, which then had 95 engineers. He worked on the Hell Gate Bridge as deputy chief engineer and wrote a detailed report on this work. In 1923 Ammann began to design and lobby for a suspension bridge over the Hudson (facing 179th Street), thus competing with his former boss. Two bridges were built to Staten Island on Arthur Kill between 1925 and 1928, supervised by Ammann. Then Ammann began a beautiful project in Bayonne between Staten Island and New Jersey, heading a group of brilliant engineers, such as Leon Moisseiff (born in Latvia in 1872) and Joseph Strauss (father of the Golden Gate Bridge). He would build the longest metal arch in the world (512 meters), one meter longer than the arch of Sydney. In the meantime, the long-awaited construction of the suspension bridge over the Hudson was beginning in September 1927. Moisseiff opted for pure metallic pillars without heavy masonry coating (the Great Depression called for financial restraint and saving). Le Corbusier expressed his admiration for the purity and lightness of the structure. The George Washington Bridge later broke all records (with a span of 1,067 meters that was surpassed six years later by the Golden Gate Bridge). The George Washington Bridge, Ammann's masterpiece, was inaugurated by Franklin Roosevelt, then Governor of New York, on 24 October 1931, six months ahead of schedule. Ammann and Lindenthal came together to the ceremony. A powerful symbol. On its part, the Bayonne Bridge, inaugurated on 14 November 1931, received the prize for the most beautiful bridge in the year 1931.

George Washington Bridge across the Hudson River (1931), designed by Othmar Ammann ©Gilya/Shutterstock

The George Washington and Bayonne bridges, which were completed in the same year, confirmed Ammann as the "Pontifex Maximus" of New York. He completed the Triborough Bridge in 1936 (between the three boroughs of Manhattan, Queens and Bronx) and the Bronx-Whitestone Bridge in 1939. After the Second World War, Ammann joined Charles Whitney to design the lower deck of the George Washington Bridge, which was opened in 1962. This bridge, which now supports 14 lanes (8 on the upper deck, 6 on the lower deck), was already used by 35 million vehicles per year at the time of its inauguration. A sculpture of Ammann's bust was then unveiled by the governors of New York and New Jersey. He was then 83 years old and stated that this great bridge was a collective undertaking. His last bridge was the huge Verrazano-Narrows Bridge between Brooklyn and Staten Island carried out with Milton Brumer, the chief engineer heading two hundred engineers, and opened on 21 November 1964. A little longer than the Golden Gate (1,298 meters, that is 18 meters more), it remained the longest bridge in the world until 1981. Ammann, lost in a crowd of officials, was recognized by Commissioner Robert Moses in his speech as "perhaps the greatest engineer of all times" but his name was not mentioned. Ammann died in 1965, at the age of 86. He had by then realized all his bridge dreams and had faced no serious technical failure.

Bayonne Bridge (1931), designed by Othmar Ammann ©iofoto/Shutterstock

Born in Cincinnati in 1870, **Joseph Strauss** obtained his engineering degree in 1892 with a proposed bridge over the Bering Strait. He worked in Chicago on bascule bridges. From 1921 he became interested in crossing the Golden Gate that opens San Francisco Bay to the Pacific Ocean. He recruited Leon Moisseiff and Othmar Ammann as consultants. Moisseiff and Charles Ellis, and later Clifford Paine, proposed a suspension bridge which was presented on 27 August 1930 and funded by subscriptions (bonds and shares). This monumental bridge (1,280 meters) was inaugurated on 27 May 1937 in the presence of 200,000 people. At that time the calculation of structures seemed well established, but the effects of wind were still poorly understood, as would be found out a few years later. Aerodynamics as a science was still in its infancy.

Manhattan Bridge (1909), designed by Gustav Lindenthal ©Joshua Haviv/ Shutterstock

Leon Moisseiff was also a great engineer, who graduated from Columbia in 1895. He worked on many bridges in New York, including the Manhattan Bridge, and influenced the design of most large suspension bridges in the U.S.A. between 1910 and 1940, including those of San Francisco. He conceived the excessively slender Tacoma Narrows, south of Seattle, completed in 1940 (the third in length after the Golden Gate and George Washington bridges), which waved and collapsed in November 1940, without causing any human casualty. The collapse came as a shock to the profession, but the war became the new priority. Moisseiff died of a heart attack in 1943. He had committed a single error: ignoring that flexibility has some limits and that aerodynamic oscillations, both longitudinal and lateral, could be fatal.

The last great American engineer to shape New York's cityscape was **David Steinman**, who was born in 1886 in Belarus. He arrived in New York at the age of four and spent his childhood at the foot of the Brooklyn Bridge while the Williamsburg Bridge was under construction. He came from a poor family, but graduated from Columbia in 1909 with a proposal for the Henry Hudson Bridge (Manhattan-Bronx) which would be implemented in 1936. He worked with Lindenthal on the Hell Gate between 1914 and 1917 and proposed in 1926 the Liberty Bridge which foreshadowed the Verrazano-Narrows. He also published several theoretical works and the history of the Roeblings in 1945. He was often in competition with Ammann. He won the tender for the suspension bridge of Florianópolis in Brazil which, once completed in 1926, was the longest bridge in South America. He built many bridges, including the Thousand Islands on the Saint-Lawrence River in 1938 and the Deer Isle in Maine in 1939, and theorized on bridge aerodynamics. The great work of Steinman was the Mackinac Bridge in Michigan, for which he was contracted in 1953. A very impressive bridge of 2,600 meters, its main suspended span is 1,160 meters long. At the end of his life, Steinman renovated the Brooklyn Bridge in 1960 and proposed a project for the Strait of Messina[2]. He died before his great rival Ammann, without gaining the recognition of the latter. Steinman was a writer in his spare time: he compared bridges to poems thrown over the waves, as markers of civilization.

There is no doubt that American engineers were at the forefront of bridge-design between 1870 and 1970. Many of them came from Europe where bridge-building had a long history. Australia took an increasingly important role in bridge-building in the 1930s (a prosperous decade following the Great Depression), followed by Japan in the 1960s, and China from the 1990s. But Europe, despite its narrow waterways, has not been left out and continues to innovate with its cable-stayed bridges. Santiago Calatrava, in particular, has positioned himself as "the" architect-engineer of the late 20th century and early 21st century, an authentic "bridge sculptor" who has managed to place aesthetics above financial constraints.

2   This project re-appeared periodically later on. In March 2009, Silvio Berlusconi announced a budget of 1.3 billion Euros, out of a total of 6 billion, for what would be the largest suspension span in the world (3,300 meters). The global economic crisis has so far postponed this project indefinitely.

The Brooklyn Bridge spans over the East River to connect New York and Brooklyn, which in 1898 became the Manhattan and Brooklyn boroughs of Greater New York. It must be recalled that the East River is not a river but an inlet with strong currents, subject to tidal movements and with heavy traffic. The Brooklyn Bridge was the first steel suspension bridge. With 486 meters between two huge granite piles, it remained the longest bridge in the world for twenty years. Inaugurated on 24 May 1883 after a 13-year construction process, it was designed by John Roebling and built under the direction of Washington Roebling, who took over from his father after his accidental death in 1869. Washington himself suffered health problems three years later (resulting from the caisson disease also known as "the bends"), and his wife Emily played a crucial role in directing the work for ten years. Washington remained bedridden and could not even participate in the grand opening ceremonies. Trained on the job, Emily (1843-1903) was, in fact, one of the first female engineers in history, using her husband's daily advice, negotiating with all parties involved, and controlling the quality of the work.

Brooklyn Bridge under a tumultuous sky ©Ilja Masik/ Shutterstock

The Brooklyn Bridge was experimental in many ways and has tested several innovations, in terms of foundations as well as metal cables, but it also caused the death of twenty men, mainly due to the phenomenon of fast uncontrolled decompression experienced by workers after laboring in compressed air chambers (or caissons) – a condition well known now to deep sea divers. The compressed-air chambers allowed workers to dig foundations in the riverbed. Aside from the casualties, the worksite did not suffer any major setback and was not even affected by the severe economic crisis of 1873-1877.

One of the two neo-gothic pillars ©Stuart Monk/ Shutterstock

The main inaugural address, on 24 May 1883 (coincidentally on Queen Victoria's birthday), was delivered by Abram Hewitt, the future mayor of New York, in the presence of the President of the United States. Fittingly, it was a speech worthy of an anthology that portrayed the Brooklyn Bridge as a marvel of civilization, comparing it to the pyramids, using it to illustrate the power of technology and democracy (the civil war was still fresh in American memories), and depicting it as a key link between two independent cities. One could associate the Brooklyn Bridge to the Chain Bridge, which after its inauguration 34 earlier, united the rival cities of Buda and Pest, before the invention of steel, and to the Bosphorus Bridge that would much later link two continents, thanks to steel and pre-stressed concrete.

The world was then entering a new era with the expanding industrial revolution that allowed rich countries, primarily the United States, to reap its full benefits. That same year (1883) the New York metropolitan area had two million inhabitants. It was the largest city in the USA. Its population would increase from 3.4 million in 1900 (including Brooklyn, and 4.2 million if one considers Newark), to 5.6 million in 1920 and 21 million in 2014 (again, including Newark). It would become the largest city in the world in 1925 and remain so for more than 30 years. In 1886 the Statue of Liberty, a gift from France, was inaugurated, symbolically opening a new era of free enterprise, of extensive building programs, of freedom of expression… and of world domination.

On 1 January 1898 New York and Brooklyn finally merged into Greater New York, which took precedence over London to become the most important port in the world. That same year George Gershwin was born in Brooklyn. Manhattan was fully subdivided in 1900, and the metro was constructed at the beginning of the twentieth century. Grand Central Station was rebuilt, the Municipal Building was raised and the first skyscrapers appeared, reaching 26 floors in 1890, 47 floors in 1908 (Singer Building, 186 meters, destroyed in 1968) and 57 floors in 1913 (Woolworth Building, 241 meters). In 1929 there would be 188 buildings with more than twenty stories, all with metal structures. The Chrysler Building (77 floors, 319 meters, 1930) and the Empire State Building (102 floors, 381 meters, built in 410 days in 1931) in turn became the tallest buildings in the world, the new pyramids or ziggurats of modernity.

Chrysler Building and Queensboro Bridge ©Steve Collender/Shutterstock

But slums persisted in the Bronx, Queens and Brooklyn. With the economic crisis of 1929 they even reached Central Park. Social housing would have to wait for the New Deal and Mayor La Guardia (1933-1945) to benefit from strong political will. The city became a major cultural capital in the inter-war period, but rather than a melting pot, it remained a gigantic mosaic of communities that did not mix.

In 1944 the railway on the Brooklyn Bridge was dismantled and in 1945 the bridge was re-opened to pedestrians and vehicles. In 1948 the first United Nations Secretary-General, Trygve Lie, saluted New York as the present and future "capital of the world". While Europe had to be reconstructed after the Second World War, New York seemed invincible. The United Nations headquarters, under construction on the banks of the East River, were inaugurated in 1952.

United Nations headquarters along the East River ©Sean Pavone Photo/Shutterstock

Today 150 million people use the Brooklyn Bridge each year – some 400,000 per day. The bridge, with its elevated walkway five meters above the road, is open to pedestrians and rushing employees. It offers a magnificent view of the skyscrapers of Manhattan, all of which were built after its construction, as if Roebling had planned skyscrapers fifty years ahead of his time. In 1883 the buildings of Manhattan had only four floors, and the bridge piers were five times higher. Of course the most beautiful view is the one from Brooklyn, with the bridge in the foreground and the Manhattan skyline in the background, the subject of millions of photographs and postcards.

Walkway at the top of the bridge

Many poets would praise the Brooklyn Bridge, including Hart Crane ("To Brooklyn Bridge", 1930, which launched the image of the harp) and Vladimir Mayakovski ("Bruklinski Most", 1925), because this bridge has become a symbol of an aesthetic modernity reflecting the economic success of the West and also, before even the Empire State Building, the symbol of a new world that was taking off. Brooklyn Bridge announced an American twentieth century – airplanes, motorcars, cinemascope, jazz music, urban lights ... and the beginning of the great migration and the urban transition. A few steps away, Ellis Island was poised to receive millions of Europeans in search of Eldorado. Brooklyn Bridge would impress them as it appeared as one of the first and most successful American feats.

"If the world explodes, if chaos reduces our planet into dust, what will remain is that bridge, emerging above the destruction ... Thanks to the bridge, future geologists will be able to recreate our contemporary world." (Mayakovski). And the Brooklyn Bridge can still claim – despite the loss in 2001 of the World Trade Centre's Twin Towers that embellished its night-time panorama – to be the most beautiful bridge in the world and also the most photographed. It was renovated in the 1950s by David Steinman, but not without controversy. New York remains today the capital of the world, in many areas (primarily financial and cultural). American public opinion cites Brooklyn Bridge as one of the most beautiful monuments on earth. Americans are (it will not hurt to admit it once!) absolutely right about this.

The USA is very rich in bridges and large rivers. As the Franco-American painter Marcel Duchamp said in his typically understated way: "the only American contributions to world art are plumbing and bridges". Many American bridges of the first half of the twentieth century are indeed splendid works of art, as well as durable demonstrations of impressive building techniques and of the genius of engineers. The City of New York, with its two large rivers, is a paradise for all bridge-lovers. It hosts a dozen of very fine metallic structures. On the East River one can admire in particular, near the UN headquarters, the Queensboro Bridge (cantilever, 1909) of Gustav Lindenthal, and further down the Manhattan Bridge (also from 1909, started by Lindenthal and completed by Moisseiff) near the Brooklyn Bridge. At the entrance of the Manhattan Bridge, the well-travelled tourist or cultured New Yorker may note the unexpected presence of clones of Porte Saint-Denis in Paris (1872) and of the colonnade of Saint-Peter's in Rome.

Entrance of the Manhattan Bridge

On the Hudson River one can admire (for once I am in agreement with Le Corbusier) the great George Washington Bridge opened with fanfare in October 1931 by Franklin D. Roosevelt, the longest suspension bridge in the world at the time (1,067 meters of central span with towers of 183 meters using four cables from the Roebling Company), designed by Othmar Ammann. It now bears fourteen traffic lanes, on two superimposed decks. And at the entrance of New York harbor between Staten Island and Brooklyn, one should admire the impressive Verrazano Narrows Bridge, which was also in its time (1964) the longest suspension bridge in the world (2,038 meters of suspended structure, central span 1,298 meters, total length 4,176 meters, width 31 meters, height of towers above water 210 meters, clearance above water 69 meters, four cables of 91 centimeters diameter with 26,108 steel wires and 61 strands per cable).

Incidentally, the Bayonne Bridge between Staten Island and New Jersey, also designed by O. Ammann, and the splendid contemporary Australian Sydney Harbour Bridge (both from 1932) have almost the same length and use the same technique (single metal arch). They were for decades the longest bridges of this type in the world. At the bridge's inauguration, on 15 November 1931, the Basque town of Bayonne fittingly sent a congratulatory telegram to the Port Authority of New York and New Jersey. Quite a distance from Manhattan, the Bayonne Bridge is unknown to New Yorkers and visitors alike, but it is nevertheless worth a visit, despite its two edges that could have deserved better treatment. Today engineers envisage raising it to let the huge container ships pass, those that will transit though the widened Panama Canal. Another great work of the 1930s is the Triborough bridge(s), a gigantic set of four bridges connecting the boroughs of Manhattan, Queens and the Bronx, which were initiated by Robert Moses as the head of the contracting authority. This American Haussmann ruled all infrastructure work in New York from 1934 till 1968, building twelve large bridges, many expressways (1,000 kilometers in total) and hundreds of parks and sport fields! With eighty bridges, including some truly monumental ones, New York City arguably holds the world record for the linear and aggregate mass of urban crossings. And many of them are real wonders that justify the legitimate pride of the city's inhabitants.

Queensboro Bridge (cantilever, 1909) designed by Gustav Lindenthal ©Sean Pavone Photo/Shutterstock

But the Brooklyn Bridge remains the one and only true icon, not only of the city but of the whole country. We know that New York has served as the backdrop for hundreds of movies and thousands of books while tens of thousands of articles have attempted to identify its magic, often associating it with its bridges. As an example we could quote an excerpt from a nice article in the French Le Monde newspaper: "New York has always something new that surprises and an enormous vitality that leaves you breathless, this mixture of old bricks, young ruins and sparkling sites, these hastening crowds, rushing yellow taxis, hot steams escaping from the pavement like sighs from industrial monsters, working obscurely, under the asphalt, perhaps supporting the naves of steel and glass of skyscrapers that never sleep, do not stop pushing their antennas in the night. It is said that New York is a standing city. This is a beautiful picture, as its silhouette on the sky (which Americans rightly call the skyline) is lofty, bristling with pride and ambition, with urban enthusiasm and the exhilaration of heights." (Michel Braudeau, Le Monde, 19 July 1995.)

Manhattan Bridge at full moon ©East Village Images/ Shutterstock

As a symbol of the city, the Brooklyn Bridge has inspired countless paintings and novels in all languages. Sartre himself was impressed: "I love New York. I learned to love it. This is the most amazing monument that man has ever erected to himself."

Paul Morand wrote in 1930: "It is difficult to speak of the Brooklyn Bridge without succumbing to excessive lyricism. I like to walk there, at nightfall ... It controls the perspective and sets a key deep black haze of distant horizons embedded in the shadow, between its steel nets. Go to the center of Brooklyn Bridge at dusk, and in fifteen seconds you will understand New York."

A book by Richard Haw, published in 2005, offers a well-documented cultural history of the bridge and its representations, from its origins to the present day (see box).

CULTURAL HISTORY OF A CULT OBJECT

The Brooklyn Bridge is a national obsession, a fascination. For most Americans it is the most important work of engineering of the nineteenth century, an exemplary icon of social progress and industrial technology. The bridge is a symbol of unity and aestheticized hope, a hyphen between wealthy Manhattan and needy Brooklyn. Its 50th and 100th anniversaries were celebrated in style. On 24 May 1983 New Yorkers celebrated the centenary of this massive monument, advertised through a poster by Andy Warhol; they celebrated its 125th anniversary in 2008 over five days. They remain convinced that the most popular bridge in the world, a monumental statue representing freedom and unity of the nation, will outlive their city.

The cultural construction of the bridge ran parallel to its physical construction. In an extremely detailed book, British Professor Richard Haw, who lives in New York, explores how people, artists, writers, journalists and politicians have interpreted the bridge since its creation, how they have somehow canonized it and brought it to the pinnacle of national imagination. Prof. Haw casts a critical eye on the idealization of the bridge, stating in passing that John Roebling was a domestic tyrant, and emphasizing the dichotomy between the romanticism and materialism that the bridge simultaneously represents.

Brooklyn had a million inhabitants in 1898 when the municipal consolidation took place. It was the third largest U.S. city, having quintupled since 1862. Its industrial and cultural development was dramatic during these 36 years, particularly after the opening of the bridge which increased its proximity to Manhattan, the borough of jobs and wealth.

The Brooklyn Bridge symbolized restored unity in the aftermath of the civil war. It was as important a public space as Manhattan's Central Park, New York's great leveler, which opened in 1859. However, the public was kept away from the opening ceremony on 24 May 1883, the same day that Alexander III, who would have his bridge in Paris, was crowned Tsar of Russia. A week later, on 30 May, twelve people died on Brooklyn Bridge, crushed by a panicking crowd (an event known as the Memorial Day Tragedy).

Abram Hewitt lyrically called the bridge "a monument to the skill of a free people, to the arts of peace" and compared it to the pyramids of Egypt, "recalling the magnificence of a tyrannical dynasty". But he forgot to mention his own involvement in a corruption scandal. Vladimir Mayakovski dedicated a poem to the Brooklyn Bridge in 1925. The Russian poet admired the bridge in which he recognized his constructivist ideal, dialectically combining stone archways representing the past and metallic cables symbolizing a socialist future. He imagined a bridge announcing the rise of socialism. Federico Garcia Lorca, on the other hand, was not impressed. He came to New York in 1929 and wrote a few poems about the city, including one on the bridge, which he described as an "incredible crocodile resting beneath the tender protest of the stars, in a sleepless city". Henry Miller hated the bridge, in which he saw a "harp of death". Lewis Mumford wrote a socially progressive play titled The Builders of the Bridge. Hundreds of essays and novels are devoted to the Brooklyn Bridge or use it as backdrop. Richard Haw has read them all.

The bridge has elicited thousands of interpretations and emotions in the last 130 years. Although Roland Barthes seems to have forgotten it, unlike his American alter ego Alan Trachtenberg (1965), the Brooklyn Bridge is a "semiotic object" par excellence. Many analysts compare the bridge's technical and aesthetic success with persistent inequalities, slums, overcrowding and violence in the city. This contradiction has constituted a classic paradigm of urban sociology (physical space versus social space) since 1925. Others compare the poetic bridge to the rigidity of the orthogonal grid of the city, as if the bridge was representing freedom in a normative and oppressive urban set up. On 24 May 1933, when the Great Depression hit the country the hardest (25% of the population was unemployed at that time), optimistic 50th anniversary speeches ignored the crisis and did not mention the most recent achievement, the George Washington Bridge (the only bridge over the Hudson).

Hart Crane associated the bridge with a harp to better glorify it. Lovers take countless pictures of themselves in front of it. Protesters know how to use it to alert public opinion. Advertising agencies fight to make the best use of it. According to Professor Haw, the cultural history of the Brooklyn Bridge is the product of two disorganized but distinct communities. The first, formalist, is fascinated by the aesthetic quality, elegance and strength of the structure and ignores its context, its environment, its impact. The second seeks to look beyond the sublime effect and to relate the bridge to the city's vast humanity, to its history, and to the peoples who built, maintained, used and celebrated it.

Anniversary stamp ©Solodov Alexey/
Shutterstock

Urban monuments that are wonders of the world can be counted on the fingers of one hand, maybe two. They include the Giza Pyramids, Hagia Sophia, the Parthenon, the Forbidden City, the Taj Mahal, the Eiffel Tower, the Golden Gate Bridge and the Brooklyn Bridge. Most of these monuments can be visited but are not part of the ordinary life of residents. This is not so with the two American bridges, which are used daily by thousands of citizens, which connect people to their history and to their present and which are an integral part of urban life. These works of art and scientific prowess are not fossilized remnants of a distant past, but witnesses to human interactions, both functionally and culturally. The Brooklyn Bridge is by far the monument that has attracted the most ink (and paint) over the last hundred years and yet it lives with New York City, every day, every hour. An exceptional icon.

Despite its industrial decline in the 1970s and 1980s, New York today remains the world center of international capital, a city in perpetual motion, but also a city in a state of unstable equilibrium. It is a landmark of modern architecture. Among the recent achievements one may mention the IAC Building (555 West 18th St.) by Frank Gehry, and the New Museum of Contemporary Art (235 Bowery) by Kazuyo Sejima and Ryue Nishizawa. Also of note is the "High Line" of Hudson River Park on the banks of the Hudson. New York is a successful product of the twentieth century because it has managed to combine an undeniable urban aesthetic, multiple social and cultural dynamics and global financial transactions. But it is also a product fragmented by a heterogeneous patchwork of sub-spaces, and a fragile one precisely because it is so symbolic and strategic – as evidenced by the attacks of 11 September 2001 and the crisis that began in the fall of 2008 on Wall Street.

The destruction of the Twin Towers had a huge impact on the Brooklyn Bridge, not only because the bridge allowed tens of thousands of people to flee the scene of the tragedy, but also because its symbolic role was revived in 2002, as a place of solidarity. It has also served as a public space open to all and taking on a new dimension, for example, during the great blackout of 14 August 2003. The great bridge serves as a therapist; it helps boost the morale of the population. The disappearance of the Twin Towers (now replaced by the One World Trade Center, 417 meters high, not including its tall spire) from New York's stunning skyline saddens many visitors but the presence and strength of the magnificent Brooklyn Bridge is a reassuring symbol of resilience for New Yorkers. Brooklyn Bridge brings freshness and vitality to those who cross it. It generates friendliness and sometimes euphoria; it frees hikers, cyclists, and even employees who work in the neighboring skyscrapers. It hosts anti-Wall Street protesters as well as advertising photographers. It is the epitome of urbanity.

"Occupy Wall Street, Occupy Brooklyn Bridge", October 2011

My friend Michael Cohen, Professor of International Relations at the New School in New York and former urban strategist at the World Bank, emphasizes the social role of the bridge: "In October 2011, as the Occupy Wall Street Movement was gaining momentum, the police attacked demonstrators on a beautiful weekend and pushed them off the area near Wall Street and on to the Brooklyn Bridge where they then arrested many peaceful people. So the Brooklyn Bridge became a space for protestors and took on a new, contemporary meaning! A student commented the next day, 'How could the police do that? Push us onto the Brooklyn Bridge! Don't they know that the Bridge is a space of recreation and peace?' The protestors were angry at the police, but they were particularly offended that the police used the Bridge in their repression of the people. During the next few days, this use of the Bridge was the subject of a lot of commentaries on television and the internet."

The Big Apple fascinates newcomers. This fascination is perhaps the biggest mystery of the multifaceted and orderly city, where impressive skyscrapers coexist with provincial streets, where nomadic tribes still manage to settle, where an inexplicable feeling of freedom hangs in the air. A young and always moving city. It is said that New Yorkers are like sharks, that if they stop moving they die. They drink their coffee in paper cups, while walking, not wasting a second. They sometimes worry visitors with their excitement and constant determination.

Williamsburg Bridge (1903) with Manhattan
and Brooklyn bridges in the background
©iofoto/Shutterstock

A former industrial city and land of immigrants, Brooklyn on its part is currently witnessing an artistic revival in the neighborhood of Down Under Manhattan Bridge Overpass (DUMBO). The old warehouses are being converted into lofts (Brooklyn native Woody Allen probably appreciates this change.) Indeed gentrification is making great strides. Williamsburg ("Billburg") is becoming an unconventional and bohemian village. The Fulton Ferry State Park, opened in 1979, offers beautiful views of Manhattan and serves as a standard backdrop for wedding photos.

The alleys and squares of Central Park and the walkway at the top of the Brooklyn Bridge remain the two most fabulous public spaces in New York. The Brooklyn Bridge is probably the archetype of post-modern space as it provides meeting opportunities without sacrificing mobility, potentially associating the convivial city to the one that moves ahead.

A wonderful two kilometer promenade, open to pedestrians and cyclists ©Jeremy Meek

PORTO AND ITS
PONTE DOM LUIS

Porto is Portugal's second largest city, the capital of the north. It is located at the mouth of the Douro, on the right bank of this golden river, near the ocean. The Douro River, which is 850 kilometers long, starts in Spain, in Old Castile, where it is called Duero. Porto – the port – was born around a cathedral in the twelfth century. The city has two beautiful arch bridges that were built before the Eiffel Tower and prefigured it.

PORTO AND ITS PONTE DOM LUIS

The Douro, golden river, towards its mouth ©Martin Lehmann/Shutterstock

With its twin city on the left bank named Cale (a former Roman Castro, or fortified settlement), and which is now called Vila Nova de Gaia, Porto gave the country its name (Portu-Cale) when it separated from Spain, specifically from the Kingdom of León in the twelfth century and then in 1385 when the Avis family was brought to the throne in Lisbon.

Portugal dominated a large part of the world at the beginning of Europe's colonial expansion. In 1460 its first explorer, Prince Henry the Navigator, passed away after organizing maritime conquests over four decades. In 1498, Vasco da Gama became the first European to make the voyage to India by sea, through the Cape of Good Hope and Malindi on the East African coast and onward to Calicut on India's west coast, a journey that would be known as "the spice route". In 1500 Cabral discovered Brazil; in 1515 Albuquerque occupied Goa, Malacca and Hormuz. But in 1580 Portugal returned to the bosom of Spain and the two countries began to decline. The House of Braganza took over in 1640, and in 1668 Spain permanently recognized the independence of Portugal, which was immediately allied to England. From the eighteenth century the wealth of Portugal came mainly from Brazil, making Dom João V (1689-1750) the richest monarch in Europe. The republic was proclaimed in 1910.

Looking upstream, Porto on the left ©Javier Gil/ Shutterstock

Porto has always been a rebellious city, a city of wine and tripe. In the fifteenth century the shipyards of Porto contributed significantly to providing the fleet of the king of Portugal with the ships needed to conquer the world. With its Baroque architecture and granite cathedral, Porto is home to some beautiful churches, including Sao Francisco, but the old city is chaotic, awaiting restoration. And it is sometimes a victim of Douro's overflows, as in 1909 when the water level came dangerously close to the lower deck of Dom Luis Bridge.

In 1809 the city withstood Napoleon's troops who invaded the region under the command of Soult, while King Dom João and the court had fled to Brazil in November 1807. The floating bridge, or Ponte de Las Barcas, which enabled the inhabitants to flee to the south, disintegrated, causing the death of some 5,000 people on 29 March 1809. A bronze bas-relief on the wall of the Ribeira pays tribute to the victims of this tragedy. Wellington counter-attacked immediately, expelled Soult, and the English continued to control the trade in port, a wine originating in the upper Douro, and to name the city Oporto. Portugal and England, historic allies, had in 1703 signed the Methuen Treaty which gave the British exceptional trade privileges that they intended to keep.

A few decades later, in 1876-1877, another famous Frenchman, less aggressive than Bonaparte, Gustave Eiffel, built a metal structure, in wrought iron (not steel), the Maria Pia railway arch bridge, named in honor of Maria Pia of Savoy, then Queen of Portugal. A few years later he built the longer Garabit viaduct (1880 -1884) in France's Massif Central, an example of superb technical prowess (a parabolic 165-metre iron arch), which was one of his last bridges. Then he devoted himself to the Parisian Tower that bears his name. His elegant bridge over the Douro was used by trains until 1991. The four arches supporting the first floor of the Eiffel Tower seem directly inspired by the Maria Pia Bridge and the Garabit viaduct. These openwork structures, very light and quick to implement, have the important advantage of not catching the wind.

GUSTAVE EIFFEL, ENGINEER OF METALLIC LACE

Gustave Eiffel

Gustave Eiffel, famously known for the tower that bears his name, was also one of the most brilliant bridge builders of the nineteenth century. His trademark became so famous that he is wrongly attributed with all metal structures of his time. He was a great engineer, a successful entrepreneur, an aesthete and a businessman. He began his career as a bridge designer and ended it with the construction of the world's most visited tower. Born in 1832 in Dijon, he was educated in that city before entering the Ecole Centrale de Paris where he graduated in 1855. His career evolved in three distinct phases.

Bridges and Viaducts

Eiffel collaborated initially with Charles Nepveu, a contractor specializing in metal construction, which was undergoing a spectacular boom. Durable, lightweight and easy to handle, iron was then preferred to stone as it was less expensive. The young engineer learned fast and demonstrated his potential. His first great achievement was a 500-metre railway bridge in Bordeaux, built in 1858. He then used for the first time compressed air chambers to build the foundation of the piers. The success of his collaboration with Nepveu gained their company recognition, and also made Eiffel known.

In 1864 Eiffel set up his own company as a consulting and structural engineer, and established his workshops in Levallois Perret near Paris. The company obtained several orders for major viaducts and buildings with metal structures. Eiffel did not hesitate to seek contracts in other parts of the world. Between 1872 and 1874 he worked in South America (Chile, Bolivia and Peru) and in 1875 he built the Western Railway Station in Budapest.

In 1876, the Maria Pia Bridge over the Douro River in Porto (353 meters) sealed his international reputation, due to its cantilever construction process, and opened doors to new markets, including the Viana Bridge (736 meters). His favorite technique was to precast metallic components in the factory and rivet them in situ. This allowed for lighter, faster to build, cheaper and stylish structures that will forever remain the signature of Eiffel and his disciples.

Eiffel's engineering talent, his enthusiasm to seize any new idea, but also his ability to surround himself with brilliant technicians contributed to the company's success. Three associated engineers deserve to be mentioned: Théophile Seyrig (designer of Dom Luis Bridge in Porto in 1886), who joined Eiffel in 1868, Émile Nouguier (designer of the Saint-Louis Bridge in 1897), working with Eiffel from 1875, and Maurice Koechlin, who joined the company in 1879.

For the Universal Exhibition of 1878, Eiffel proposed a project for a bridge and cultural space, above the bridge of Iena in Paris, which would eventually not be built. In 1880 he was awarded the contract of the Garabit viaduct which quickly became famous because of its height (122 meters) and its parabolic shape. The completion of this bridge, located in the Cantal departement, and based on an initial concept by Leon Boyer, constituted another success. Its arch of 165 meters that supports the deck then held a world record. The image of the Garabit Viaduct also graced the last 200 franc banknote.

In 1883 Eiffel built his final bridge, the Tardes viaduct in the Creuse departement. The second phase of his career began then.

Garabit Viaduct (1884)

The one-thousand-foot tower

In preparation for the 1889 Universal Exposition, Maurice Koechlin and Emile Nouguier had the idea of building a large metal tower. Their draft, developed in June 1884, benefitted from the collaboration of architect Stéphane Sauvestre, who refined the design. At first reluctant, Gustave Eiffel appropriated the idea of his associates by acquiring the patent from Koechlin and filing it on 18 September 1884.

In 1886 he was awarded the contract for a tower of 300 meters (1000 feet) to serve as a monumental portal to the Universal Exposition. His proposal unanimously outweighed those of the other candidates, though it had its critics. Indeed some French artists opposed to the construction described as "a giddy, ridiculous tower dominating Paris like a gigantic smokestack". He signed an agreement with the government on 8 January 1887 and advanced from his own pocket 80% of the cost of the work, estimated at 8.5 million gold francs. Governmental authorities granted him a concession of twenty years, from 1 January 1890, after which the tower would return to the city of Paris, which would be allowed to demolish it.

It took only two years, two months and five days to build the tower. Its lower part actually looks like four bridge arches assembled on the first floor. Construction started on 28 January 1887. Craters were dug in the Champ-de-Mars to receive the foundation pillars, the terrain was drained, hydraulic jacks were installed, and innovative solutions were invented at each stage. All the tower's structures were prepared at the factory in Levallois-Perret before being transferred to the site.

Parisians observed the majestic elevation of the building at the incredible pace of two meters per month. On 14 July 1888 the second floor was reached and on 31 March 1889, the third floor was completed. This stunning technical achievement allowed the tallest, yet very light (8,000 tons), tower in the world to be delivered on time. Eiffel received the Legion of Honor, a rare distinction at the time. His 225 workers, sky carpenters, shared his glory. The year 1889 was one of triumph for Eiffel and the peak of his dual career as an engineer and entrepreneur. His landmark tower would be the highlight of the centenary of the French Revolution.

From mid-May 1889, the monument was open to the public who was amazed not only by the sheer beauty of the structure, but also by the ultra-fast and totally new hydraulic lifts. And in less than six months until the end of the Expo, the Tower received two million visitors, almost reimbursing Eiffel for his personal investments. The tower was the tallest building in the world, a glorification of industrial technology, whose construction was not marked by any death and experienced only one strike. A profitable business for a "useless" object that spoke to the soul of the city and would later become a symbol of freedom as the antenna of Radio Paris.

The post-Tower

In 1893 Gustave Eiffel was convicted and pardoned for his role in the Panama Canal affair. He had not been able to work with Ferdinand de Lesseps. A better engineer than he was a financial expert, his new career was plagued by controversy, and he retired from business to devote himself entirely to the sustainability of his masterpiece. Since Eiffel's management of the Tower was only guaranteed until 1910, and there was always the threat that the authorities might one day demolish it, he tried desperately to demonstrate the usefulness of the structure. He set up a weather forecast laboratory at its top in 1898 and then in 1901, a permanent radio transmitter. The advent of aviation and the strategic interest of the French army saved the monument from a possible dismantling.

Gustave Eiffel died on 27 December 1923 at the age of 91 in his mansion at Rue Rabelais in Paris. He was buried in the cemetery at Levallois-Perret with all honors. He remains one of the most prominent personalities of his time and a successful industrial engineer who had also been a great bridge builder.

Porto and Eiffel Avenue ©Martin Lehmann/Shutterstock

In 1885 a brilliant Belgian engineer, formerly member of Eiffel's company and who had participated in the Maria Pia Bridge project, Théophile Seyrig, built another beautiful bridge of the same type, again on the Douro, connecting the center of Porto and Vila Nova de Gaia. This second two-hinged single arch steel bridge, 172 meters long and 60 meters high, supports two paths, the top deck (392 meters) being now used by the metro, the lower (174 meters) by cars. Both paths are lined with sidewalks for pedestrians. This magnificent Ponte Dom Luis, named after the King of Portugal who reigned between 1861 and 1889, became the symbol of a city of bridges. It was opened on 31 October 1886. It remains today an important element in the life of Porto and is essential for intra-urban communications. Metallic lace of absolute lightness (only 3,000 tons against 8,000 tons for the Eiffel Tower), the bridge is revered by the Portuenses and attracts many visitors. It is without a doubt the most beautiful latticework arch bridge of the planet and deserves to be as famous as its big sister, the Eiffel Tower.

Perfect maintenance ©Jorge Felix Costa/Shutterstock

Porto now has six bridges, three of which have been built since 1990. The Arrabida Bridge, which is nearest to the ocean, has a huge concrete arch of 278 meters. It was designed by engineer Edgar Cardoso and was inaugurated in 1963, 77 years after the opening of Dom Luis Bridge. The Ponte Sao Joao, also designed by Edgar Cardoso, replaced the Maria Pia Bridge as a railway crossing in 1991. The eight-lane flyover Freixo buckled the Via de Cintura Interna, a ring road, in 1996. Finally, the Infante

Dom Henrique Bridge, designed by Antonio Adao da Fonseca, a pre-stressed concrete arch of 280 meters of central span, located between Dom Luis and Maria Pia Bridges, was inaugurated in 2002.

Porto was designated the "cultural capital of Europe" for the year 2001. To promote this event, the city chose a beautiful motto: "Pontes para o Futuro" (Bridges to the Future), stressing the symbolic value of its bridges that synthesize into a single image its vitality and openness.

The metropolitan area has around 1.4 million inhabitants, downtown Porto having approximately 300,000 inhabitants. The quay between Dom Luis and Maria Pia Bridges is aptly named Avenida Gustave Eiffel.

Luis the First Bridge and its lower deck ©Philip Lange/ Shutterstock

Iberian Bridges, From Trajan To Calatrava

The Iberian Peninsula possesses many bridges that have marked its history. They can be classified into three groups: Roman, medieval and modern bridges. Most have significantly contributed to urban development, both to facilitate communications and to beautify the architectural landscape.

Roman Bridges

Baetica Province, with its capital in Cordoba, was colonized by the Romans after the conquest of Cadiz in 206 BCE. It was the most Romanized region of the peninsula. A road led from Rome to Cadiz. Emperor Marcus Ulpius Traianus (Trajan), born in 53 in Italica, near Seville, was adopted by Nerva in 97 and succeeded him that year. He extended the empire to the east and died in 117. Most Roman bridges in Spain date from his reign. Publius Aelius Hadrianus (Hadrian), born in 76 and adopted by Trajan, also spent part of his youth in Italica. He inherited the empire, stabilized it and died in 138. The two greatest Roman emperors (forty-one years of rule between them) were therefore builders of Spanish origin. This explains the presence of a large number of Roman buildings in Spain.

The imposing Roman Bridge in Cordoba on the Guadalquivir, composed of 16 arches and 330 meters long, was periodically renovated. It is near the Great Mosque which once became a cathedral, the Mezquita, and appears on many views of the city. Probably the dean of Spanish urban bridges, it is 2,000 years old.

The Alcantara Bridge on the Tagus, built between 104 and 106 on the road from Cadiz to Salamanca, is one of the most original works. Its name comes from the Arabic word for bridge, and was given to it by the Moors. It is 194 meters long and 47 meters high, with six semi-circular arches. It supports a central triumphal arch of 14 meters symbolizing the glory of the Emperor. Periodically attacked and consolidated, it still retains a proud aura and reassuring solidity.

The aqueduct of Segovia, also built during the reign of Trajan, is impressive in its size (700 meters long and 28 meters high) and slenderness. It sits in the center of the city. Built without mortar, it has 167 arches on a double row, and is somehow the urban equivalent of the Pont du Gard in Provence.

The Roman bridge of Merida on the Guadiana, 790 meters in length, is perhaps the longest Roman bridge. It has sixty low arches, 12 meters in height each. The stocky bridge over the Tormes in Salamanca, 360 meters long and 10 meters high, was rebuilt and extended in the seventeenth century and is also a symbol of its host city.

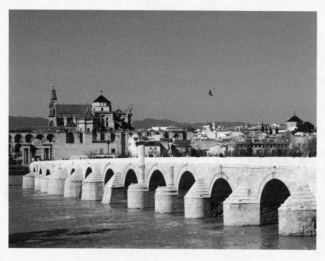

Cordoba Bridge across the Guadalquivir, the oldest Spanish bridge ©pinggr/Shutterstock

The Roman bridge of Alcantara (106) ©LianeM/Shutterstock

Medieval bridges

During their long occupation of Spain, the Moors rebuilt several Roman bridges. In Toledo they built the Puente de San Martin (1212) over the Tagus River with five arches, including one of 40 meters, and the Puente de Alcántara (1380), with an arch of 30 meters. In Navarre, Puente la Reina on the Arga, on the way to Santiago de Compostela, has existed since the eleventh century. It is a harmonious and balanced bridge of six arches, which gave its name to the small town. The Puente Nuevo in Ronda, Andalusia (1751-1793), has a very short but steep rise of 98 meters above the Guadalevin canyon. Its construction was marked by the loss of many lives.

In the seventeenth and eighteenth centuries large masonry aqueducts, including those of Pegões and Águas Libres in Lisbon, Portugal, were built. They were precursors of the Arcos de Carioca in Rio de Janeiro. Portuguese engineers were among the last builders of aqueducts.

Modern bridges

The transporter bridge in Bilbao (1893), still in use, is probably the oldest transporter bridge in the world. This Vizcaya Bridge, which is 164 meters long, connects the districts of Portugalete and Las Arenas at the mouth of the Nervión. It can carry six cars and dozens of pedestrians in its gondola and complete the crossing in 90 seconds. The supporting pillars are 50 meters high.

Lisbon has two large bridges over the Tagus estuary. The first one, a suspension bridge, is called Bridge of 25 April to celebrate the Carnation Revolution. Inaugurated in 1966, its foundations are very deep (79 meters below water level). It is 2,277 meters long with a main span of 1,013 meters. Both towers are 190 meters high. It was designed by the American engineering company Steinman-Boynton, and was the last bridge bearing the imprint of Steinman, who died in 1962. The second bridge, cable-stayed with a main span of 420 meters, is the endless Vasco da Gama Bridge, opened in 1998. These two bridges represent quite well the current hegemonic bridge-building techniques.

Since the 1990s, Santiago Calatrava's achievements have gained worldwide fame. In Spain we find his works in several cities (Seville, Merida, Valencia, Barcelona, Bilbao). His first bridges immediately revealed him to the public, particularly the Puente Alamillo in Seville, built for the Universal Exhibition of 1992. This icon of Spanish revival has a span of 200 meters attached to a single pylon of 142 meters inclined at 58 degrees. It became the symbol of Seville and has been reproduced or copied throughout the world.

Calatrava, the Spanish architect-engineer born in 1951 in Valencia, has initiated a renaissance in the aesthetics of bridges. He managed to put formal research in the foreground, above financial considerations. Calatrava is a post-Baroque designer, a dynamic and prolific sculptor, lover of tense "organic" forms and spatial geometry, who has been able to find an urban market in all latitudes. Many publications have been devoted to his work.

The suspended 25-April Bridge in Lisbon (1966) ©artono/Shutterstock

Alamillo Bridge in Seville (1992) ©vlas2000/ Shutterstock

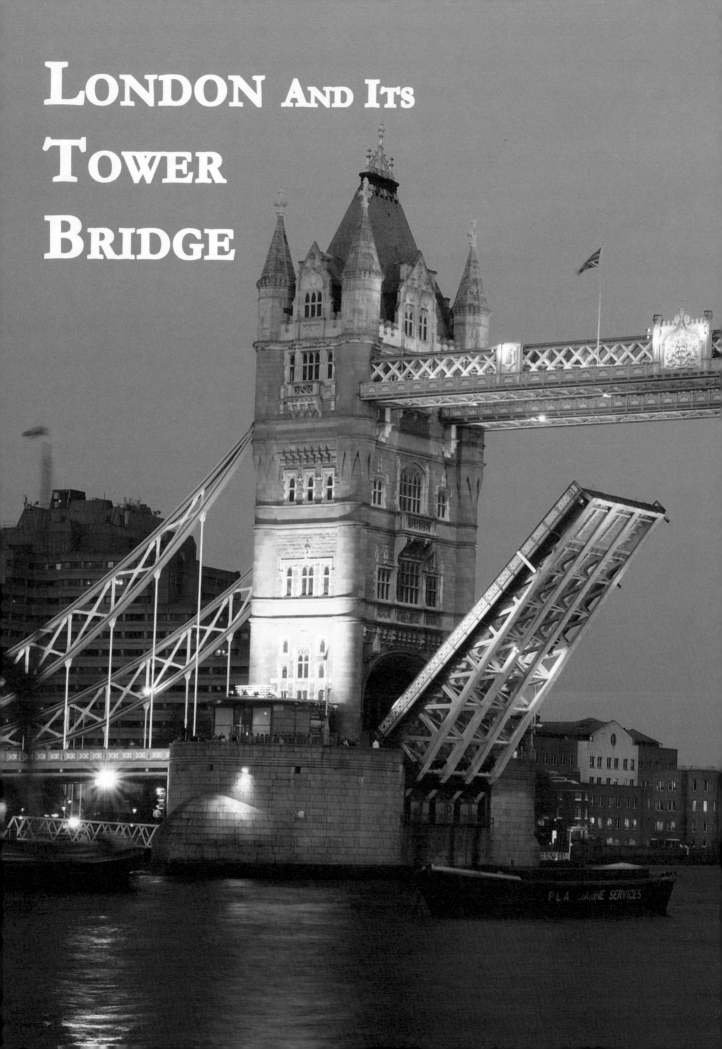

London And Its Tower Bridge

London was founded by Julius Caesar and grew around a place where people arriving from the east could finally cross the Thames. From the beginning, its location was based on the possibility of crossing a river, the downstream area being too swampy. The Romans built the first wooden bridge across the Thames around the year 80 CE. One thousand years later, in 1066, William the Conqueror was crowned king there and imposed the French language on the kingdom for several centuries. The Old London Bridge, opened in 1209, long remained a distinctive symbol of London. Tower Bridge, the jewel of the Victorian era, is now the emblem of the city, and was celebrated during the 2012 Olympics.

Tower Bridge and the City
©David Iliff/Shutterstock

LONDON AND ITS TOWER BRIDGE

London had only 50,000 inhabitants in 1500, but this number increased to 190,000 in 1600 and 550,000 in 1700, just after the city was destroyed by the great fire of 1666. The population grew rapidly throughout the nineteenth century – without a plan, without a right angle, without a center, without harmony. It was a low-lying green city, an attractive urban jumble, a city where the working class was born (and died?), where the first slums appeared, along with urban shanties of all kinds. It built its railway stations in the middle of the century, then the first metro in the world from 1863, followed by long-lasting sewers.

From 1209, when it was commissioned, until 1750, the famous Old London Bridge, overcrowded with houses, was the only bridge over the Thames, and the very lively and resilient victim of many fires. It was completely rebuilt between 1821 and 1831 and eventually sold to the United States in the 1970s (to be rebuilt in Lake Havasu City, Arizona!)

The Old London Bridge was the longest inhabited bridge in the world (285 meters) until its houses were demolished in 1762. The second London crossing, Westminster Bridge, was inaugurated in November 1750.

The Tower Bridge, the first bridge to the east of London Bridge, was built to celebrate the fiftieth anniversary of the accession to the throne of Queen Victoria, who reigned from 1837 to 1901. The idea of neo-Gothic stone towers was inspired by the nearby medieval Tower of London and the architectural model of the Houses of Parliament (1860), also neo-Gothic.

The Old London Bridge, rebuilt in Arizona in 1970 ©Jim Feliciano/Shutterstock

The Neo-Gothic, Paradoxical Expression Of Victorian Supremacy

England dominated the world for a century, between 1815 and 1914. Because the country was the first to complete the industrial revolution, because it had annexed India, because it had a powerful navy and a dynamic American backyard, this small nation could impose its law all over the world, from Shanghai to Calcutta, from Cape Town to Cairo, from Sydney to Kingston. France only managed to somewhat challenge this hegemony, until the United States and Germany took over in the late nineteenth century. The longest reign in history (1837-1901), that of Queen Victoria, Empress of India, symbolized this domination.

The neo-Gothic architectural style paradoxically appeared at a time of triumphant industrial and technological development. Was it just an anachronistic wrapping or a glorification of history, an attempt to go back ideologically to the blessed time of the Middle Ages?

The neo-Gothic style is sometimes divided into Medievalism and Victorianism. These twin currents grew in parallel to the birth of modernism, which was rationalist and industrialist, and which on its part took advantage of metal structures that would culminate in the Art Nouveau of the 1900s, an art form combining decoration and industry that directly reflected the evolution of the economy and the dominance of engineers, and whose emblematic flagships are large public buildings, such as the Amsterdam Stock Exchange (1903), the National Library (1868) and Sainte-Geneviève Library (1850) in Paris, and Paddington (1854) and King's Cross (1852) stations in London.

Medievalism, meanwhile, reflected the nostalgia of bygone moral virtues undermined by progress and the crisis of the 1840s. It aimed at reintroducing these values through a deliberately neo-Gothic style, that is to say, strictly imitating the past Gothic architecture that was considered to be divine. Its main architects were Augustus Pugin, William Butterfield and George Edmund Street, and in France, Eugène Viollet-le-Duc.

Victorianism was the other component of neo-Gothicism. It attempted to associate new technologies and new materials (bricks, glass, and steel) with architectural tradition. It perfectly reflected a time when the extraordinary progress of industry was not supposed to challenge authority, especially the stability of the monarchy. Its buildings combined modern engineering techniques with forms derived from the Gothic era, or sometimes from classicism. Its most famous building is the Saint Pancras station, recently restored, which combines the Gothic Midland Hotel (1874) and the metal technology of the railway station (1865), a symbol of the Victorian dilemma. The first Victorian architects were Charles Barry and Augustus Pugin (designers of the two Houses of Parliament, 1840-1860) and George Gilbert Scott. Their style is found exclusively in England. John Wolfe-Barry would follow in the footsteps of his father by designing the Tower Bridge as a mirror of the Houses of Parliament, at the other end of the pool of London.

The British Parliament, Charles Barry (1860) ©Giancarlo Liguori/Shutterstock

The neo-Gothic style appeared as a rejection of the symmetry and proportions of the Renaissance and a revival of Catholic Baroque by adapting it to a modern but puritanical Protestant society through a formal return to Gothic sources from before the Reformation. It illustrated the tensions between a capitalist economy and a thriving culture marked by traditional values in an era of colonial empires (1875-1914), a trend that was well analyzed by Eric Hobsbawm. The British historian writes: "In 1890 about a third of the world was British, economically and culturally (...). Until the dawn of the twentieth century there was no break between 'modernity' in politics and 'modernity' in art. The revolution that started in England and affected architecture illustrates both what united them and what would eventually separate them (...). Curiously, English 'modernism' had Gothic roots. In the smoky workshop of the world, medieval peasants and artisans passed for a model of society and artistic creation." William Morris (1834-1896), dreaming of a revival of traditional methods and an admirer of Gothic cathedrals, had a strong ideological influence on architects. The result of this socio-aesthetic marriage between craft, architecture and desire for reform was the "Art Nouveau" style that invaded the European continent, combining the necessary modern technology with a profusion of decorative motifs. An early environmentalism.

The neo-Gothic school was rooted in English Gothic that is generally broken down into three phases. The first (1170-1240) started in Canterbury (1184), continued to Lincoln (1240) and concluded with the Salisbury Cathedral, which was influenced by French Gothic while being less high and more massive. The second phase (1240-1330) began with Westminster Abbey (1269), which was inspired by the Cathedral of Reims, and continued to York and Bristol. The last phase (1330-1530) was more independent, marked by the so-called perpendicular style, which was brighter and rational, and was initiated in Gloucester (1360), Winchester (1394) and Cambridge (King's College). Although influenced by France, English Gothic had important specificities and extended over a period of more than three centuries, which stretched beyond the Hundred Years War (1337-1453).

In the sixteenth century Henry VIII (1509-1547) introduced the Reformation and dispersed religious orders. Gothic then gave way to the Renaissance that was brought from Italy but remained present and imposing in cities of southern England. This no doubt impressed William Morris and his peers who saw themselves as heirs to an era of opulence and elevation of the soul. Neo-Gothic was a way for them to introduce supposedly eternal aesthetic values into an era of rapid socio-economic changes, to provide moral and symbolic references to a rapidly evolving bourgeois society in a world that was becoming industrialized and chaotically urbanized. In fact, this style would remain confined to the nineteenth century and would find its conclusion in the Tower Bridge, at a time when the decline of the empire was about to begin. The two towers of the bridge look a little like the steeple of the cathedral of Salisbury (1220-1266) and a lot like the Chambers of Parliament. Its eight pinnacles are similar to those of the Chambers. John Wolfe-Barry, while inspired by the work of his father, would eventually bring neo-Gothic style to a close.

The Tower Bridge, John Wolfe-Barry (1894)

Tower Bridge was opened on 30 June 1894. Its towers are 63 meters high, connected by two metal footpaths 43 meters above the river. They contain a hydraulic mechanism used to lift its central leaves, while the side spans are suspended on steel cables. This bascule bridge marks the apotheosis of the Victorian era. The invisible motorized hydraulic machinery constituted a major technological innovation: each half-span weighing 1,000 tons could be raised in 90 seconds, at least fifteen times a day, to allow ships to enter the pool of London.

H.G. Wells described the Tower Bridge as "a stockbroker in armour". A certain resemblance could be noted with the Valentré Bridge in the French city of Cahors, which was paradoxically designed by the French to withstand the English during the Hundred Years War.

"A stockbroker in armor"?
©Mike Liu/Shutterstock

The original design of the bridge, including its two massive towers, is from Sir Horace Jones, the city architect who died in 1887. Its implementation was led by the engineer Sir John Wolfe-Barry, whose father had designed the Houses of Parliament. Many proposals for mobile bridges (duplex bridge, bridge with lifts, sliding deck) had been outlined, always with the idea of letting the boats enter the pool of London. In fact, this port was extremely active; in 1800, 20,000 workers were handling 300,000 tons of cargo weekly. Import-export companies, therefore, feared that the Tower Bridge could impede traffic on the Thames. But ordinary people demanded the creation of a free crossing in the eastern part of the city.

By 1876 the site was chosen, near the Tower of London. The option of a metal structure was immediately adopted. In 1884 the concept of two towers and a double deck was retained, as well as the controversial idea to hide the metal structure under stonework, granite and limestone from Portland. A budget of 750,000 pounds was passed by parliament in 1885 and work began in 1886. It took four years to build the two piers, the largest in the world, because of the conditions imposed by boat safety. The towers had to contain all the lifting mechanisms, including hydraulic motors and counterbalances. The construction of the metal structure (using three million rivets)

Aerial view of the Thames towards the west ©Maryna Khabarova/Shutterstock

began in 1890 and masonry work followed, as amended by Jones's successor, George Stevenson. The hydraulic machines designed by the scientist William Armstrong had to be absolutely reliable to ensure fluid river traffic in all tidal conditions. Armstrong doubled all systems and engines, which functioned perfectly until 1976. By the time the bridge was inaugurated by the Prince of Wales on 30 June 1894, it had cost 1.2 million pounds or about 70 million pounds at current prices. Although the architecture of the bridge ("monstrous and grotesque" according to The Builder magazine of 30 June 1894) was initially criticized, the Tower Bridge was to become the monument that best symbolizes London.

During its first year the bridge was used by 8,000 carriages and 60,000 pedestrians per day. The upper walkways did not really fulfill their function as pedestrian crossings (people preferred to wait for the spans to close after the passage of boats), but they did give rise to several suicides. They were closed from 1908 to 1982. The bridge was the site of exploits and journalistic scoops - in 1912 Frank McClean flew between the towers, and 42 years later a bus crossed over the bridge as it was opening. In 1976 the old engines were replaced with electric motors, and it was envisaged that the bridge be closed to boat traffic and that the lower deck be blocked, as the pool had no longer any commercial value. This idea was rejected and the bridge continues to open at least twice a day, much to the delight of tourists and sometimes the discontent of rushing motorists. It is crossed daily by an average of 40,000 vehicles but is limited to trucks of less than 18 tons.

The Thames is subject to North Sea tides ©S. Borisov/ Shutterstock

THE CITY OF LONDON, A CITY WITHIN THE CITY

In the Middle Ages the City constituted the entire agglomeration of London. Its boundaries along the Thames have not changed since then, but London has grown around the original core and now the City is only a tiny part of London. Strangely, the City has retained an autonomous status, independent of London, to this day. It has elected its mayor since 1215. Its takeoff as a financial hub dates back to the sixteenth century with the founding of the Royal Exchange in 1565. Its main monument, Saint Paul's Cathedral, a Baroque masterpiece, was consecrated in 1708. The Bank of England moved there in 1734, at the beginning of the industrial revolution, while the town grew rapidly.

London exploded in the nineteenth century, as the City provided credit and financial expertise to the imperial expansionist project. All attempts at municipal reform to institutionally integrate the City into London were unsuccessful. In theory, the City is one of London's 32 boroughs but it is an independent borough with its elected officials and separate police, and especially its own financial rules. The City itself is divided into 25 wards, one of which, called "Bridge", includes the London Bridge. The City maintains five bridges, including the Tower Bridge (which, however, is not in its territory).

In the mid-nineteenth century, the City had 140,000 inhabitants. Today it has barely 12,000 residents but provides jobs – better paid than anywhere else in the UK – to 320,000 people. It is one of the three major financial capitals of the world, along with New York and Tokyo, whose transactions amount to more than a trillion pounds per day. Hundreds of banks and insurance companies have their headquarters or major offices there.

The electoral system of the City is unique insofar as not only residents but also companies have the right to vote – the interests of 32,000 companies and their shareholders in all major issues clearly outweighing those of residents. As during the era of the Medici in Florence, the City is led by the financial aristocracy. The Lord Mayor of the City and the Corporation of the City represent the interests of banks, insurance companies and investment firms, and defend the City against all attempted interferences from London municipal authorities and the British government.

Sometimes the City is called "The Square Mile" because that is roughly its size (less than 3 km²) i.e. about one thousandth of the total area of Greater London. This center of European financial capitalism occupies, therefore, a very small part of the metropolis, and houses only one-thousandth of the population of the British capital. Such a concentration has no equivalent in the world.

The Bank of England, heart of the City ©Godrick/Shutterstock

Since the beginning of the global financial crisis in 2008, the City has been subjected to a lot of criticism. Its lack of controls and regulations, its obscure activities, its lack of transparency, its taste for secrecy, its outstanding bonuses and its junk bonds, have been addressed in numerous articles and even documentaries. The French channel France 5, for example, released in November 2011 a report by Mathieu Verboud titled: "The City, finance in troubled waters" in which the author tries to answer a crucial question: "How did the City manage to be one of the major players in financial deregulation, extravagant bonuses, a culture of short-term profit and soft taxation in addition to bank secrecy, tax evasion and money laundering?" The film aims to show how the discrete organization of the City with its strange and secretive customs influenced all political attempts to regulate the financial world. And even, when it suited its interest, bring states to their knees, as was the case with Greece.

However, all these investigations have only touched the tip of the iceberg. The City is a complex inter-twined entity or authority consisting of a multitude of visible and invisible networks, which form a complex and inextricable web, where few economists, even those of the highest caliber, dare to venture.

Geographically, the City is a small enclave in central London, just as the Vatican is a small enclave in the center of Rome. These are areas outside norms, outside common law, which have retained their medieval privileges in order to thrive, even when everything collapses around them. They are untouchable, sacred and offshore ghettos, global hubs out of the control of states and intergovernmental institutions. There are few such "cities within the city" that have taken advantage of past privileges to conquer and sometimes subjugate the contemporary world. Incredible but true.

The City with its new skyscrapers ©QQ7/Shutterstock

Some have called the Tower Bridge a masterpiece of engineering disguised as King Arthur's castle. It is, in fact, a bewildering building – pompous, Baroque, medieval, Gothic, modern and ... mesmerizing, all at once, both a summary of English history and a celebration of the British Empire at its peak. A concealment of the most advanced metal and hydraulic technologies under a kitsch masonry packaging? A bridge or a tower? Or two towers? Tower Bridge, a hybrid of a suspension bridge, a bascule bridge and a (pseudo) inhabited bridge, a link between Brooklyn with its granite towers and Saint-Petersburg which was also crossing the Neva with bascule spans, perhaps the precursor of the romantic and fantastic novels of J.R.R. Tolkien.

Tower Bridge is often abused by its critics. In his masterly biography of London, Peter Ackroyd devotes only four lines out of eight hundred pages to the monument! He tells us that the Tower Bridge is too complex, too large, not on a human scale: "It was an extraordinary feat of engineering but it seems deliberately to have been built upon an impersonal and somewhat forbidding scale." According to the author, this architecture was celebrating imperialism and British wealth, which is not wrong but is only one part of the story. The other part is that the Tower Bridge also symbolized the power and spirit of a country – by then already 70% urbanized – and a city which was the political center of the planet. With 6.6 million inhabitants in 1900, London was the largest city in the world, far ahead of New York (4.2 million) and Paris (3.3 million). It remained the largest city in the world for most of the nineteenth century - the successor in 1825 to Beijing, reaching two million in 1840 and three million in 1865 - and would only be overtaken by New York after the First World War, around 1925. Tokyo would take over by 1960, then home to more than 14 million inhabitants, and remains the largest city in the world to this day. London now has 10 million inhabitants, and its population has not grown much in the twentieth century. Tower Bridge, one of its most prestigious emblems, has seen its nocturnal illumination system completely renovated by the French firm Citelum, on the occasion of the 2012 Olympic Games.

Night lighting under upgrading
©Akva/Shutterstock

When admiring Tower Bridge one cannot help but wonder: is it still possible and feasible today to build such spectacular bridges in major cities? Maybe in some Asian and Middle Eastern countries. In Europe, with basic infrastructure needs generally considered met, the authorities prefer to focus on footbridges and enhancement or renovation of the existing heritage. If the time of Western economic expansion is over, London still poses a challenge to Paris for the title of capital of Europe. It is one of the most globalized cities in the world, well connected to other major cities, primarily to New York. It is one of the great capitals of financial globalization, information and business, and even sports. It attracts thousands of migrants, as during the time of the opening of Tower Bridge, but on a new premise. While its defunct industry has given way to services and physical communication has been replaced by virtual networks, bridges keep their indispensable presence in the fabric and flesh of the city. Even in London, virtual human beings have not yet been invented.

Big Ben and Westminster Bridge ©Samot/Shutterstock

My friend Yves Cabannes, Professor at the Development Planning Unit of University College, London, likes to stroll along the Thames. He says: "Each of the bridges spanning the river is a hyphen between complementary areas and varied stories. The Millennium Bridge, the only pedestrian crossing, is my favorite. The tumult of cars, trains and subways is replaced by the cries of gulls and murmurs of strollers admiring the new Babylon. Downstream, Tower Bridge opens its wings. Heavy barges echo past clippers, charged with teas and spices from distant lands. To the south, we recognize the mass of the Tate Modern, a fine example of an industrial building that became a cultural temple, and the open and circular Globe Theatre where Shakespeare presented his first works to the mob in a disreputable area. To the north, one must ignore the charmless buildings born on the banks bombed during the Second World War. Fortunately, in the axis, Saint Paul's Cathedral, surrounded by the spires of Wren's chapels, recalls the victory of London's people over the fires and epidemics that often ravaged the city. When night falls, the clouds above the bridges invite bystanders to daydream, especially when a breeze manages to dispel the famous London fog."

The Millennium Footbridge (2002), in front of St. Paul Cathedral ©Dan Breckwoldt/ Shutterstock

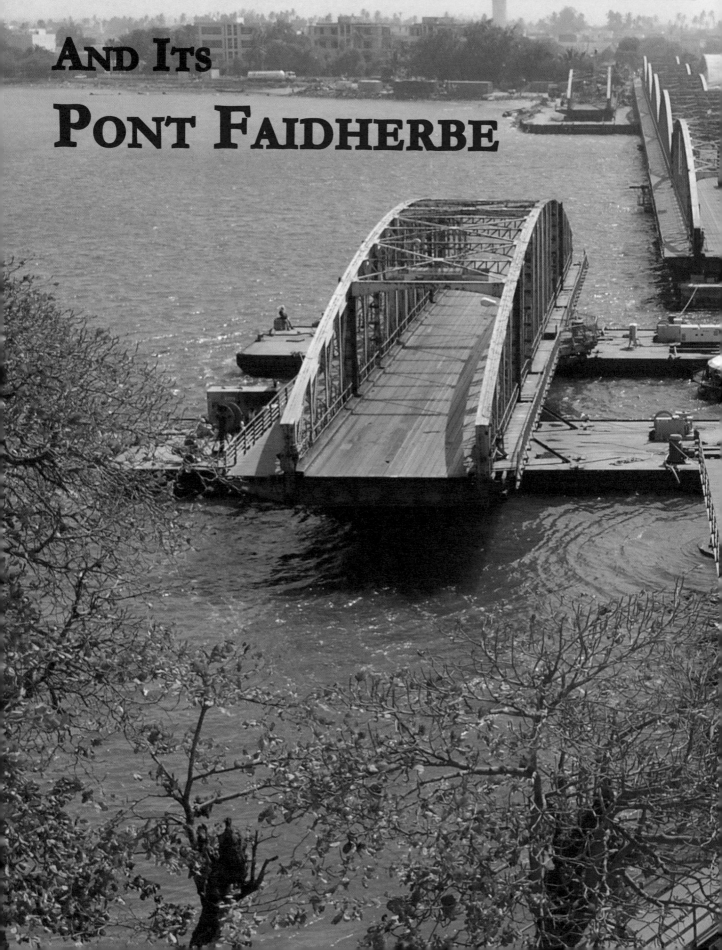

SAINT-LOUIS DU SENEGAL
AND ITS
PONT FAIDHERBE

The city of Saint-Louis occupies a strategic position between two arms of the Senegal River, a few miles from its mouth. In Wolof language this island is called Ndar, a name that simply means "city". Saint-Louis was the capital of Senegal for three centuries and of French West Africa (A.O.F. created in 1895) until 1957 and of Mauritania from 1902 to 1960. Saint-Louis is a mythical city. This is indeed where the French colonization of Africa began in the eighteenth century, where Senegalese elites were trained for ages, and where one can admire a majestic half-a-kilometer long bridge, renovated in 2011.

SAINT-LOUIS DU SENEGAL AND ITS PONT FAIDHERBE

Sunset on the Senegal River
©Djibril Sy

In 1445 the Portuguese arrived in Gorée and made this small island a preferred port for their ships en route to India and South America. Two centuries later, in 1638, a small village was founded in Ndar by Captain Thomas Lambert. This village became a trading post and was named Saint-Louis in 1659 in honor of young King Louis XIV (then in power) and of Louis IX (Saint Louis). Close to the ocean and protected from floods, the site was strategic and almost impregnable. Thanks to the river, it was also a good starting point for all kinds of expeditions to the interior. Between 1677 and 1758 Saint-Louis and Gorée were administered by French companies enjoying a monopoly on gold, slaves and gum. In 1754 Saint-Louis still had only 800 inhabitants, including 80% slaves ("captives"). Although it was the main French settlement on the West African coast, the town remained a fairly marginal trading post. The first governor of Senegal, Lauzun, was appointed in 1779, after 21 years of English occupation.

The growth of Saint-Louis began in the nineteenth century. From 1822 till 1827 Baron Roger established the first building of the Maurel & Prom Company, which was for long the most imposing building in the colony. In 1840 the first Local Council was created. Until then an economic hub, Saint-Louis became the political capital of Senegal. The population of the island soon rose to 10,000 and many marriages between French men and freed local women gave rise to a people of mixed descent who gradually formed the wealthy elite of the city.

Louis Faidherbe arrived in Saint-Louis in 1854 at the age of 36. Slavery had just been abolished by the decree of 27 April 1848 in all French colonies. Faidherbe (1818-1889) would be Governor of Senegal until 1865. This army engineer born in Lille, and a graduate of Ecole Polytechnique, who also created the port of Dakar (Captain Protet had founded Dakar in 1857) would impact the history of the city, both in terms of public buildings, urban planning and economic growth. He would connect the island to both banks of the river and demonstrate, long before independence, the key role of infrastructure in economic development at the time when Baron Haussmann was radically transforming the streets and avenues of Paris. Faidherbe later became senator and wrote a number of essays on African history, geography and archeology. Lille, his hometown, is today twinned with Saint-Louis. Faidherbe was, in fact, the first real colonizer, the first to have an overview of the possible role of France in West Africa, the first colonial geo-strategist.

A SPAHI'S LOVE STORY, TYPICAL EXAMPLE OF COLONIAL EXOTICISM

"Sailing down the West Coast of Africa, a ship, once she has left behind the extreme southerly point of Morocco, runs for days and nights along an interminable stretch of utterly barren shore. This is the edge of the Sahara, the 'great sea without water', which the Moors likewise call 'Bled-el-Ateuch', the Land of Thirst.

The shores of the desert extend for five hundred leagues on end without one spot that a passing vessel can use as a landmark, without a plant or living thing. The solitude is unbroken; the same depressing monotony is ever before the eye, shifting sand hills, horizons lost in haze; and the heat grows fiercer and fiercer every day.

And then at the very last appears rising above the sands an old-time city, a few scanty yellow palms waving over its white houses; this is Saint-Louis du Senegal, the capital of Senegambia. A church, a mosque, a tower, houses of Moorish architecture, all seem fast asleep under the blazing sun, like those Portuguese towns that once were flourishing communities on the Congo coast, Saint-Paul and Saint-Philippe de Benguela.

As you approach you are surprised to find that the place is not built on the sea-shore at all, that it possesses no harbor, no direct communication with the outside world ; the coast, low-lying and without an inlet anywhere, is as inhospitable as that of the Sahara itself, and an unbroken line of breakers forbids all access to shipping. Further you see what was invisible from out at sea, immense human ant-hills lining the beach, thousands and thousands of Lilliputian huts with pointed roofs of thatch, swarming with a queer nondescript Negro population. These are two big Yolof villages, or rather towns, Guet-n'dar and N'dartoute, separating Saint-Louis from the sea.

As soon as a vessel drops anchor, long sharp-pointed canoes, noses like fish, lines like a shark, dart out, manned by blacks, who row standing. These oarsmen are tall lean fellows, magnificently built, with the muscles of a Hercules, and faces like gorillas. Crossing the breakers, they are swamped half a score times over and more; but with Negro obstinacy and the agility and strength of demons, they right their canoe again and again, and start afresh ; a mixture of sea water and sweat streams down from their naked skins, which shine like polished ebony.

At last they reach the ship's side, wearing a grin of triumph."

Pierre Loti, Le Roman d'un Spahi (A Spahi's love-story), Introduction, 1881

Construction completion in 1897 with the old floating bridge still in service (left)

The Servitius (now Malick Gaye) bridge and Geole Bridge that provide access to Guet-Ndar and Ndar-Tout and to the ocean were built in 1856. In 1860 Upper Senegal became a French protectorate, which corresponded to an intensification of territorial conquest towards the Walo (annexed in 1858), Fouta, Djoloff and the coast. In 1872 Saint-Louis was elevated to commune status; it was equipped with a water supply network in 1886 and public lighting in 1889.

Looking at a map one can see that this small island, two kilometers long and 400 meters wide, is surrounded by the two arms of the river, themselves parallel to the Atlantic coastline. The large arm is 500 meters wide, and the small arm 100 meters wide. Between the small arm and the ocean, the long Langue de Barbarie (host to many fishermen), barely 300 meters wide, is threatened by rising sea levels and the continued expansion of a breach created in 2003 that unfortunately widened. The site is obviously unique, extraordinary.

Aerial view of Saint-Louis
©Laurent Gerrer

Historically people had to use small boats to get to Saint-Louis from Sor, itself a large island in the Senegal River delta on the left bank of the main river. From 1858 a ferry was installed, making ten trips per day. A floating bridge of 40 boats, 680 meters long, already baptized Faidherbe Bridge, was opened in 1865 when Louis Faidherbe was leaving the country. Since then the city never ceased to grow out of the small island. Despite the fierce resistance of the Damel of Cayor, Lat Dior, a railway was built from 1882 between Dakar and Saint-Louis. In 1885 the opening of the railway line led to the saturation of the narrow pontoon, a process that Calcutta would face a few decades later. As a result, the construction of a metal bridge between Saint-Louis and Sor came on the agenda.

In 1892 a loan was obtained, and a tender launched. The Nouguier, Kessler & Co. firm was selected for a contract of 1,885,000 Francs (the total cost would reach 2.114 million Francs, fully funded by the budget of the colony). For justified aesthetic reasons its bid was preferred by the General Council of Senegal, against the advice of Parisian engineer Résal (author of Alexandre III Bridge), who preferred the bid of the Levallois-Perret (formerly Eiffel) company. Note that Emile Nouguier, a brilliant engineer, worked with Eiffel on the design of his Tower and of the Maria Pia Bridge in Porto. In fact, he was with Maurice Koechlin, one of the two authors of the original concept of the Eiffel Tower, that Gustave Eiffel further developed himself. Another bidder who also worked in the Eiffel firm, Théophile Seyrig, author of the great Dom Luis Bridge in Porto, was eliminated for financial reasons.

The finest metal bridge-builders were indeed very interested in the Saint-Louis project. Nouguier proposed a metal bridge of 510 meters and 2,000 tons, comprising parabolic beams, 9 meters high in the middle and 3.5 meters at the piers, and a swing span to allow boats to pass, a rare system at the time. The bridge was built from 1894 to 1897 by a contractor named Mairesse. It was temporarily opened on 14 July 1897, and officially inaugurated by Minister André Lebon on 19 October the same year. Thus the most beautiful bridge in sub-Saharan Africa was born. Maintenance has not been easy, especially that of its swing span. The bridge was renovated between 1929 and 1933. The legend that it was originally intended to bridge the Danube has been denied by several historians, but it reappears from time to time. A meticulous publication by Guy Thilmans provides comprehensive information on all repair and paint work on the bridge from 1913 to 2001.

The Faidherbe Bridge is a girder bridge with parabolic beams and discontinuity between independent spans. It includes seven piers founded according to the technique of compressed air caissons, including a tower of nine meters in diameter and 17.5 meters in height that supports the swing span. This corresponds to the second span from Saint-Louis; it consists of two parts of 36 meters each. The first span, from Saint-Louis, is only 44 meters long while the five major spans are 78 meters long. The metal parts were assembled using 600,000 rivets, compared with 2.5 million rivets for the Eiffel Tower. The total width of the bridge is 11.25 meters, its width between beams, available to road traffic, being 7 meters. It includes two sidewalks, two meters wide each, essential for pedestrians, and supports water pipes and electric cables. The opening of the swing span required thirty minutes in 1898, which was much longer than the time taken by other similar structures, such as those in Cairo.

Extreme corrosion
©Watchtheworld/Shutterstock

Since Senegal's independence, the bridge had been open only on very rare occasions, once in 1990 and a final time on 16 October 2005. Its mechanism actually needed a full replacement. It symbolized the decadence of a city about which reporter Jean-Pierre Péroncel-Hugoz wrote: "This is a call to be avoided at all costs, unless you are an arrant colonialist looking for arguments showing that Africans are bloody jokers unable to maintain the colonial legacy." He added: "Today as soon as you cross the 500 meters Faidherbe Bridge, with its horizontal Eiffel Tower style, you reach quays collapsing amidst garbage." Tristes Tropiques. Is it time to rename the city and the bridge?

Mechanism totally out of
order (2008)

But the cultural renaissance of Ndar-Geej (Ndar-on-Sea) may have already started. For this "old French town, center of elegance and good taste," says Ousmane Socé Diop, is now representing under its Wolof name of Ndar "the sublime expression of Sénégality." Boubacar Boris Diop elaborates: "Saint-Louis is a city that sticks to your skin. There always remain some discrete but indelible marks, hidden in a secret corner of memory. A narrow and shady alley between old houses, the majesty of the Faidherbe Bridge and, seen from the Henry Jay quay, the night dance of long columns of light on the river."

Car rapide on the old bridge
(2008)

The Faidherbe Bridge recently went through a complete renovation. On 10 June 2008, engineer Mor Gueye Gaye, welcoming us at the Public Works Agency in Saint-Louis, presented an ambitious project which followed a visit by presidents Chirac and Wade in January 2005.

Car rapide on the new bridge
(2012) ©Djibril Sy

Funding of 34 million euros (36% from the French Development Agency, AFD) allowed for the reconstruction of the seven piers and all the metal superstructure of the bridge. Eiffage Senegal was selected to lead this major project, in collaboration with Eiffage Construction Metallique and Berthold, on behalf of AGEROUTE. The metal structure was prefabricated by Eiffage in eastern France, at Maizières-les-Metz and Lauterbourg in 2009.

The bridge in 2012 ©Djibril Sy

The impact study of SETEC indicated that profitability calculation had little meaning as the economic utility of the bridge was obvious. Twenty thousand vehicles, of which 60% are taxis, and more than 20,000 pedestrians cross the bridge every day, representing a total of over 80,000 daily users. The new bridge was opened on 19 November 2011 by President Abdoulaye Wade who, commending the "symbol of friendship and cooperation between France and Senegal," then launched an electoral campaign that would end with the victory of his young rival, Macky Sall, now President of the Republic of Senegal.

President Wade on inauguration day, 19 November 2011 ©Seyllou Diallo

MOVEABLE BRIDGES, AN ENDANGERED SPECIES

In the group of moveable bridges capable of allowing boats to pass temporarily, one must include not only the swing bridge (a span rotating around a vertical axis, as in Saint-Louis and Cairo) and the bascule bridge (around a horizontal axis, as in Saint-Petersburg, London and Amsterdam) but also transporter bridges (in which a gondola supported by cables from an overhead frame undergoes a horizontal translation).

The latter are spectacular and generally located at the mouth of a river, like in Bilbao (still in service), to permit seagoing traffic. The magnificent transporter bridge of Nantes, dismantled in 1958, appears in some pictures and old postcards. Only one of these bridges remains in France, in Rochefort-sur-Mer. Allowing only a slow flow of vehicles, transporter bridges belong to history. Finally there are also a few vertical lift bridges, rare and sophisticated, whose deck is lifted on supporting towers while remaining horizontal, such as in two recent bridges over the Seine in Rouen (2008) and across the Garonne in Bordeaux (inaugurated in 2013).

Generally moveable bridges reflect a bygone era when river traffic was of great economic importance. But interesting exceptions retain their charm, as in Saint-Petersburg and Saint-Louis.

Transporter bridge in Bilbao, Spain

The renovated Faidherbe Bridge is identical to the original one. It measures 515 meters and includes seven spans. All piers were strengthened by injection of concrete, as well as addition of reinforced concrete skirts and gabion protection. An assembling and painting area of precast elements was set up on the east bank, on the Sor side, each new span being then transported by barge to replace the former by shifting with an interruption of traffic of less than 24 hours during the weekend. The replacement of the swing span was more complex, with its completely renewed mechanism, requiring 48 hours in February 2011. The old bridge was then dismantled, cut into pieces that could have been auctioned...

Test of the swing span (March 2011) ©Eiffage C.M.

Installation of the new swing span (February 2011) ©Eiffage C.M.

The city now has more than 200,000 inhabitants, including 150,000 in the popular suburb of Sor and 70,000 in the Island and the Langue de Barbarie. A world heritage site within a fragile ecosystem, about two-thirds of its area being flood-prone, the city has been recognized as being particularly vulnerable to climate change. In addition, the reckless breach, a gap of some ten meters, has been widening gradually since 2003, causing salinization of the river. Degraded infrastructure and inadequate pumping units explain the current pessimism. Despite the cooperation of Lille, Toulouse, Liege and Saint-Louis (Missouri), the former capital could one day be submerged in water. Then only the new bridge would emerge from the waves, the last vestige of a deceased colonial empire, Raft of the Medusa anchored in a limitless estuary.

20.000 pedestrians per day ©Djibril Sy

AFRICAN CITIES IN TRANSITION

In 2013, Africa had 1.1 billion people, including 440 million in urban areas, which represents an urbanization level of 41%. It is expected that the continent's population will reach 1.72 billion by 2035, including 860 million in urban areas (50% of the total). In sub-Saharan Africa alone cities had 340 million people in 2013; their population is expected to double in a generation to reach 680 million in 2034. Rural populations will begin to decline in absolute terms by 2050. Urban growth will take place mainly in medium-sized towns like Saint-Louis. The absolute growth should not hide the fact that the annual rates of urban growth are diminishing. About 4% in 1990, they are now down to 3.3% on average and are expected to reach 3% around 2020. This trend should normally contribute to facilitate city management, but the needs for land and basic services will continue to increase, not only because of the absolute growth of the population but also because of the accumulated shortage.

Poverty: Mathare slum in Nairobi

In sub-Saharan Africa there are only a few very large cities. However hundreds of towns, often resembling large villages, are growing fast. Only three cities exceeded a population of five million in 2013 (Lagos, Kinshasa and Luanda); a fourth, Khartoum, is classified as part of North Africa. In 2025 there will be six cities of that size (including Abidjan, Nairobi and Dar es Salaam) and two megacities (with populations of over 10 million), namely, Lagos and Kinshasa.

Cities of more than five million people comprise less than 10% of the total urban population; those with less than 500,000 inhabitants account for nearly 60%. The average density of the urban fabric remains low despite pockets of high density, making the provision of services very expensive. For the last twenty years many cities have been fueled by conflict, drought, traditional rural exodus (generated by the search for urban jobs) and their own population growth. But urbanization levels remain modest: in East Africa they only reach 25%, in Central and West Africa 45%, and in Southern Africa 60%. The urban transition is far from being complete.

In African cities it is customary to distinguish "modern" planned neighborhoods from informal, unplanned, under-equipped settlements. These comprise, depending on the country, between 30% and 95% of the urban population. They can themselves be divided between actual slums where water supply and sanitation are scarce and expensive, and administratively irregular areas which have some access to services and where security of tenure is relatively guaranteed. The formal sector and the informal sector are not waterproof; they are intertwined, the former frequently using casual or unskilled workers from the latter, which itself provides all kinds of products and services to the formal sector.

Abidjan and Dakar plateaus, as well as the Central Business Districts of Anglophone capitals, belong to the modern world. Lagos and Nairobi would like to be as international as Johannesburg (with motorway networks and separated bus lanes), while Luanda dreams of imitating Chinese cities. On the other hand, Kinshasa is very informal, with minimum rules and infra-minimum infrastructure. The capital of the Democratic Republic of Congo is a kind of miracle of self-urbanization. A huge city continuously fed by civil unrest that affects the country, it is expected to host 15 million inhabitants in 2015. A rural or "rurban" city, a place of refuge, socially resilient, innovative at the neighborhood level, where commuting times between home and workplace are probably the longest in the world, Kinshasa shows that the lure of the urban ignores all difficulties.

Congestion in Lagos, crime in Johannesburg, lack of drinking water, power cuts and repeated outages, flooding in the rainy season, giant potholes, long hours of walking, acrobatic motor-taxis carrying three passengers, crowded minibuses and "cars rapides", African cities operate despite all these evils ... Urban Africans, with their impressive survival skills, are the unsung heroes of our time. They truly deserve a Nobel Prize.

Because cities are centers of economic opportunities and poverty reduction, the national level of human development is related to the rate of urbanization in all regions of the world. The urban economy provides more employment opportunities than rural areas and facilitates synergies between productive actors, especially between formal and informal sectors and between rural production and urban markets. However, African cities were often developed in the colonial era with little regard for issues of vulnerability to climate change and other environmental risks (Saint-Louis is a good example of the absence of anticipation). They lack coherent policies while urban development, even less than economic development, cannot be left to individual and private initiatives. Governments should guide the process of urbanization and support urban growth, while fighting social inequality and environmental degradation that often accompany this growth. Some are gradually aware of this need while urban regions or corridors emerge spontaneously in some countries (e.g. Dakar-Touba in Senegal and Johannesburg-Pretoria in South Africa) or even across borders (such as the axis Ibadan-Lagos-Accra along the Gulf of Guinea), foreshadowing the Africa of tomorrow.

Two problems are common to all African cities: unevenly distributed land that is difficult to acquire, monopolized by elite groups, and insufficient, unreliable, expensive, and sometimes non-existent basic services (water, sanitation, transport). In theory, these problems can be solved by, on the one hand, the formulation and implementation of land regulations governing land use, registration and transactions, and, on the other, resource mobilization to finance infrastructure and services. Land tenure rules should cover the informal sector (to be regulated) and formal sector (to make it more transparent and fluid). Municipal finance can come from three sources: transfers (subsidies, grants, and concessional loans), fees and charges (for marketable services, such as water, electricity, transport) and municipal taxes (including land rates). Ultimately African cities have to solve two equations - about land and finance - that are not specific to the continent. But the political will to influence the course of urbanization is often lacking in concerned countries, a will that all experts are calling for. That is certainly a main problem, but governmental determination to change the world does not fall from the sky. It is the result of a certain optimization of different and often opposed interests, such as those of powerful landowners, poorly organized urban squatters, civil society organizations, industries in need of electricity and water, banks requiring guaranteed investments, water vendors and waste recyclers, multinational companies bidding for subways and highways, producers of building materials, landlords of all kinds, tenants fearing rent increases, and, of course, the peasantry, the rural world to which most African politicians of the last half century belonged.

In addition, the two major physical ingredients of urban development (land and services) cannot be managed independently. They must be integrated into smart urban planning and efficient urban management in everyday life. This requires, in turn, capable institutions, at central and local levels, with appropriate human resources and powers of intervention. These institutions begin to exist but are rarely a priority in public policy.

After all, if the national wealth comes essentially from urban areas, the city should manage to tax this wealth and self-finance its development. An irrefutable argument, but which overlooks the redistributive role of the State, especially in oil-exporting countries, and ignores the insufficient prerogatives of municipal authorities.

Sub-Saharan Africa will be predominantly urban in twenty years. Cities, engines of socio-economic development, should not wait so long to receive the priority that they deserve.

Wealth: Nelson Mandela Bridge and the business district in Johannesburg ©MikeE/Shutterstock

My friend and colleague Alioune Badiane, a Senegalese planner born in a village between Dakar and Saint-Louis, and a director at the United Nations, does not hide his concern about the future of his country and Saint-Louis in particular: "In sub-Saharan Africa, we have very few bridges of interest as rivers like the Congo and Niger are too broad and our investment capabilities too limited. Saint-Louis is an exceptional case, magnificent but in great danger, especially since the city has little support from the central government. It should build dykes, follow Amsterdam's example, but it needs external support." At a time when adaptation to climate change becomes a top international priority, this warning should be heard. The new Faidherbe Bridge could then constitute a first step in the rescue of Saint-Louis.

Night traffic on Faidherbe
Bridge ©Djibril Sy

HANOI AND ITS
CAU LONG BIEN

Hanoi is one of the oldest cities in South-East Asia, a region that has a long and turbulent history but which has been experiencing rapid urban and economic transformation in recent decades. Officially the city was founded on 10 October 1010 (10/10/1010). It recently celebrated its millennium. Long Bien Bridge, awaiting renovation, looks like a great dragon, delicately lying on the Red River.

◄On the banks of the Red River, close to Long Bien Bridge

HANOI AND ITS CAU LONG BIEN

Urban agriculture
©Dominique De Miscault

The Red River has played an important role in the birth and development of Hanoi by connecting the city with the region and the outside world. But the river had to be dyked to reduce the impact of its devastating floods. It flows above the level of the city, and the dyke is 15 meters high in some places. Hanoi means "inside the loop of the river"; it was born in the elbow formed by the Red River and the To-Lich River.

During the first millennium Long Bien was several times the political center of Nam Viet, in particular from 544 to 607. The Chinese established a fortified settlement on the site of Hanoi in the eighth century. At the end of the ninth century a Chinese governor reinforced this enclosure and built mounds to prevent flooding on the site (Dai-La). The Ly Vietnamese monarchy emerged in the tenth century. It asserted its autonomy and Ly Thai To moved the capital to Dai-La in 1010, naming the city Thang Long ("City of the Dragon Which Rises" while Ha Long is "Where the Dragon Lands") and constructing several palaces. Pagodas and monasteries followed, as well as the Temple of Literature, the first university in the country (1070).

The next dynasty, the Tran (1225-1400), set up institutions, an authoritarian administration, and contained the Red River. A craft began to grow, but the city was attacked twice by the Mongols, who were in power in China, in 1258 and 1285, then by the troops of Champa (central Vietnam) in 1371 and 1377, and by the Ming in 1406. With the new Lê Dynasty, the country rose again and enjoyed a golden age (1428-1497). The state was strengthened with the recruitment of hundreds of mandarins. The capital was named Dong Kinh. The sixteenth century was marked by political instability; the city became a vast market that the English and the Dutch discovered from 1650. Hanoi was then known as the "City of Thirty-Six Streets", each street specializing in a product or service.

The decline of the city began with the Nguyen Dynasty (1802-1945), especially after the transfer of the capital to Hue in 1806. In 1831, Vietnam was divided into 31 provinces and Thang Long became Hanoi, a simple provincial capital.

Sampans under the old bridge

The French seized Saigon in 1859 and the entire southern part of the country that they called Cochin China. They sent two successive expeditions to Hanoi (1873 and 1882) and transformed the Tonkin (northern Vietnam) into a protectorate in 1884. The Chinese withdrew permanently and Hanoi came under French domination.

Biking towards the village market ©Dung54

A colonial city started to grow from 1890 onwards, with significant public investment. Philippe Papin denounces this development in his History of Hanoi as "a disproportionate, unreasonable and costly policy of public buildings". Despite its small size (only 50,000 people) Hanoi was promoted capital of Indochina (Tonkin, Annam, Cochin China, Laos and Cambodia) in 1902 when the Doumer Bridge was inaugurated.

Crossing the Long Bien Bridge, towards the city center ©Le Thi Mai Huong

Recurrent repairs

Many official buildings (Art Nouveau Opera-Municipal Theatre, University, Department of Finance, Museum ...) and opulent villas of this period are still standing and used by Vietnamese institutions. The Doumer Bridge was one of those prestigious investments aimed at making the city a small tropical Paris. Built between 1899 and 1902 by the Parisian company Daydé and Pillé, it is a bridge of 19 spans with a total length of 1,680 meters, a typical cantilever metal bridge. With an investment of 6.2 million French francs at the time, the bridge was initially designed to support a railway. The two narrow roads bordering each side of the track were built 19 years later. The Doumer Bridge was then one of the four longest bridges in the world, and the longest in Asia. It played a strategic role in the first trans-Indochina railway, linking Hanoi to Hai Phong and Kunming.

The city's population reached 200,000 in 1940, including 5,000 Europeans who owned half of the urban land. Hanoi was a bustling city with many small shops. Hundreds of "street leaders" appointed by the colonial power were in charge of urban management. But they could not prevent protests, nor the rise of the Communist Party.

In 1941 the Japanese invaded Indochina but immediately after the surrender of Japan in August 1945, the Communist Party, the core of the Vietminh Front, peacefully declared independence and the advent of the Republic on 2 September 1945. The following year the French were back in Hanoi and the war began. It would culminate in the fall of Dien Bien Phu on 7 May 1954 and the Geneva Accords signed on 21 July the same year, which divided Vietnam into two parts, along the 17th parallel. The departure of the last French troops and the entry of Vietnamese troops in Hanoi through the Doumer Bridge took place on 10 October 1954. The capital was independent, but the country remained divided. Hanoi had only 420,000 inhabitants in 1960. The American administration then came on board to "stop communism".

In 1965 the U.S. Air Force began to bomb North Vietnam. Hanoi was affected in 1966 and more seriously in 1967. That year the city was shelled several times. The Long Bien Bridge, the new name of the Doumer Bridge, was hit in August (100 tons of bombs on 11 August), October and December. It was temporarily repaired and re-opened in May 1968. It became a legend and now symbolizes the resistance of the Vietnamese people. Thousands of casualties during the war did not prevent the growth of the city's population, which reached 750,000 inhabitants in 1975. The Long Bien Bridge was bombed again in September and December 1972, particularly in its central part, and repaired in March 1973.

American troops were finally defeated and the country was reunified in April 1975. Saigon became Ho Chi Minh City and is the most populous city (7 million inhabitants in 2014) in Vietnam but Hanoi remains the capital (3.5 million inhabitants in 2014), a city initially "ruralized" by the revolutionaries, up to 1990, then quickly modernized, densified and extended from the mid-1990s.

Hanoi today aims to become an international metropolis of the twenty-first century, following the examples of Hong Kong, Singapore and Shanghai. Ambitious investments are planned. The Red River is no longer a barrier. Gia Lam district thrives on the left bank but the Bai Giua Island remains wild and flood-prone.

The Dragon-Bridge ©Thor Jorgen Udvang/Shutterstock

Street life in Hanoi ©Le Thi Mai Huong

BRIDGES OF SOUTH-EAST ASIA

South-East Asia had a total population of 610 million in 2013, and comprises economic dragons such as Indonesia (240 million), the Philippines (95 million), Vietnam (90 million), Thailand (70 million), Malaysia (30 million) and soon Myanmar (50 million). Its population is as large as that of Latin America. The average level of urbanization is only 43% and should reach 50% by 2020. Cities have played a key role in the economic growth experienced by most countries in the region since the beginning of the twenty-first century, and rivers, seas, gulfs and straits constitute the common bases of this dynamism. Development has indeed followed maritime and fluvial waterways, ports and bridges being its key elements. South-East Asia, a strategic region, has also constituted a giant trading viaduct between East Asia (China, Japan, and Korea) and South Asia (India, Pakistan, Bangladesh) for centuries. Singapore symbolizes its growing success.

In South-East Asia (which used to be called the East Indies) important bridges can be admired in three cities near rather large rivers, namely, Bangkok, Hanoi and Palembang, not to mention Singapore and its small British bridges of the nineteenth century. It is worth highlighting here the most interesting urban bridges in these cities.

Palembang is a historic city, capital of South Sumatra (Sumatra, the neglected island). With 1.5 million inhabitants, it is the fifth largest city in Indonesia, straddling the Musi River. Formerly known as Srivijaya, it was the most important port of the archipelago from the seventh to the thirteenth century, a crossing point between China and India in a strategic position near the Strait of Malacca, an area of archipelagos where sea arms look like huge rivers. Palembang was sometimes called the Venice of the East because urban life has historically been organized on and around the river.

Buddhist Srivijaya was a thalassocracy frequented by Javanese, Chinese, Indian and Persian ships. It was destroyed by the Javanese in the late fourteenth century. Under the leadership of Prince Parameswara, the survivors founded Malacca on the Malay shore of the Strait. This city-state replaced Srivijaya as the main port of the region, while Islam came from India and entered the Malay Peninsula, Sumatra and Java. Admiral Zheng He visited Malacca many times where a large Chinese colony had settled. Malacca was conquered by the Portuguese in 1511 and by the Dutch in 1641. The Sultanate of Palembang was revived in the seventeenth century, while the Dutch concentrated on Java, where they founded Batavia in 1619. In 1818 the British founded Singapore, a port that gradually replaced Malacca in southern Malaysia, and became a showcase of the British Empire. In 1824 the Treaty of London divided the region into two zones of influence, British in the north of the Straits (future Malaysia) and Dutch in the south (future Indonesia).

Ampera Bridge, started in 1962 and inaugurated in 1965, is an enduring symbol of Palembang. The bridge is 1,177 meters long and 22 meters wide, and is the longest bridge in Indonesia. Its two towers are 78 meters high. Originally it had a bascule span, like the bridges of St. Petersburg, to let the big boats pass but the mechanism deteriorated in the 1970s due to lack of a real need. Recently, the bridge has faced some structural problems, due in particular to "the corrosive effects of human urine on one of its piers" according to the Jakarta Post (27 November 2004)!

Ampera Bridge (1965) in Palembang, Indonesia ©Veronica Wijaya

The longest bridge in Indonesia may soon be built between the north of Java and Sumatra, over the Sunda Strait. It would cost US$15 billion and support the crossing of vehicles, trains, and all kinds of cables. This 31 kilometer-long suspension bridge would be high enough to allow the passage of the largest vessels. An even more massive bridge joining Sumatra to Malaysia is also envisaged, which would make it possible to go from Paris to Jakarta by car (a dream!).

Bangkok (Krung Thep, the City of Angels, in Thai), is itself a recent city, established as the capital of Siam in 1782 by King Rama I on the country's longest river, the Chao Phraya, near the Gulf of Thailand. It was, and still is, a city of canals, also known as the Venice of the East. Today it is a sprawling city of seven million people, fairly well managed, where traffic and pollution have begun to be mastered, but where flooding seems inevitable, as witnessed in October 2011. Its metallic Memorial Bridge (Saphan Phra Buddha Yodfa, dedicated to Rama I) connects Chinatown to the western district of Thonburi. It was inaugurated in 1932 to celebrate 150 years of the dynasty and of Bangkok. Its access is marked by a monument and a statue dedicated to Rama I. From a historical point of view, it is more meaningful than the impressive cable-stayed mega-bridges, called Rama VIII and Rama IX (the other name of King Bhumibol), built as part of the city's ring-road.

Large highway bridges at the periphery of Bangkok ©watchara/Shutterstock

Although water has played a very important role in its development, Bangkok did not build spectacular urban bridges, preferring to concentrate on temples. But a cruise on the canals is still strongly recommended. Of course, the famous Bridge on the River Kwai is not far away, part of the Death Railway in Kanchanaburi. A symbol of the Japanese occupation, it is not urban, as every moviegoer knows, but remains an important memorial site.

Historically Singapore was the first city in South-East Asia that benefitted from modern techniques of crossing, because of its strategic importance to the British Empire. Today it is a city-state of five million people, predominantly Chinese (three-quarters of the population), a major maritime hub where West meets East. It owes its prosperity to its location (on the southern tip of the Malay Peninsula), a far-sighted leadership and the commercial dynamism of its multi-ethnic population, which is a successful melting pot of people of Chinese, Malay and Indian origins. A British colony since 1819, the island became independent in 1965. Its closest rival is Hong Kong, a dynamic economic powerhouse that is now part of mainland China.

Bangkok Sky-train (1999), an efficient metro on a 55-km viaduct ©1000words/Shutterstock

Cavenagh Bridge (1869) on Singapore River

Singapore has many small bridges, including on the Singapore River. The oldest is the Cavenagh Bridge, inaugurated in 1869 to commemorate the territory's new status as a "Colony of the Crown". It owes its name to Governor Orfeur Cavenagh, who served between 1859 and 1867. The Cavenagh family crest is still visible on the piers of a bridge that is only 80 meters long and 10 meters wide. It is reserved for pedestrians and cyclists. It connects the administrative center (north bank) to the commercial district (south bank). This is a nice little suspension bridge, a bit kitsch, in riveted steel, a bonsai of a bridge. It cost 80,000 Singapore dollars to build and was prefabricated in Glasgow before being assembled in Singapore by Indian forced laborers. Ox-carts and rickshaws jostled on this bridge that greatly facilitated local trade (before there was a ferry). In 1910 traffic was limited to vehicles and animals of less than 152 kg. Other bridges were built later (Anderson Bridge, 1910) for heavy vehicles, including automobiles.

Singapore is a thriving and well managed city that organizes international events and continues to build beautiful bridges, such as the recent double helix footbridge over the Marina.

The new Helix Footbridge in Singapore (2010) ©Byelikova Oksana/Shutterstock

The majestic and historic Cau Long Bien (was it built 100 years too early?) should be renovated. It is presently used by trains, pedestrians and two-wheelers. France has pledged 60 million euros to enlarge it (to 15 meters) and raise it (by 3 meters) but is waiting for a specific project to be defined. The recent renovation of the Pont Faidherbe in Saint-Louis, Senegal (a bridge of the same type, inaugurated in 1897), represents a precedent from which interesting lessons could be drawn. Other major bridges are being planned in Hanoi, including a railway bridge near the Long Bien, 200 meters upstream, which will host the track. Two major road bridges were inaugurated in 2010 to open up areas of the rapidly expanding left bank. The risk of flooding has been reduced due to upstream dams. But newlyweds continue to be photographed on Long Bien Bridge, as on the Brooklyn Bridge in New York.

A very popular observatory ©Dominique De Miscault

In August 2008 Hanoi's area tripled, due to the incorporation of the neighboring province. A master plan to the year 2030 has been designed. It proposes five subway lines, skyscrapers, gated neighborhoods, social housing and private villas, satellite towns, highways and expressways, in short, all the attributes of a conquering Asian metropolis in the era of globalization. The Hanoi-Haiphong region could soon become a mega-conurbation and an engine of the Vietnamese economy. For now tens of thousands of noisy motorcycles characterize the city and prove that urban poverty reduction is well underway, although social and spatial inequalities persist. As elsewhere, economic growth leads to an improvement but not a leveling of incomes. And public transport still remains underdeveloped.

Heavy motorcycle traffic on Long Bien Bridge ©Le Thi Mai Huong

In October 2009 the first festival of Long Bien Bridge was held, upon Mrs. Nguyen Nga's initiative. It was a great success that demonstrated the commitment of the people of Hanoi to the bridge, an internationally known and recognized icon. A second festival was held the following year to celebrate Hanoi's millennium.

First Long Bien Bridge Festival (2009)

The renovation of the Long Bien Bridge should be a national priority, as this bridge symbolizes the spirit of the city. It daily carries to Hanoi large amounts of fruits, vegetables and meat from the surrounding countryside. It serves as a refuge for marginal people in the central Bai Giua Island and as a place of relaxation and tranquility for workers fleeing the urban hustle and bustle. It should remain an essential link between the two banks, not only in terms of urban transport but also as a catalyst of social relations. As with the Pont de Pierre in Bordeaux, it could support a light train and as with the Pont des Arts in Paris it should remain open to pedestrians. Cultural spaces on the banks of the river could also be integrated in a renovation program. An international planning competition would be welcome, combining the bridge itself, its surroundings and the island of Bai Giua.

Improving the interface between the bridge and the city should be a priority

Worldwide, bridges are key markers of urban history. Hanoi will really enter into the new century when its Dragon Bridge regains its shine and takes its true place in the landscape of the city. Both sides of the Red River will then meet and Hanoi's takeoff would be ensured and showcased to the world.

Downtown Hanoi, the main means of transportation ©skphotography/Shutterstock

My friend and former colleague, Vietnamese planner Nguyen Quang, insists on the role of Long Bien Bridge as a cultural icon and a potential lever for general improvement of the urban environment: "The Long Bien Bridge can testify the history of Hanoi, which has experienced periods of war and peace but also urban steps, from feudal citadel to colonial town, from socialist city to capital of a market economy representing the integration of Vietnam in the global economy. It was and remains a major part of our national culture. Because of its historical importance and economic significance, the renovation of the Long Bien Bridge will contribute substantially to the future development of Hanoi. This bridge should be an icon that will help forge a new image of the city as an internationally competitive metropolis. Following this transformation, the Bridge could be the beginning of a green city, resulting in slum upgrading along the river banks, renovation of the Old Quarter nearby and facilitating urban expansion on both sides of the Red River." A beautiful vision that the authorities would certainly wish to transform into reality.

Artist' views of the Bridge, Paintings exposed in 2009 at the Long Bien Bridge Festival

Hoàng Xuân Huo'ng

Phan Thi Minh Chau

Nguyen Minh Tan

Nguyen Lam

Le Cong Thanh

Hà Hông Ngân

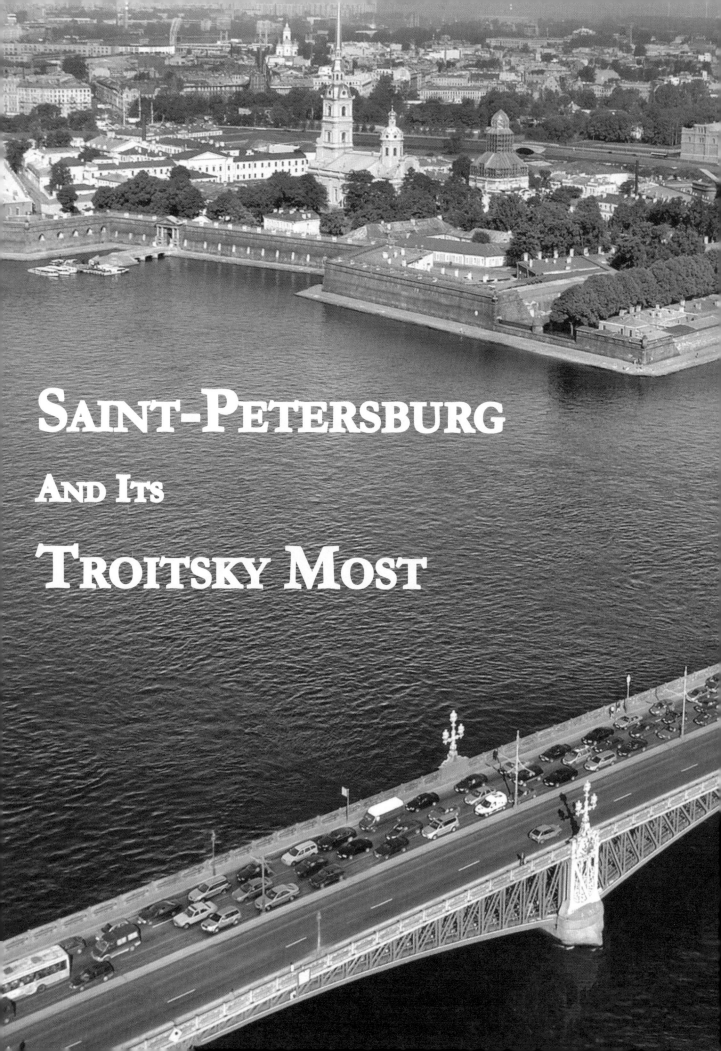

SAINT-PETERSBURG

AND ITS

TROITSKY MOST

Saint-Petersburg was founded by Tsar Peter the Great on 27 May 1703. At that time Russia was mainly rural and comprised only two classes: enslaved peasants and nobles. The latter lived on their lands and sometimes in Moscow. The Tsar decided that they should move to the Baltic Sea and to the beautiful new city that he was to build. A large number of canals and bridges were soon constructed on both sides of the Neva, before the great river was crossed by magnificent permanent bridges from

◀The Trinity Bridge
(Troitsky Most, 1903),
skyview with Zayatchi
Island in the background

SAINT-PETERSBURG AND ITS TROITSKY MOST

Until the late nineteenth century, Russia remained extremely rural. The first census of the Russian Empire, conducted in 1897, showed that only 5% of Russians lived in urban areas. The country then had two major cities, Saint-Petersburg (1,265,000 inhabitants) and Moscow (1,039,000 inhabitants) and a few towns, all with less than 150,000 inhabitants. Rapid urbanization would only begin in the 1930s. The proportion of urban dwellers would reach 34% in 1940, 44% in 1950, 62% in 1970 and 73% in 1990. This rate would then stabilize while the Russian population would begin to decline and many cities, with the noticeable exception of Moscow, would lose 0.5% of their population each year. Saint-Petersburg grew from 2.9 million people in 1950 to 4 million in 1970 and 5 million in 1990, and its population is now stabilizing at around 5 million, compared to 12 million for Moscow. This Baltic city remains the capital of culture, scientific research, education and tourism, the Russian city where the poverty rate is the lowest.

Other Russian cities are relatively small. The third largest city in Russia, Novosibirsk in Siberia, born between 1893 and 1897 during the construction of the railway bridge across the Ob, has 1.5 million inhabitants. The country has only ten cities with more than a million inhabitants and 160 cities with populations between 100,000 and one million inhabitants. Urban Russia thus revolves mainly around its two historical capitals, Moscow on the Moskva and Saint-Petersburg on the Neva.

Saint-Petersburg, one of the most beautiful cities in the world, is said to have over 500 bridges (315 in the ancient city, including 20 bascule spans, out of which 9 on the Great Neva) compared to 400 in Venice (3 on the Grand Canal). An accurate count seems impossible and sources differ. The city has also experienced 300 floods over 300 years.

St. Isaac Bridge, first floating
bridge on the Neva, Y.V.
Vassiliev (1753)

The city of Peter the Great was probably the first new town in the history of modern urbanism. A port on the Baltic Sea, it occupies the estuary of the Neva, a very short river of 74 kilometers that joins the huge Lake Ladoga to the Gulf of Finland, the marshes of which have been transformed into a multitude of canals. The site might appear illogical or absurd, but it reflected the personal and political interests of the Tsar; his goal was not only to celebrate his victory over the invading Swedes but also to open a window to Western Europe that he had secretly visited. The city now covers 42 islands of various sizes, dozens of islets and 68 rivers and canals. During the eighteenth century many small bridges were built over these canals, mainly south of the Neva, which then seemed impassable by a permanent structure. The first Winter Bridge (a small bascule timber span) was built between 1718 and 1720 on the Winter Canal while the first floating bridge on the Neva was established in 1727 at the initiative of Prince Menshikov, who had to wait until the death of Peter the Great to complete a project that was dear to his heart. Indeed Menshikov, second personage of the state, had a magnificent palace on the north bank of the Neva (still in place) and wanted to cross the river more quickly to get to the Admiralty. A few months later, he was unfortunately arrested, tried and exiled to Siberia. He did not use his bridge for long. This pontoon of boats, removable in the fall before the first frost, and originally tolled, was called Saint- Isaac and would be repaired several times and finally destroyed in a fire in 1916. It had served for 189 years and contributed greatly to the prosperity of the city.

A futuristic project of a permanent bridge across the Neva, with a single span of 294 meters, was proposed by a Russian engineer, Kulibin at the end of the eighteenth century but rejected by Tsar Paul. The Institute of Civil Engineering was founded in 1809 by the great engineer Betancourt and focused on bridge design. In 1824 the construction of a new floating bridge across the Neva started, from the Champ de Mars. The Suvorovsky Bridge, opened in 1827, would be replaced at the end of the century by the great Trinity Bridge (Troitsky Most, see below).

PETER THE GREAT, ENLIGHTENED DESPOT AND URBAN PLANNER

Statue of Peter the Great in Kronstadt, T. Jacques (1841)

Despite the efforts of Ivan the Terrible (1530-1584) and his successors, seventeenth-century Russia was still lagging far behind the rest of Europe. Weak, it was constantly harassed by Swedish troops. The succession of Tsar Alexis, who passed away in 1676, was chaotic. Peter, son of his second wife, became full-fledged Tsar at the age of 22 in 1694 and created the Russian Empire. Peter was a giant with an iron will, a man of action eager for new ideas. He travelled the country in 1697 and then went incognito to Sweden, Prussia, Holland and France. He was amazed and impressed by Amsterdam, Paris and Versailles. The idea of a new capital gradually took shape in his mind. He recruited engineers, architects and master builders in Western Europe.

But he first had to repel Swedish troops, and defend the northern border and the shores of the Gulf of Finland. On 16 May 1703 he established a basic fortress on Zayatchi Island (or Hare Island on the Neva) and named it Peter and Paul, and another on the island of Kronstadt, in the open sea. He then decided to establish a port and city, Saint-Petersburg, around the fortress. It was an impulsive decision, taken without any feasibility study – which is fortunate because such a study would have undoubtedly demonstrated the absurdity of creating a city, let alone a capital, on unhealthy swamps that are frozen six months of the year. It was, in fact, an absolutely insane gamble.

Peter built a shed in a few days from where he led the construction work. At the cost of thousands of lives, the marshes were drained by digging canals and building platforms out of the water on a million stilts. Twenty thousand forced laborers arrived in the summer of 1703 and the massive project began, as well summarized by Michel Pétuaud-Letang in his comparison of Bordeaux and Saint-Petersburg: "By only the will of one man, and his authoritarian decision, a future capital rose against all common sense, in order to open a backward country to the modernity of his time."

First Winter Bridge built in 1718-1720, anonymous (c. 1740), Hermitage Museum

From 1704, the Tsar would bring 40,000 workers for six months each year to build his capital. Italian architects arrived and planned the layout of roads and canals. Amsterdam was the reference for Vasilievsky Island. On the left bank of the Neva, the Moika and Fontanka were channeled, the Admiralty was built and a shipyard was established in 1709. That same year the Swedish troops were crushed by a modernized Russian army at Poltava.

The construction of the Summer Palace started in 1710. Aristocrats began timidly to build their own palaces. The future Winter Palace was initiated in 1711. On 16 January 1712 Saint-Petersburg officially became the capital of Russia. Moscow's nobles and merchants were strongly encouraged to move to the site, which was considered among the most inhospitable in Europe. French planner Le Blond was appointed chief architect. He botched a master plan (1717) that was rejected by the Tsar. Amended by the Academy of Sciences, the plan was eventually adopted. This was the first plan in modern history to be for an entirely new city.

Baroque architecture invaded the city along three streets converging to the Admiralty. As in Amsterdam, merchants were associated with municipal management. Twelve colleges hosted the administrations that gradually settled in the city. The Tsar chose the colors of the buildings and established standard plans that all had to follow. Planning regulations were strict but sensible.

Despite the uncertainties that would follow his death in 1725, Peter the Great largely won his bet: he sowed the seeds of a city that Russian architects would expand, densify and homogenize, despite floods and fires, throughout the eighteenth century, particularly during the reign of Elizabeth (1741-1761) and Catherine II (1762-1796). After the death of Catherine the Great, Saint-Petersburg would become, less than a century after its ex nihilo creation, the effective capital of Russia. With 200,000 inhabitants, it was already one of the most visited cities in Europe. Against all odds, the delusional ambition of a young man aged 31 had become a reality. Despotism and urban planning had woven their first relationship; this relationship would persist in other climes.

The violent reforms of Peter the Great and the ferocious exploitation of peasants gave Russia the confidence to open itself to Europe. But Saint-Petersburg would remain until the early twentieth century a brilliant exception in a vast rural countryside that would heavily hamper the country's development.

Today Peter the Great is revered by the Russian hagiography and the population as the founder of modern Russia. Dozens of statues and paintings celebrate him, from the mythical Bronze Horseman commissioned to Etienne Falconet by Catherine II to the impressive statues in the parks of Kronstadt and Peterhof.

The oldest bridges in the city are on the canals and not on the Neva. The oldest and very beautiful bridge still in service is the Anichkov (1715, in wood until 1785, rebuilt in 1841) which allows the Nevsky Prospekt to cross the Fontanka. Fifty-five meters long and thirty-eight meters wide, it has four superb equestrian statues at its ends, which were added between 1841 and 1850 by sculptor Pyotr Klodt. Two other bridges are notable for their statues, the Lions Bridge and the Bank Bridge, built by G. Traitteur (1825-1826) on the Griboyedov canal. These are small footbridges supported by chains coming out of the mouths of majestic sculptures (lions or griffins).

Lomonosov, Lechtoukov, Semionovski and Oboukhovski bridges, each sixty meters long, on the Fontanka River

Lions Bridge (1826) over Griboyedov Canal ©Pinaev Sergey/Shutterstock

In fact, many bridges were built on the Fontanka (Fountain), then on the Moika, at this time, some bearing the names of colors (Blue Bridge of 1818, the largest), as well as chain bridges (such as the Egyptian Bridge, which collapsed due to the resonance created by a cavalry squadron). The Lomonosov Bridge (1787), with four small towers, offers a beautiful view on the Fontanka, a channeled 6.7-kilometre long river, starting from the Neva and returning to the great river, spanned by fifteen bridges.

The population of Saint-Petersburg increased from 200,000 in 1800 to 500,000 in 1860; it rose to more than one million in 1890 and two million in 1914. This rapid growth reflected the hyper-dynamism of Russia's largest city, a cradle of capitalism, whose brightness lasted until 1914. The czarinas-builders Elizabeth Petrovna and Catherine II had played a decisive role in the development of the city in the eighteenth century. Entrepreneurs took over during the following century. But a permanent bridge on the Great Neva was only built between 1843 and 1850 at the beginning of the industrial revolution. This metal bridge (in cast iron) called Blagovechenski (or Annunciation) became the Nikolayevski bridge, then the Lieutenant Schmidt bridge after the October Revolution, and reverted to it old name, Annunciation, in 2007.

Lomonosov Bridge (1787) ©Potapov Alexander/ Shutterstock

It was designed by engineer Kerbedz. At its inauguration, on 21 November 1850, a newspaper called it "a marvelous necklace worn by our gracious beauty, the Neva." The last bridge across the Neva before the Gulf of Finland, it was rebuilt between 1936 and 1938 and recently renovated. A second large metal bridge (Liteiny or Alexandrovski) was built upstream in 1875-1879.

From 1860 onwards Saint-Petersburg entered a period of vigorous expansion, marked by a rapid growth of the industrial proletariat and some infrastructure improvements.

Annunciation Bridge, first permanent bridge (in cast iron) across the Neva, V.S. Sadovnikov (1851)

Trinity Bridge in front of the Marble Palace and the Church of the Resurrection ©Alexander Petrosian

Candelabras and Art Nouveau parapet ©Serge Lamere/ Shutterstock

Trinity Bridge enlightened ©jetkat/Shutterstock

On 9 October 1891, the Duma of Saint-Petersburg decided to build a third permanent bridge across the Neva. An international tender was launched in 1892, which received sixteen responses. Although having not bid for it, the French company Batignolles was chosen to build the central Trinity Bridge (Troitsky Most), arguably the most elegant bridge over the Neva, especially when the night lights are on.

Design engineers Ivan Landau and Arthur Flanchet directed the project, which was launched by Tsar Nicolas II and French President Félix Faure on 12 August 1897. The bridge, a contemporary of the Alexander III Bridge in Paris, was inaugurated by the Tsar in May 1903 to mark the bicentenary of the city, which then had 1.5 million inhabitants and was the third largest city in Europe after London and Paris. As the bridge took more than the stipulated four years to build, Batignolles had to pay penalties. Initially the bridge consisted of a double bascule first span (from the left bank), which was replaced in 1967 by a simple bascule of 43 meters. The bridge was renovated between 2001 and 2003 to mark its centenary. Its modernist style, its Art Nouveau candelabra (due to architects V. Chabrol and R. Patouillard), its spans with length increasing toward the center, make it the best example of the lightness allowed by metallic structures. It originally was 582 meters long and 23 meters wide (it was widened a little in 1967) and its structure weighed 11,242 tons. The terms of the 5.2 million rubles contract indicated that the company would only use Russian materials and workers and should regularly consult Russian engineers.

A few years later, two other large metal bridges were built; they would mark the urban space of Saint- Petersburg, which would be re-named Petrograd (from 1914 to 1924) and later Leningrad (from 1924 to 1991). Upstream is the Bolcheokhtinski or Peter the Great Bridge (1908-1911), near the Smolny Convent, with its imposing central granite towers flanking the Rastrelli cathedral in the background.

Peter the Great Bridge (or Bolcheokhtinski, 1911) ©Yury Zakharov/Shutterstock

It has a fairy tale quality, especially when a ship sails the Neva under the first snow and moves on between the light-towers that evoke the Tower Bridge in London. It is 335 meters long and 24 meters wide. And finally the Palace Bridge (1912-1917) between the Winter Palace and Vasilievsky Island, which became, by virtue of its location, a symbol of Saint-Petersburg (upstream of the Saint Isaac bridge destroyed in 1916).

Night opening of the Palace Bridge ©Selyutina Olga/ Shutterstock

All these bridges with bascule span(s) open a few hours a day to let boats pass. The central span of the Palace Bridge opens at half past one in the morning. In June and July, during the White Nights, it is an unforgettable sight. Only the newest cable-stayed bridge across the Neva (Obukhovski, 2004) does not open. Its deck is, in fact, 30 meters above the river, its central span being 380 meters long. Part of the city's ring road, it symbolizes the entry of Russia into the era of globalized techniques. But the most beautiful bridge over the Neva could very well be – it is our runner up – the Bolcheokhtinski (or Peter the Great), if one could redesign its surroundings, disfigured by excessive traffic, and contain the Neva correctly. One could compare the facades on the Neva to those of the Garonne in Bordeaux, also from the eighteenth century; both offer magical Baroque perspectives.

Palace Bridge in front of the Hermitage (Winter Palace) ©Maslov Dmitry/Shutterstock

Despite its role as the theatre of the October Revolution, in which control over Neva bridges was critical – to facilitate access of the revolutionaries to the left bank on 24 October 1917, which was followed by the taking of the Winter Palace by the Bolsheviks on the night of 25 October – Red Petrograd lost its status as capital in March 1918 when peace was signed with Germany at Brest-Litovsk. Its population then dropped sharply, from 2.4 million in 1917 to 740,000 in 1920. The city experienced terrible flooding (more than three meters in September 1924), when it had been renamed Leningrad. But it quickly recovered and began a large reconstruction program in the 1930s. The siege of Leningrad, from 8 September 1941 to 27 January 1944 (872 days!) by the Nazi army caused a terrible famine, leaving more than 600,000 dead and 700,000 homeless. Once again, the city rose from its ashes. It built a subway, new monuments, stadiums, and even "Khroutshobs" (Khrushchev slums). And in 1991, it reclaimed its original name Saint-Petersburg and initiated a gradual restoration of its fantastic heritage.

Access to Trinity Bridge from
the left bank, Suvorov Square
©Alexander Petrosian

Photographic comparisons by Vladimir Balabnev of Saint-Petersburg and Amsterdam, on the one hand, and Venice, on the other, show so many similarities that one can only admire the art of synthesis and adaptation that influenced the development of the city. Santa Maria della Salute and Saint-Isaac, Doge's Palace and Winter Palace, theatricality of urban forms, islands, canals and bridges (including the bridge of sighs which has its replica in Saint-Petersburg), stone lions symbolizing power, repeated flooding, status as global cities and bridge-cities between East and West: the parallels are obvious. But there are differences between architectural styles, such as Gothic and

Renaissance versus Baroque. In 1698 Peter the Great was in Vienna and wanted to visit Venice but had to return urgently to Moscow to restore order. He was inspired, without visiting it, by the city of doges, including the Arsenal, and recruited many Italian architects. He threw a bridge between the Adriatic and the Baltic, between an ancient window to the East and his new window to the West.

Freshly married couple pausing on Peter the Great Bridge, July 2012

My friend and colleague, urban planner Tatiana Roskoshnaya, lives in Saint-Petersburg. She loves her city, but is also aware of the existing problems. She says: "Saint-Petersburg is home to more than two hundred museums, including the Hermitage, many parks, including the Summer Garden, more than eighty theaters, including the Marinsky. This is one of the world capitals of culture and tourism. It is also a major hub of communication that maintains an extensive public transport system consisting of trams, trolleybuses, buses, subway, boats, etc…In my opinion the most interesting aspect of the city is the fact that it is a living museum of urban architecture, rooted in the culture of ancient Russia and Europe. This gives it a special dimension. Despite a terrible mixture of outdated bureaucracy and an unregulated developing market, Saint-Petersburg progresses while preserving its heritage, palaces, churches, bridges, and the Marinsky. You must preferably visit this city during its White Nights."

The Moika River seen from Singer's Bridge

Responding to this invitation, we were, like many other visitors, fascinated by this spectacular city: "Imagine a city where during summer nights at half past one in the morning, bridges open under applauses of a cheering crowd. The city is Petersburg, Petrograd or Leningrad. And its White Nights, when the sun never sets…The Palace Bridge and Trinity Bridge, illuminated on the vast Neva, then let boats pass while cars are waiting. These bridges are very popular – the Palace Bridge is used by 30,000 vehicles per day and the Trinity Bridge by 100,000. Between the open spans, silhouettes of the fortress and of Saint Peter and Saint Paul cathedral appear in the background on Zayatchi Island. One cannot help but be captured by the nocturnal beauty of the city of Peter the Great, and to be captivated by the unique atmosphere of Baroque and Art Nouveau, the beautifully lit canals and bridges, to deliciously breathe the fresh air of the polar night and be overcome by an inexplicable euphoria." (Text of an imaginary message sent in the blogosphere).

The Central Post Bridge across the Moika got its own stamp (of course)

St. Petersburg-Beach on Zayatchi Island in front of Trinity Bridge

The Palace Bridge with Peter and Paul Cathedral in the background ©Andrey Kekyalyaynen/ Shutterstock

In 1833 Alexander Pushkin, considered the founder of modern Russian literature and second icon of the city after Peter the Great, paid tribute to Peter and their common city: "One hundred years have passed. The juvenile city, wonderful ornament of Midnight countries, born of gloomy forests and muddy marshes, stands proud, luxurious (...) Today along the shores full of life, rise graceful, powerful palaces and towers, ships board around opulent docks, the Neva is clad in granite and bridges over-span its waters, and islands are covered with dusky green parks." Images of the Bronze Horseman's prologue, an emblematic Russian poem, appear eternal.

THE BRONZE HORSEMAN

"Standing in front of deserted waves, meditating serious intentions, he stared at the horizon. At his feet, the magnificent river, where passed a poor and lonely skiff, the marshy shore, spotted by sad hamlets sheltering needy Finnish, and the immense forest, closed to sunlight, he thought: 'From here we will threaten the proud Swedes, I want here to be founded the city that will open a window to the West. Here, splitting new waters, all vessels will come to our call to enjoy an eternal feast."

"I love you, city, masterpiece of Peter, I love your severe harmony, the majestic course of the river, the granite that adorns its banks, the interlacing iron railings, clear dark nights bringing dreams where, without lighting my candle in my room, I read, I write, in the light that bathes the sleepy streets and the glittering spire of the Admiralty; where, without leaving the nocturnal shade dwelling on golden skies, dawn is eager to replace unfinished dusk, leaving less than an hour to the night. I like, in your bitter winters, the deep freeze in still air and the sledge race on the Neva and the bright pink on girls' faces and the noise and the brightness and the sound of balls and boys' dinners, the foam skimming in the cups and the punch with blue sparks."

Alexander Pushkin, The Bronze Horseman (excerpt), 1833

Equestrian statue of Peter the Great, Etienne Falconet, 1782

CONSTANTINE AND ITS PONT SIDI RACHED

Constantine, formerly Cirta ("the Rock"), was founded by the Phoenicians. This is a very old city, which has celebrated its 2,500 years of existence. Under the reign of Masinissa, who died in 148 BCE, Cirta was the capital of Numidia (corresponding to north-eastern Algeria and Tunisia), in competition with Carthage. It was Roman until the sixth century and was conquered by the Arabs in the eighth century. As with Constantinople, it owes its name to Emperor Constantine, who rebuilt it after his predecessor and enemy Maxentius destroyed it in the year 311. Different Arab dynasties ruled it until the arrival of the Ottomans in the sixteenth century. In the Arab world Constantine is undoubtedly "the" city of bridges, which were necessitated by its spectacular landscape.

◀Sidi Rached Bridge
(1912), last stone bridge
and symbol of the city

CONSTANTINE AND ITS PONT SIDI RACHED

Constantine, vertiginous
citadel ©Pichugin Dmitry/
Shutterstock

Constantine is built on a grandiose site, "blazing with insolence", on a cliff overlooking the deep gorges of the Rhumel River. The capital of the Beylik of east Algeria, it was conquered by French troops in October 1837 after a fierce resistance led by the last Ottoman ruler, Ahmed Bey, a builder who bequeathed the city a magnificent palace, built in the years 1827-1835.

The city was celebrated by Théophile Gautier, Gustave Flaubert, Guy de Maupassant, Alexandre Dumas, and many contemporary Algerian writers, such as Kateb Yacine, Ahlam Mosteghanemi and Tahar Ouettar. Théophile Gautier exclaimed in 1845: "What hallucinating oriental city, this stunning nest of houses perched on a rock eight hundred feet high, and waving, in the blinding light of the Midi, the ocean of its tiled roofs." Maupassant added in 1881: "And here is the phenomenal city guarded by the Rummel. It overlooks wonderful valleys, full of Roman ruins, aqueducts with giant arcades, also full of wonderful vegetation. It appears standing on a rock, guarded by its river like a queen." Constantine also gave rise to superb Orientalist paintings from 1837 until the 1940s that can be found in major museums. Some of these works depict its bridges, including those of El Kantara and Sidi Rached. Constantine was considered by Romantic painters, first by Théodore Chassériau, as the most authentic Arab city in Africa, as they jostled to capture its picturesque vistas.

Patio of Ahmed Bey Palace,
built in 1827-1835

In 1900 Constantine was an important city with 50,000 inhabitants. Between 1901 and 1934, lawyer Émile Morinaud, Mayor and repeatedly Member of Parliament, deeply transformed the city and gave it the appearance that it still boasts today. Among the works undertaken during this period one should mention the Sidi Rached and Sidi M'Cid bridges Perregaux and Lamy footbridges, the rebuilding of the El Kantara and Roman arches bridges, the widening of avenues and streets, the reservoir of Mansoura, sewer renovation, Panis and El Kantara squares and bandstands, the elevators of Perregaux footbridge and Sidi M'Cid, Boulevard of the Abyss, war memorials of Sidi M'Cid, the Cemetery, ten schools including Jules Ferry school and the Medersa, large public buildings, such as the Post Office, the Consular Palace, the Worker's House, the Casino, the People's University and the Museum, the Sidi Mabrouk Orphanage, the House of Agriculture, the Courthouse, social housing in Bellevue, Lamy, Cité Gaillard, Mansoura, Camp des Oliviers, Viviani and Forcioli Avenues, the transformation of Sidi M'Cid and the complete overhaul of the hospital, and the creation of meeting rooms at Sidi Mabrouk-les Ateliers and El Kantara, infirmaries and local clinics. The list is very impressive, particularly if one remembers that the anti-Semitic Émile Morinaud considered voting to be "incompatible with the social condition of the natives".

Construction of Sidi M'Cid
Bridge (postcard of 1911)

CITIES OF THE MAGHREB

In 2013 the five Maghreb countries (Algeria, Libya, Mauritania, Morocco and Tunisia) had a total of 92 million people, a population close to that of Egypt (87 million). Algeria is the most populous country in the Maghreb (37 million), followed by Morocco (33 million). The urban population (60 million) accounts for two-thirds of the total and is growing at a moderate rate of 2% per year. Population growth was rapid after independence, but has slowed considerably over the last twenty years. It has to be noted, for example, that Algeria, whose population increased from 11 million in 1962 to 23 million in 1987 (doubling in twenty-five years) had only 37 million people in 2013, fifty-one years after its independence. And its rural population has been decreasing in absolute terms since 1995.

Algiers at sunrise and its new tramway

The largest Maghreb cities are Casablanca and Algiers (3.2 million each), followed by Rabat (1.9 million) and "millionaire" cities (whose populations are around one million), such as Tripoli, Fez, Marrakesh, Tunis, Oran, Agadir, Tangiers and Constantine. The majority of the urban population lives in medium-sized towns and not in big cities. In Morocco, 51% of urban residents live in cities with less than 500,000 inhabitants, compared to 84% in Algeria. Most cities are ports or located near the coast, reflecting the region's colonial heritage. In fact, the only large inland cities – Fez, Marrakech and Constantine – are historic towns that existed long before colonization.

The urban region under development around Rabat, the political capital of Morocco, and Casablanca, the economic capital, foreshadows a momentum that has already happened in Western Europe, East Asia and the United States. This "territorial banana" starts from El Jadida in the South and reaches Tangiers in the North. It represents more than 50% of the GNP of the kingdom, and less than a quarter of the population. A region of the same type could develop between eastern Morocco and western Algeria, along the axis Nador-Oujda-Oran-Tlemcen, as soon as political relations between the two countries become more relaxed.

The mode of economic development differs greatly between, on the one side, oil-exporting Algeria and Libya and, on the other, Morocco and Tunisia, which produce services and consumer goods. Paradoxically, these latter countries are much more integrated into the global economy than OPEC members as energy exports are less sensitive to international crises than industrial or agricultural products. But jobs are provided by two main sectors: services (63% of urban employment in Algeria) and construction (18% in Algeria). Primary education is widespread and the number of graduates is growing faster than the availability of skilled jobs. Graduate unemployment has become a serious problem, causing frustration, discontent and revolts. But absolute poverty has almost disappeared and social inequalities are less pronounced than in other developing regions.

If slums are gradually eliminated, decent housing could still remain unaffordable for half of the urbanites who rely on informal housing in areas where land is cheaper and unregistered, but where high rents result in overcrowding and promiscuity. In Algeria, low rents in the public housing sector discourage private investment and contribute to the housing shortage. The country produces 70,000 public rental units per year, fully funded by the state. The price of "good" urban land doubles every five years while property taxes are low, sometimes nonexistent, and poorly collected. Municipal budgets are, therefore, dependent on government transfers and decentralization remains theoretical.

Urban transport is slowly improving, thanks to buses, minibuses, trams, and the relatively low rate of car ownership (rapidly growing in Algeria, where fuel is extremely cheap). Constantine has recently built a tramway of twenty-two kilometers and eleven stations. Tunis, Algiers and Rabat, and more recently Oran, have shown the interest of such a mode of urban transportation.

Water is scarce and the resource is not renewable. Algeria's desalination of sea water is a costly method requiring a lot of energy. The country already has thirteen desalination plants, modeled on the Gulf countries, and subsidizes the production and distribution of water. Renewable energies (solar and wind) receive public funding but are not yet a top priority.

In recent years civil society has been organizing itself into various associations, both religious and secular, and making its voice heard in urban deliberations. This is a new and unexpected factor that forces politicians and technocrats to better weigh the issues and options related to urban development. The completion of the urban transition in the Maghreb could thus be viewed in a positive light. However, in all countries public policies related to housing, planning and urban management should be reassessed and refocused, particularly in the areas of land, basic services and the strengthening of responsibilities and resources of local authorities.

Rabat-Sale tramway, inaugurated in 2011 ©cglua

At the time of the 1931 census the city had 100,000 inhabitants (53% Muslim, 13% Jewish and 34% European). In 1960 the population had doubled to 220,000, 80% of which was Muslim. Before the independence of Algeria, the city was multi-religious with an ancient and important Jewish community, of which musician Raymond Leyris (1915-1961) was an iconic figure. A city of high culture, music and literature for decades, Constantine remains the cultural and academic capital of east Algeria. The great historian Fernand Braudel made his debuts there in 1923, as a teacher in the madrasa which later became a national secondary school and the Benbadis Foundation.

The oldest bridge in the city is named El Kantara ("bridge" in Arabic). Originally Roman it was destroyed several times throughout its history, in 1304 and in 1857, and restored in 1788-1782 by Salah Bey. The current bridge, dating from 1863, has long been closed by a gate, Bab El Kantara. It is 128 meters long and dominates the Rhumel from a height of 125 meters, connecting the Rock to the railway station.

The M'Cid suspended bridge, seen from the cable-car

Downstream the Sidi M'Cid Bridge, thrown on the canyon in 1912 and 164 meters long, is meanwhile suspended 175 meters above the river. Magnificent, narrow and breathtaking. One must also add the Slimane Mellah footbridge (ex-Perregaux, 1925), 125 meters long and oscillating under the weight of pedestrians (106 meters above the Rhumel it would be ideal for practicing bungee jumping), and downstream at the outlet of the gorge, the Falls' bridge of five arches, opened in 1928.

The most important bridge in Constantine, Pont Sidi Rached, was built between 1907 and 1912 at the southern end of the city.

Roger-Marius Debat (1906-1972), Le Pont Sidi Rached, oil on canvas, private collection

This stone bridge is 447 meters long and 12 meters wide. The deck follows a series of three curves based on 27 arches, the larger one of 70 meters crossing the Rhumel at 105 meters. These arches widen towards the center. Designed by Paul Séjourné and overlooking the mosque-mausoleum of Sidi Rached, it was at its inauguration, on 19 April 1912, the tallest stone bridge in the world. It is sometimes compared to the Adolphe Bridge in the Grand Duchy of Luxembourg, authored by the same architect. This is the last traditional bridge in our selection, one of the last great stone bridges in the world that benefited from the structural contribution of reinforced concrete.

FOUR HISTORIC CROSSINGS

El Kantara Bridge (1863) rebuilt several times since Roman times

Sidi M'Cid Bridge built simultaneously with Sidi Rached Bridge

Mellah footbridge (1925) link to the Medina

Waterfalls Bridge (1928), North of the gorges

The bridge connects the city center, the Medina, to the railway station area and provides access to the route of the Aures. In 2010 the traffic on it was estimated to be 40,000 vehicles per day. However a permanent landslide resulted in a shear in the first arch and eastern abutment, which affected the deck and the central vault. It was necessary to re-build this abutment on more stable ground, a problem already diagnosed in 1952 by Engineer of Ponts et Chaussées René Mayer. The bridge was closed on 21 August 2011 for 70 days, and from 16 June 2012 for 55 days, for rehabilitation work that was carried out by the Algerian company SAPTA with the support of an Italian design office. But it is not complete and further work is planned, including to reinforcing the arches.

The renovated bridge celebrated very discreetly its one hundred years in 2012. It provides a vital link between the two banks of Constantine and remains one of the main symbols of the city. A Brazilian company has now completed a large cable-stayed viaduct, 1,119 meters long (with a central span of 259 meters), between the UN square and Mansura (on the southeastern shore, towards Batna), immediately upstream of Sidi Rached. This Transrhumel Bridge, "the 8th wonder of the city", was inaugurated in July 2014. The old and tiny Devil's Bridge (1850), visible inside the abyss under Sidi Rached, is its exact opposite in terms of size.

Curves of Sidi Rached Bridge, seen from West

Over the 2,000 meters of Rhumel's gorges, one thus encounters from upstream to downstream the new Transrhumel viaduct and the Sidi Rached bridge, followed east by the Mellah footbridge after 400 meters and El Kantara another 400 meters further. Then going north one finds Sidi M'Cid bridge, 600 meters from the El Kantara elbow, and finally the Falls Bridge 400 meters further at the exit of the ravine. Constantine, a city developed on an extraordinary site but whose urban potential remains underutilized, is truly "the" City of Bridges.

As elsewhere, the agglomeration grew beyond its traditional boundaries and a new town called Ali Mendjeli had to be created. This modern suburb located near the Ain El Bey airport includes a new university center that complements the university designed by the famous Brazilian architect Oscar Niemeyer. It is growing fast and welcomes both inhabitants displaced from Constantine and rural migrants.

Medina (old town), standing
on the Rocher (the Rock)

Algeria had a population of 37 million in 2013, 75% of which being urban. Its population growth of 1.4% per annum is moderate and its annual urban growth rate of 2.5% seems quite manageable. But reforms are needed, especially in the field of land and housing policy. Infrastructure is improving, thanks to oil revenues, but this is not enough to ensure sustainable development. Informal settlements, both poor and rich, often dominate the urban landscape.

Constantine on its part is a crossroad. Austere, "a city that goes to bed early", but also rebellious and religious (the Ulema Association was founded here in 1931 by Abdelhamid Benbadis). However, it is also a tolerant city, pressed by the challenges of the future, but proud of its past. The third city of Algeria, and an industrial and academic hub, Constantine has nearly one million inhabitants (including its satellite towns).

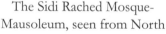

The Sidi Rached Mosque-
Mausoleum, seen from North

Its brand new tram that goes from Constantine to Ali Mendjeli, a distance of over twenty kilometers, is expected to signal a long overdue modernity. Its recent cable car (2008), that links district Emir Abdelkader to Souk El Acer downtown, allows residents to slide over the city to get to their workplaces and offers impressive views of the Rhumel's gorge.

CONSTANTINE NOVELS

Several major contemporary Algerian writers used Constantine as the background to their novels. Tahar Ouettar and Ahlam Mosteghanemi, who were among the most creative of these writers, and who both wrote in Arabic, spoke wonderfully of this fascinating city that gives rise to metaphor and fantasy.

Tahar Ouettar in Ez-Zilzel (The Earthquake) describes the hostility aroused by the influx of rural migrants who are unable to adapt to urban ways of life. One may recall a recurring theme of the 1970s, when President Boumediene denounced "the shack spirit", that is to say, the backward mentality that then permeated the Algerian countryside. Noting the ruralization of habitat and the difficult coexistence of ancient urbanites and new entrants, the hero laments: "The authentic Constantine no longer exists. It has faced its earthquake and has lost its true children."

The Earthquake (translated by William Granara) includes seven chapters whose titles correspond to the seven bridges of Constantine. The author admires them all: "The Sidi Rached Bridge takes the form of a crescent soaring in the heart of the city on graceful and redoubled arches. At the height of the sanctuary, it crosses the gorge with superb pride, overhanging buildings, single spots of brilliant colors. Around the brink, in a fight of Titans, the cliffs are trying to bend the arch that prevents them to unite. The gaping maw of the precipice chokes in the depths."

The hero, a rich owner hostile to change, begs Sidi Rached to perform a miracle and trigger an earthquake that would swallow Constantine, "which is now crammed by half a million inhabitants, bare-feet that have crossed the river, the seven bridges, ramps and narrow streets to climb and assault the Casbah and invade the city."

Yet hope remains: "The earthquake might show an excessive violence, but the Sidi Rached Bridge will resist. It will remain, even after the river below its apron has disappeared, after the piers that support it have been uprooted. It is a bastion witnessing the stubbornness of man to exalt and challenge, or rather it symbolizes the desire that man has to participate in the creation. The day of the big shake, the day the city collapses, those installed on the bridge are likely to be saved." And "the rabble will be gone"... A cynical and disillusioned novel about the tensions of the first years of independence.

Twenty years later, Ahlam Mosteghanemi in Dakirat el-djassed (Memory in the Flesh, translated by Baria Ahmar Sreih) opens a very different perspective, with the story of an impossible love between a former mujahid (the narrator), who becomes a painter and goes into exile, and a young woman (perhaps the author?) who represents for the artist Algeria and Constantine, the beloved city that he continues to draw in his paintings, and his own youth: a painful and exhilarating past woven with struggles, pride, idealism and hope. With her Baroque lyricism and unconventional characters, Ahlam Mosteghanemi "looks like a firework in the Algerian literary landscape" (Yasmina Belkacem). Denouncing all corruption, revealing hidden desires, she reflects the aspirations of Arab youth in search of a new liberation:

"Painting, yes, painting, putting all strengths of my reversals, of my contradictions – my madness, my reason, my memory, my forgetfulness, not to perish of despair that summer in a town populated only by tourists and pigeons.

I made a new bridge that morning, the Sidi Rached, and entered without realizing it the most mysterious artistic experience of my life. Ten other bridges followed in a month and a half. I would stop for a few hours of sleep in the middle of which I would awake with a mad desire to return to work. I drew in the colors of my memory, experiencing an impossible to strangle hemorrhage. I had not finished a painting that I had to start another; I had not yet crossed an area that I had to move to another, I had not yet completed a bridge that a second would suspend inside me.

I wanted to kiss Constantine stone by stone, a bridge after another, one neighborhood after another, as a lover embracing the body of a woman who is no longer his. I wandered with my brush over the city as if I was wandering with my lips, kissed its land, stones, trees, its wadis, spreading my passion over its entire surface, watering it with love, multicolored kisses and fervor. Hours of combat, sweating, shirt sticking to the skin, a delight!

Sweat, the tears of a crying body. In love as in painting, the body does not cry for any woman or for any canvas. The body chooses for whom to sweat. Constantine! The canvas that had mourned my body. I was happy."

My good friend Farouk Tebbal, an engineer of Ponts et Chaussées, former minister and international expert (and painter in his spare time), likes to compare Constantine to other cities in Algeria and to his beloved city of Tlemcen, but focuses particularly on the unique topography of the old city: "Constantine was one of the two biggest cities in Algeria, along with Tlemcen, before the Ottoman period. It remains a major regional capital and a city of culture. A first visit to Constantine is always an occasion for a double shock. The first is caused by the large crowd, the hustle and impossible traffic flow recalling Asian cities, which makes you wish to escape. The second, that

Farouk Tebbal, Le Pont Sidi Rached et la Medina, oil on canvas, June 2012

justifies all returns to Constantine, is the city's unique location on a rock suspended over the gorges of Oued Rhumel, the 'river from the sands'. The houses of the old medina cling to the rock, not to get lost in the ravine, not to succumb to vertigo. Crossing the terrifying gap, bold bridges everyday carry the multitude from one bank to another, but also attract sometimes desperate people. In the writings of poets the city becomes 'Madinat el joussours', the city hosting multiple bridges that painters have immortalized since colonial times and today inspire new generations of artists."

SYDNEY AND ITS
HARBOUR BRIDGE

Sydney Harbour is certainly one of the most beautiful sights in the world. It was, however, neglected by its inhabitants until the late 1950s. Sydney then discovered its recreational potential, its beaches and parks, and its cultural and ethnic diversity increased rapidly. This fjord of 55 square kilometers has been transformed into a deep-water port extending over 240 kilometers of coastline. The Sydney Harbour Bridge constitutes its majestic heart, complemented since 1973 by the magnificent Sydney Opera House, a masterpiece by the Danish architect Jorn Utzon, located near the Circular Quay ferry terminal.

SYDNEY AND ITS HARBOUR BRIDGE

Sydney was named after Viscount Sydney, who held the title of British Home and Colonial Secretary in 1788 when a fleet of eleven ships under the command of Captain Arthur Phillip anchored on this faraway land. There they founded both a small village, Sydney Cove, and an unsafe penitentiary, on the present site of Circular Quay. This penitentiary held 700 convicts who had been deported in the holds of the expedition's ships.

The colony underwent a boom in the early nineteenth century and was admired by Charles Darwin during the passage of the Beagle in 1836. The first bridges were raised over the Parramatta River circa 1825, at about the same time that the oldest bridge in the country was being built by forced laborers in Richmond, Tasmania. Australia was originally intended to accommodate delinquents from the British Empire. Yet by mid-century the composition of the population of Sydney had changed. The city grew from 50,000 to 400,000 inhabitants between 1850 and 1890, as trade with the British metropolis developed rapidly around the port, based on the export of gold, copper, meat, and other valued commodities.

Construction work in 1930

On 19 March 1932, the Sydney Harbour Bridge was opened with great fanfare and endless celebration by the Labour Premier of New South Wales, Jack Lang, after six years of construction. The bridge cost 13.5 million Australian dollars. Known locally by the nickname "coat hanger", it accommodates about 160,000 vehicles a day between the center and the north of the city. The nearby construction of the Opera, for its part, raised many controversies and took more than fifteen years. By 2013 the agglomeration had 4.5 million residents and had become the largest city in the country. It now surpasses Melbourne as the most dynamic city in Australia.

The bay of Sydney, north view ©Xavier Marchant/ Shutterstock

The metal arch Sydney Harbour Bridge was built starting from each side, the two arms gradually joining during the winter of 1930. There were previously two Sydneys. The north shore (300,000 inhabitants) was isolated from the south (600,000 inhabitants), the birthplace of the city. The south itself was divided between rich neighborhoods, along the eastern beach front, and poor areas in the west. The 500 meters between north and south could only be crossed by ferry (opened in 1816) or by road, a journey that involved riding 50 kilometers around the bay. In 1890 ferries carried as many as five million passengers, 378,500 vehicles and 43,800 horsemen a year, averaging 14,000 people and 1,000 vehicles a day. They crossed many cargo ships, passenger liners, steamers and coasters. In 1908 they carried 13 million passengers per year, a situation that was becoming chaotic and dangerous.

The Bridge-in-Curve, famous painting from Grace Cossington Smith (1930)

This was the Sydney which John Job Crew Bradfield, the son of a migrant railway worker from Ipswich, Queensland, stepped into out of a steamship at the age of eighteen, during the summer of 1886. Bradfield would devote his life and all his energy to creating this most iconic symbol of Australia, the Sydney Harbour Bridge. Better known in his time than the opera star Nellie Melba, Bradfield was a national celebrity during the 1920s and 1930s. First a draughtsman who became an engineer in 1889, he was a visionary planner, patient negotiator, workaholic and aesthete, who became the source of immense pride for his country.

With its large bridge, the young British colony strived to be technically at par with Europe and America, and to assert its independent identity. Bradfield's source of inspiration was the Hell Gate Bridge in New York, designed by Gustav Lindenthal in 1914, the first steel arch to span 300 meters. At that time Bradfield was the chief of the engineering bureau of Sydney, in charge of transport infrastructure. He had become chief engineer in 1913, and was responsible for the construction of all railways and bridges in the city. The Committee of Public Works of New South Wales decided that a large bridge had become indispensable and Bradfield began to go on fact-finding missions around the world. He vacillated between two technical options: cantilever (Quebec) and arch (New York). In England he was convinced by the Cleveland Bridge Company, on the advice of Georges Imbault, a French engineer of Arts et Métiers and the designer of the arch bridge on Victoria Falls, to include the arch option in the tender. In 1920 he persuaded local politicians to establish a property tax to help finance the bridge. In November 1922 the Legislative Council of New South Wales approved the funding and in July 1923 the first stone was laid. But five hundred houses had to be demolished and the ground prepared before launching the bidding process. The Department of Public Works took charge.

In London, a brilliant engineer, Ralph Freeman, born in 1880, prepared the winning proposal, again with the support of George Imbault, on behalf of Dorman Long & Co. Meanwhile the Cleveland Bridge Company had withdrawn from

A colossal masterpiece, icon of Australia since 1932 ©iofoto/ Shutterstock

the project following the death of its president. The selection among the twenty proposals was conducted in early 1924 by the developer, under the direction of Bradfield and his team, and endorsed by the State Government. The total cost was initially estimated at 5.5 million pounds and finally surpassed 7 million. Detailed plans were developed in 1925 by Freeman and Imbault and approved by Bradfield. Prefabrication workshops were installed, including cutting and bringing from Moruya the granite needed to build the spectacular towers. Steel was imported from England and wood from Oregon. Huge 575-ton cranes, some mobile to follow the progress of the structure, were installed. Expansion of steel had to be taken into account in the calculations and in the joints with the foundations. These were dug in 1927. The construction of the two steel arms began only in 1929. Workers fleeing the Great Depression came from everywhere. English, American, French and Russian workers met in Sydney, where 40% of the men were out of work. Sixteen men died during construction, including two on the arch itself.

Held back by thick cables, the two half arches approached one another gradually, element after element, rivet after rivet, to join on 19 August 1930. That night there was a public celebration and the horns of ships resounded throughout the port.

BRIDGE-CLIMBING IN SYDNEY

An organized visit to the Sydney Harbour Bridge, which attracts many visitors and residents, combines mountain climbing and aerial speleology. The bridge has become an important element of sight-seeing in Sydney. Since 1998 BridgeClimb Sydney has been organizing these visits throughout the day – be it dawn, noon, twilight or nighttime. Three options are proposed, the most interesting of which, for bridge lovers, is called "Discovery Climb". It allows visitors to explore the heart of the structure before reaching the top of the arch. After climbing 465 steps one beholds a stunning panorama 134 meters above the water. The tour lasts approximately three hours; it is conducted in small groups, and is guided by well-equipped specialists. People suffering from acrophobia (fear of heights) are particularly taken care of, and often succeed in dominating their fear.

It took ten years for the project initiator, Paul Cave, to convince all concerned parties about the interest that such an unprecedented attraction would generate. This was to become a world first. Issues of security and heritage preservation were, of course, central and required absolute guarantees. Today the company is very profitable and has received several awards. It has been recognized by Lonely Planet as one of the world's top 10 "Biggest Adrenaline Rush" experiences.

Many of the three million visitors (from 140 different nationalities) who have climbed the bridge so far have stories to tell. For instance, the first official wedding ceremony, between two British citizens, took place on the summit of the bridge on 3 June 2008. The most frequent climber is 85 year-old Lloyd Poulton, who has climbed the bridge over fifty times and who really enjoys the 360-degree view that is on offer at the top of the arch.

BridgeClimb constitutes a successful and rather unique example of promoting bridge heritage in a large metropolis. This experience could be replicated in other cities, provided entrepreneurial spirit and support from the authorities are combined. One may dream of guided tours dubbed "Bridges of …" that combine the discovery of a historical heritage with a bit of adrenaline. Sydney offers a nice model which could be adopted or adapted in other urban contexts.

Fantastic urban landscape and adrenaline rush ©BridgeClimb

At the end of the construction work, a controversy developed in the press about the paternity of the bridge. Who could claim to have conceived it? Bradfield was undoubtedly the driving force behind the whole project for two decades but Freeman wanted to be recognized as the true designer of the Harbour Bridge. It was a conflict of egos between the public developer, initiating, financing and controlling the work, and the designer who had submitted a detailed bid and whose company was running the site. In fact, both sides deserved joint recognition. It is known that Bradfield initially favored the cantilever option and that he had changed his mind after his visit to London, encouraging and selecting the proposal from Dorman, Long & Co. for the metal arch. As a consultant with that company, Freeman worked closely with Bradfield between 1924 and 1926 to finalize the detailed project but did not participate directly in the construction. In fact, the man who had tipped the balance and who had performed most of the calculations, Engineer Georges Imbault (1877-1951), remained in the shadows and was not involved in the controversy. Without him, and without Lindenthal, whose Hell Gate Bridge on the East River opened in 1917, the Sydney Bridge would have looked quite different. If Bradfield was the leader, Freeman and Imbault were the technicians. All three deserve to share the glory of having created the icon of modern Australia. The Minister of Public Works finally decided to put on the dedication plaque the following wording: "The general design and specification were prepared and the whole supervised on behalf of the Government of N.S.W. by J.J.C. Bradfield, Chief Engineer. Contractors for the design and construction of the main structure: Dorman, Long & Co. Ltd under the responsibility of Lawrence Ennis, Director of Construction, in collaboration with Ralph Freeman, Consulting and Designing Engineer."

The business district, south of the bridge ©GTS production/ Shutterstock

The Harbour Bridge, with its 49-metre wide deck, is quite monumental. Its center span measures 503 meters, the top of the arch is 134 meters high and the pylons reach 89 meters above mean sea-level. Its construction took 6 million rivets, 52,000 tons of steel (including 13,000 tons used for approach spans), 95,000 cubic meters of concrete and 17,000 cubic meters of granite.

Panorama at sunset
©Semisatch/Shutterstock

Four months before the opening of the bridge, the Bayonne Bridge was inaugurated in New York. Almost identical to its Australian counterpart, the Bayonne Bridge was longer by 60 cm but more narrow (only 26 meters). The Sydney Harbour Bridge was a bit higher (49-metre clearance against 46 meters) and much heavier (39,000 tons against 16,520 tons) than the Bayonne Bridge. These rival bridges held the world record for arch bridges for half a century. The Lupu Bridge in Shanghai, opened in 2003, outdid them with 550 meters. The new Sheikh Rashid Bridge in Dubai, expected to be built soon, will have an even longer span, of 667 meters. Like its New York model, Hell Gate, Sydney Bridge is surrounded by four Egyptian-style purely ornamental towers (the same company was also building an important bridge in Cairo at that time!). The American engineer, David Steinman, a disciple of Lindenthal, worked as a consultant on the Sydney Harbour Bridge.

Since its opening in March 1932, the Harbour Bridge has become the geographical center of Sydney. The inauguration ceremony was magnificent and remains one of the biggest events in Australian history, perhaps even bigger than the Olympics. One million people walked the bridge on that day and viewed its first firework display. Bradfield crossed the bridge at the wheel of his Ford A the following day and entered Sydney through the new Bradfield Highway. The symbol of Australia was born and soon became a place of dreams, protests, poetry, meetings, and sometimes, suicide.

In 1958 tram lanes were converted into roads to accommodate 70,000 vehicles per day. The bridge was tolled (southbound) from the beginning, and it now has eight lanes and a large tunnel that was added in 1992 to allow for an increased flow of vehicles. On 18 March 2007, for its 75th anniversary, Sydney residents organized a huge festival on the bridge. The global transition from one year to another, on New Year's Eve, begins in Sydney and gives rise to one of the most beautiful fireworks around the illuminated bridge. For a few minutes, a pyrotechnic deluge then flares up in the sky of the city, and on television sets worldwide.

The bridge with Sydney Opera in the background ©Taras Vyshnya/Shutterstock

What Australians call "adventure tourism" has become very popular in Sydney, where you can climb the bridge for a (large) handful of dollars (see box). The city is very friendly and fond of sports, and hosted the Olympic Games in September 2000. The Darling Harbour docks area was rehabilitated from 1988, and attracts young wealthy executives in the west of the business district. It reflects the renewal and dynamism of the city. But the major renovations that took place during the 1960s and 1970s also brought their share of destruction, particularly of the Victorian heritage. The city then had to struggle to preserve the old facades and hide the horrors of the modern international style. On the whole though, this architectural melting pot has been relatively successful. Although Sydney has one of the highest per capita income levels in the world, it faces a serious inflation of real estate prices and should put an end to a chronic under-investment in public transport.

As stated by my former Australian colleague, Joe Flood, a senior housing economist: "Sydney always has to be seen in contrast to its southern companion Melbourne, the sedate home of Old Money. Sydney is the town of New Money, of bustle and clamor and color on the streets. In structure it is made of two unequal cities: around the harbour a high-rise glistening global city of young two-income professional families working in producer or service industries, and further west a dull, sometimes run-down concentric suburbia stretching for many kilometers. It has been said that Sydney was a poor place to build a major city because of the rugged topography and natural constraints. This has made it difficult to build a normal network of roads and public transport, and has restricted the land available for building. Also, during the last decade urban expansion has almost stopped under the pressure of 'smart growth' policies, and almost all the new development has been infill. New houses are no longer bought by young people, who once dominated that market, but by rental investors and speculators. For these reasons, Sydney has some of the highest house prices in the world, typically about 30% higher than other Australian cities. Sydney is in search of a new momentum but still ranks in my view over Rio and Cape Town as the most beautiful harbour city – as long as you don't head west!"

As Joe Flood used to say, "Nobody is perfect" ... except the Sydney Harbour Bridge, of course.

Pyrotechnic deluge at midnight on 31 December ©Taras Vyshnya/Shutterstock

CAIRO AND ITS
KOBRI QASR EL-NILE

Cairo was born in the ninth century on the right bank of the Nile in the neighborhood of the austere and elegant Ibn Tulun Mosque (named after the Abbasid governor of the time when the seat of political power was in Baghdad). Officially it was founded in the year 969 by the Fatimids who constructed the Al-Azhar Mosque and University. It took 900 years for the first large bridge over the Nile to be built between Qasr el-Nile and Gezira, as the city grew exclusively, until the nineteenth century, on the east bank of the river.

◄Qasr el-Nile Bridge (1933) seen from the right bank

CAIRO AND ITS KOBRI QASR EL-NILE

Between the thirteenth and sixteenth centuries, the Mamelukes, descendants of slaves and great builders, ruled Egypt. They modeled the face of Historic Cairo (see box). It is, however, customary to date the entry of Egypt into the modern era from 1798, at the beginning of the French expedition, or from 1805, the date of the accession of Mehmet Ali (1805-1848) to power. But the growth of Cairo remained slow during the first half of the nineteenth century.

Napoleon evicted and eliminated the Ottomans in July 1798 but continued with their governance systems. His engineers from Ponts et Chaussées built some roads and repaired bridges and canals in the delta, but their presence was too short (only three years) to have a serious impact on the city. Mehmet Ali developed Alexandria more than Cairo, mainly to promote the export of cotton. However, he created a School of Engineering in 1821 at Boulaq and a Bureau of Engineering in 1837. He initiated the

The Nile in Cairo, South view ©Baloncici/ Shutterstock

construction of his mosque in the Citadel in 1833, drawing inspiration from Sultan Ahmet Mosque in Istanbul. After his death, railways were built between Cairo and Alexandria (1854) and between Cairo and Suez (1858). Barracks were built near the Nile, to replace the Qasr el-Nile palace (on the site of the current Carlton hotel), which paved the way for new urban settlements towards the river.

Cairo's true urban revolution occurred during the second half of the nineteenth century, thanks to Ismail Pasha (1863-1879), the first ambitious planner, who was strongly influenced by Baron Haussmann and the Universal Exposition of 1867 in Paris. The city would then grow in an organized manner and its population would rise to one million by 1930. Khedive Ismail Pasha created a Ministry of Public Works in 1865 (he apparently visited the Ecole des Ponts in Paris in 1846), and introduced public lighting and a small water network. He inaugurated the Suez Canal in 1869. His chief engineer, Ali Pasha Mubarak, who had been trained in Paris, became minister and modernized Cairo, physically and administratively. He developed areas near the Nile and launched the first major steel bridge between Qasr el-Nile and southern Gezira between 1869 and 1872.

Cairo, Ancient Capital Of The Arab World

Cairo was officially founded in 969, though the town was born earlier, in the seventh century during the Arab conquest of Egypt, which freed the country from Byzantine rule. The first settlement was called Fustat (the tent) by Syrian General Amr who set up his camp there. The country became an Umayyad province. In 750 the Abbasid founded al-Askar northeast of Fustat, and in 870 Ibn Tulun founded al-Qata'i, northeast of al-Askar. These are the three villages that preceded Cairo and are today part of it.

Fustat is located on the right bank of the Nile. However, the river was gradually moving westward, over several hundred meters. From the outset a pontoon was built, and often rebuilt to reach the rural left bank. A canal (Khalij, filled in the nineteenth century) parallel to the Nile was also dug to divert and regulate the river. Several small bridges were built on this canal, the first one in 688. Bridges of the dam (Kantara al-Sudd) and the Lions (al-Siba) followed. Then Ibn Tulun, coming from Samarra, created his superb mosque, the oldest in the city, between 876 and 879, and an aqueduct. He acquired a high degree of autonomy vis-à-vis the Abbasids and a century later Fustat (which incorporated al-Askar and al-Qata'i) rivaled Baghdad.

The Fatimids arrived from Tunisia in 969 and ruled for two centuries. They then founded a new city, Qahira or "The Victorious", at some distance north of Fustat, and propagated Shi'aism. They officially established Cairo, a pluralist but elitist city, on the model of Kairouan. Three years later, in 972, they built one of the most prestigious buildings of Islam, the Al-Azhar Mosque. In the meantime Fustat continued to grow around its port, and had 120,000 people by the year 1100. Egypt, therefore, had two twin cities as its capital, a royal city with its mosques and palaces and a dense and industrious market town.

The decline of the Fatimids began with the capture of Palestine by the Crusaders in 1099. The Syrian sultan Nur al-Din took Damascus in 1154 and drove back the Franks. General Shirkuh and his nephew Saladin captured Cairo in 1169 and Saladin emancipated himself from the Abbasids and founded a new and brief dynasty in Cairo, the Ayyubids, who ruled not only Egypt but also Syria and Palestine. Egypt and al-Azhar returned to the Sunnis. Saladin began in 1176 the construction of the citadel on the hill of Muqattam, on the model of Syrian cities, and tried to protect Qahira and Fustat by a common enclosure. The citadel, halfway between Fustat and Cairo, would remain (with some interruptions) the place of Egyptian political and military power until 1874.

The Muski Bridge was built on the Khalij in 1188, and the bridge of Bab el-Kharq followed in 1241, but the city stagnated. Mamelukes, freed slaves, mostly from the Caucasus, organized as a military caste, overthrew the sultan in 1250. They established an efficient administrative system which lasted until 1517. The heyday of Cairo began then, reaching its peak between 1310 and 1340. This era would be followed by the Ottoman renaissance of the sixteenth to eighteenth centuries. The Mamelukes took Acre in 1291 and put an end to the adventure of the Crusades. Urban builders, they left a lasting imprint on the morphology of Cairo.

After the Mongols invaded Baghdad in 1258, Cairo became the sole capital of the Islamic world; the seat of the Caliphate was transferred there, schools and madrasas multiplied, and trade developed. The zenith of the Mamelukes occurred during the reign of Nasir Muhammad (1293-1340), when more than fifty mosques and madrasas were built. Arriving in Cairo in 1325, the Moroccan traveller Ibn Battuta marveled at a city "without equal in beauty and splendor".

A new canal (Nasiri) was dug with its waterwheels and seven bridges. New bridges were also introduced on the Khalij. The city was growing between the two canals. The construction of mosques culminated with that of Sultan Hassan, after the death of Nasir and the plague of 1348 (which led to the death of about 100,000 people or half the population). This magnificent mosque was built between 1356 and 1361. Ibn Khaldun, arriving in Cairo in 1383, exclaimed: "I welcome the capital of the world, the garden of the universe, the iwan of Islam, on the banks of the Nile, river of paradise."

Cairo's decline began with the famine of 1403. However, at the end of the fifteenth century, the reign of Sultan Qaytbay (1468-1496) was marked by an economic and architectural revival (his mosque-madrasa is a masterpiece of carved stone). The Mamelukes then reached their limits while the Ottomans were gaining momentum in Asia Minor and Syria. Cairo fell into their hands in January 1517 and Egypt became the most populous and richest province of the Ottoman Empire, governed by a Pasha and paying tribute to the Sultan in Istanbul. The Mamelukes were integrated into the management of public affairs, as were the Janissaries (military). The three groups shared the taxes while laborers lived in slums.

The city's population was estimated to be 263,000 (with significant Coptic, Catholic, Turkish, Greek and Jewish minorities) when Napoleon's troops arrived there in 1798. The city had not grown much over three centuries (50%) but had been moving a bit to the west, towards the river, in the eighteenth century. It occupied about 700 hectares. Trade was flourishing, especially in the Khan al-Khalili, the grand bazaar established in the sixteenth century. The streets were narrow, services were chaotic, and water was supplied by thousands of porters using donkeys and camels to convey water from the Nile, which flew about a mile west of the city and was separated from it by a flood-prone area. Lethargic and unplanned, Cairo, was, however about to enter modernity in the early nineteenth century with Mehmet Ali, and to definitively confirm its unofficial title as the capital of the Arab world.

Two historical mosques of Old Cairo, Sultan Hassan and Al-Rifai ©Mikael Damkier/Shutterstock

This first bridge on the Nile was thus built nine hundred years after the founding of the city, near the Palace of Princess Nazli, known as Nile Palace (Qasr el-Nile). It was 406 meters long and 10.5 meters wide, with a roadway of 8 meters and 2.5 meters of sidewalks. Its steel deck rested on masonry piers. It included two swing spans of 32 meters each, which could be opened manually to let the boats pass. At the time Gezira (island in Arabic) was completely rural as can be seen in the photos of the late nineteenth century. Designed by French engineer Linant de Bellefonds, Kobri el Gezira cost the modest sum of 110,000 Egyptian pounds and was opened to traffic in February 1872. It allowed the development of the agglomeration on the island and on the left bank of the Nile by creating a permanent link between these areas and Old Cairo, including during river floods. The bridge, which could claim to be the first bridge over the longest African river, had to be renovated in 1913, but the growth in traffic soon necessitated the construction of a new bridge that had to be wider and stronger.

The French engineer Pierre Grand designed the structure plan of Cairo in 1874, in a clearly Haussmannian logic. But Cairo's decline began at that time because of excessive public indebtedness that the British took advantage of by "temporarily" occupying the country from 1882 (this lasted in various forms until 1952!).

The frame of modern Cairo was, however, in place. The demographic takeoff occurred during the First World War. The city expanded from 10 km² in 1882 to 160 km² in 1937, and hosted then 1.3 million people. A tramway was built at the turn of the century, running over 65 kilometers in 1918. With the first Aswan Dam (1902) the banks of the Nile could be stabilized and canals filled. Four new bridges were built between 1902 and 1912, two towards Rawdah, one between Rawdah and Giza, and another one to the north of Gezira with an extension to Embabeh. The Embabeh Bridge, consisting of seven spans, including a rotating one, was built between 1913 and 1924 by a Belgian company.

Embabeh Bridge (1924)
©Baume & Marpent

The first Gezira Bridge, or Kobri Qasr el-Nile, was to be rebuilt between 1931 and 1933. The competition for the new bridge was hotly contested. Thirteen Western European companies submitted bids. Dorman, Long and Co. won the tender with an offer of 308,000 Egyptian pounds. This company, based in Middleborough, Yorkshire, specialized in metal construction, was in the process of building the Sydney Harbour Bridge on the other side of the world. Such was the Greatness of the British Empire! The design of the bridge was by Sir Ralph Freeman, also a key actor in Sydney.

In January 1931 the four bronze lions guarding the bridge were carried to Giza Zoo (to meet their peers!). These statues by the French sculptor Alfred Jacquemart returned to their original home a few years later.

One of Alfred Jacquemart's
watch-lions

The old bridge was dismantled and replaced by the new one. The first stone was laid on 4 February 1931 by King Fuad. The bridge was then called Bridge Khedive Ismail, named after the king's father, who reigned in 1872. Foundations were rebuilt deeper, 7 meters below the river bed, and the bridge was completed in thirty months. Inaugurated on 6 June 1933, the bridge is 382 meters long and 20 meters wide. There are eight steel spans, including a 67-metre one that can be opened electrically in three-and-a-half minutes to let boats through (which would happen twice a day until the 1960s), as in Saint-Louis du Senegal. It required 3,700 tons of steel and features beautiful lamps and two granite towers at each of its ends, as well as the famous lions. As in Sydney, an Opera House was built near the bridge, on the island of Gezira- Zamalek, which is now connected to the city center by two other bridges, those of 6 October and 26 July.

Qasr el-Nile Bridge with the
Opera House at the back

ASWAN'S DAMS-CUM-BRIDGES

One sometimes forgets that dams are also bridges. They allow people to cross rivers, even if this is not their primary function. Conversely, some bridges may play the role of dams, as in Isfahan. South of Egypt the two Aswan dams have improved irrigation and power generation, but also facilitated the crossing of the Nile before a bridge was built in 2002 in the north of the city (Luxor for its part had obtained its bridge in 1997).

THE OLD DAM

Human beings since ancient times have tried to stem the whims of the Nile. The left bank was endowed from the Pharaonic period with a network of dykes and ponds and with a natural canal up to the Fayum depression, which served as a reservoir to control flooding.

In 1902, the British funded the first dam south of Aswan, near the first cataract of the Nile, for the irrigation of cotton fields. One-and-a-half miles long, it was raised and expanded twice, in 1912 and 1933, flooding part of Lower Nubia. The old dam is still in operation and continues to produce hydroelectric power. However, the summer floods continued to overflow into the Nile Valley and fertilize its soil by the addition of stringers. But these floods were very irregular, resulting in alternating droughts and floods.

THE NEW DAM

In the late 1950s, the construction of a new dam was considered by President Nasser to permanently regulate floods, generate electricity and provide a reservoir of water for agriculture. To build this dam, Egypt turned to the Soviet Union, which provided 2,000 experts and technicians, and a billion dollars. The work lasted eleven years (1960-1970) and mobilized 35,000 workers.

Built six kilometers upstream of the old dam, the new dam has a huge volume of 42.7 million cubic meters. It is 3,800 meters long, 980 meters thick at the base and 40 meters at the top, and 111 meters high; 11,000 cubic meters of water can pass every second through its gates. The immense reservoir, named Lake Nasser, is 550 kilometers long and about 10 kilometers wide on average, representing an area of 5250 km² and storage of 157 km³ of water. The dam contains twelve generators with a total capacity of 2.1 gig watts. It links most Egyptian villages to the national electricity grid. With the help of UNESCO, the temples of Abu Simbel, built during the reign of Ramses II, as well as those located on the island of Philae, were moved during the 1960s to avoid being submerged – a memorable operation that also laid the foundation of the concept of World Heritage.

Among the negative consequences of the dam one could note a significant evaporation of the water of Lake Nasser, the decreasing intake of silt downstream and an erosion of the river bed. Among the often ignored positive effects, one should remember that the dam offers another option of crossing the river, especially for heavy vehicles.

The Aswan High Dam (1970), symbol of Nasser era ©Hallam creations/Shutterstock

The bridge took back its popular original name, Qasr el-Nile, after the revolution of 1952. But the famous Palace (Qasr) that lent its name to the bridge was demolished in 1955 and replaced by the Nile Hilton (now Carlton) and the headquarters of the Arab League. Hotel guests can enjoy the view and atmosphere of the Nile, especially at dusk, from the top of the panoramic terrace. The cornice and the bridge of the university were built during those years. On the 1st October 1970, dozens of heads of state and millions of Egyptians crossed the Kobri Qasr el-Nile, or Tahrir Bridge, behind the coffin of Gamal Abdel Nasser. At the time, Cairo was without a doubt the largest city in Africa and the Arab world, with 6 million inhabitants.

Warm night over the river

Today Cairo remains the largest city in Africa (though it is being overtaken by Lagos) and by far the most populous Arab city. The town is divided into three governorates. Its master plan was prepared in cooperation with France and adopted in 1983. Infrastructure (ring-roads, urban expressways, bridges) have improved while illegal or informal neighborhoods – about one hundred – have extended on farmland or desert. They are home to half the population of the city but cannot be equated with slums since the vast majority benefit from essential services, such as water and sanitation, and are gradually being regularized.

Sixth October Bridge from the left bank ©Vladimir Korostyshevsky/Shutterstock

In the Western media, Cairo has a bad reputation that is totally unjustified. It is often described as a gigantic urban sprawl, hyper-polluted, with apocalyptic traffic jams. In reality it is a modern city of contrasts, which has somehow managed its growth and has maintained a very special urban atmosphere in many friendly neighborhoods where social ties are still alive (Naguib Mahfouz's novels do not only paint portraits of a bygone era, they reflect a way of life which has not totally vanished). Cairo is a city that works and produces, that attracts, absorbs and excludes, that vibrates and moves. A noisy and dusty anthill, but warm and attractive. The poverty of millions and the income gaps certainly cannot be ignored, as cannot the unstable equilibrium of the urban environment and the invasion of arable land, but the catastrophic predictions of the 1970s have not materialized. Cairo plays its full role in the urban transition of Egypt, which is far from being completed (in 2013 the country had only 37 million urban citizens out of a total population of 87 million). Its transport system works, slowly but without major blockages. Its metro is expanding. Senior reporter Jean-Pierre Péroncel-Hugoz wrote in 1989 in the French Le Monde: "Cairo constantly gives the impression of a frightening ship sinking under the weight of its passengers. Yet, the city does not collapse. It derives, of course, but it finds every day new tricks to absorb its thousand more inhabitants." And the journalist admires an "Islamo-Rabelaisian" people with a caustic humor, and the thousands of minarets, "spears stuck in the down-to-earth of the city, sometimes grouped in clusters, with a look of Iris in its opening stage (...) that tell the long history of a contrasted and tormented Islam."

Eastern exit of Sixth
October Bridge ©Baloncici/
Shutterstock

If Egypt is a gift of the Nile (the river supplies 95% of the country's water) the Qasr el-Nile Bridge is a gift to Cairo, a bridge that played a major role in the development of the city and remains a key node of mobility and vibrant life. A bridge where in summer evenings young loving couples can be seen hand-in-hand, face-to-face while under the bridge of their arms passes ... the longest African river.

As stated twenty years ago by André Raymond, in the conclusion of his masterful history of Cairo: "For dozens of kilometers the Nile now flows between a double wall of high-rise buildings, giving an indication of the changes Egypt has undergone in the last forty years. This concrete Nile frontage, which was the despair of the celebrated Egyptian architect Hassan Fathy, is nonetheless the most spectacular and most impressive aspect of Cairo in our day, along a river that, hour after hour and season after season, preserves its majesty and magic." And further: "Modern Cairo remains an admirable, even a fascinating, city. The life and animation pulsing through it, its countless crowds, are a fabulous spectacle. The contrast between its modern districts, often broadly laid out, and the old city, so harmonious when seen from a distance, leaves an unforgettable impression. The majestic beauty of the Nile is constantly renewed with a charm, a color, and a grandeur that reflect nuances in the time of day and night and the variations in the seasons." We can only agree with this warm and admiring vision of the ancient but always renewed city, especially since the spring of 2011 that allowed the Cairene to appropriate public spaces, squares, streets and, of course, the bridges of their city.

In 1985 Jacques Lacarrière in his Sura of Cairo, wrote: "Crowd. Crowds. Many crowds. The city is not overcrowded; it is congested, bloated, thrombosed by the excessive yet peaceful crowd, almost placid despite the urgency of life. There is no lighter city despite its density of misery, a more human place despite the inhumanity of the sun, a more welcoming city in its swarming. A quiet ants' nest, a delightful dust of men, a good-natured crowd. The streets of Cairo."

Low-income incremental housing, typical of Cairo ©Steve Heap/Shutterstock

Descriptions abound, rendering these image of the city: a feverish and vibrating city; effervescence of unalterable humor; beating heart of Arabism; mother of the world; New York on the Nile; New Babylon; meeting place of Africa and the Arab world; the city of horns and loudspeakers; a city that never sleeps; the victorious, Cairo!

The Egyptian capital is certainly a magical city, the most spectacular in the Arab world. It officially had twelve million people in 2013 and is growing at an annual rate of 1.7%, representing 200,000 additional persons each year. Greater Cairo on its part has 17 million inhabitants and will gradually form with Alexandria a large "urban corridor" of 25 million people, the engine of Egypt's development. Since 1990 eight new towns ("New Communities") have been built around Cairo on desert lands, to absorb part of the urban growth. These dormitory towns work reasonably well. They attract investors and jobs, which are still insufficient, and have been created to reduce commuting to the metropolis.

My friend and former colleague, Dr. Mohamed El-Sioufi, ponders the future of his city: "A few months before the revolution of 2011, a team of planners from the General Organization for Physical Planning (GOPP) elaborated a vision of Cairo in 2050, based on a number of meetings of experts and economic actors. The diagnosis of strengths and weaknesses of the city was severe but an ambitious goal was agreed upon: to make Cairo an international metropolis able to compete with other major cities of the world, particularly in terms of living conditions, as well as environmental and socio-economic competitiveness. Unfortunately, the approach remained focused on mega-infrastructure projects rather than on mobilizing citizens. This is an undervalued resource which, I hope, will find its place in the new Egypt."

Indeed, the political context has changed and no one quite knows what shape the Egypt of tomorrow will take. But it is certain that Cairo around its Kobri Qasr el-Nile and its Tahrir Square will remain at the center of future debates and developments, since the city is the geographical, economic, social and cultural heart of the country, and has a reach far beyond Egypt's national borders.

THE BATTLE OF QASR EL-NILE
(Cairo, 28 January 2011)

While bridges have played a strategic role in most wars, urban bridges have been particularly at stake during revolutions. Bridges can easily be destroyed to stop the advance of the enemy or to block protesters: Joan of Arc defeated the English on the bridge of Orleans in 1429; Napoleon Bonaparte beat the Austrians at Arcole Bridge in 1796; the retreating Nazis destroyed many bridges in 1944 and 1945, including those in Budapest and Florence; the Hiroshima A-bomb targeted the city's T-bridge (Aioi Ohashi); the Milvian Bridge near Rome was in 312 the scene of a battle that founded Christianity; the old Bridge in Mostar, from its destruction to its reconstruction, summed up the Balkan war; the struggle for independence ended with the victory of Simon Bolivar in Boyacá Bridge in 1819; the Long Bien Bridge in Hanoi was shelled several times during the Vietnam War; control of the bridges of Saint-Petersburg was crucial during the October Revolution; the examples are many and varied. Bridges are promoters of peace and progress, their destruction acts of war, their control a common objective of revolutions.

The media has talked a lot about Tahrir Square in Cairo, which is equivalent in terms of urban geography to the Place de la Concorde in Paris, but they hardly mentioned the nearby bridge, the Kobri Qasr el-Nile, that is located a few meters away. This is where the "Arab Spring" revolution that ousted President Hosni Mubarak began in earnest in January 2011. A few journalists have described the confrontation between the demonstrators coming from the west and the police who wanted to prevent them from crossing the Nile. The envoys of the Guardian, New York Times and New Yorker were present on 28 January 2011, the "Friday of Anger" when everything changed. While the internet and mobile phone networks were put out of use, these reporters managed to publish poignant articles on 29 January and later. Their stories help to record the memory of the Cairo spring.

The first gatherings began on 25 January 2011 in Tahrir Square and continued the following days. It is well known that in Islamic countries Fridays are the most conducive days for collective action, so Friday, 28 January, was to be a day of popular mobilization. At the time of the Friday prayer large cordons of police were blocking the Qasr el-Nile bridge to prevent the demonstrators from entering the city center. Some mosques were closed "due to repair work". After Friday prayers, tens of thousands of residents, especially young people, went to the bridge, cheered on by people from balconies and windows, and arrived in Opera Square while singing the national anthem. They were greeted by a barrage of tear gas and water cannons and brutally driven back; they could not therefore leave the left bank.

At first there was relative calm; the bridge was empty, policemen caught their breath, protesters re-organized. At around 4 p.m. the crowd gathered in Opera Square was ready for action. They began to move forward, grenade explosions resumed, water cannons and batons were activated by the police to violently strike the front ranks of the demonstration. But the youngsters were determined and did not lack courage, the crowd chanting slogans that became famous: "Freedom for Egypt" and "Mubarak out!" Grenades were collected and thrown into the Nile, backs were turned to water sprays and the wounded were evacuated. Some protesters climbed onto police vehicles and on the lion statues to motivate the crowd. At 5.30 p.m., the bridge was invaded by the crowd, and the policemen slowly retreated and had to abandon their position. The call to the sunset prayer from hundreds of minarets was understood as a sign of victory, and on the bridge thousands bowed to glorify Allah. Qasr el-Nile was theirs. In the evening the army intervened with tanks to restore a fragile calm, and tried to consolidate the status quo. The curfew was ignored; police cars and the seat of the ruling party were torched. The bridge was then evacuated but Tahrir Square definitely belonged to the protesters.

The battle of Qasr el-Nile resulted in several dead, many wounded, but it had pushed the power back, it had severely eroded the regime that a few weeks before seemed invincible. Two weeks later, on 11 February, Hosni Mubarak, "the last pharaoh", resigned after thirty years of rule.

Demonstration of 28 January 2011 on Qasr el-Nile Bridge ©MOHPhoto/Shutterstock

SAN FRANCISCO AND ITS
BAY BRIDGE

On 29 June 1776, five days before the American Declaration of Independence, Spanish sailors founded a military post while celebrating a mass at the Franciscan Mission Dolores, close to a beautiful bay known since 1595 as San Francisco. Mission Dolores still exists and Saint Francis gave his name to a city that, in the 1930s, would build two of the most amazing bridges in the world.

◄**The Bay Bridge seen from downtown San Francisco, with Oakland lights in the background ©Mark Schwettmann/ Shutterstock**

SAN FRANCISCO AND ITS BAY BRIDGE

In 1821 Spanish California became Mexican, and a village was born shortly after on Yerba Buena Island. It was named San Francisco in January 1847, at which time it had only 500 inhabitants. In the mid-nineteenth century San Francisco was a very small town, which became American in 1848 as a result of the war that attached California to the United States. Its initial orthogonal grid was defined in 1847 by the Irish engineer Jasper O' Farrell who created Market Street, a hinge separating two unconnected urban areas with roadways perpendicular to Market Street in the south, and at 45 degrees in the north. This basic plan has guided the city's urban development to this day.

The Gold Rush blew over the grid from 1849 during an incredible year in which 40,000 adventurers arrived from all over the world. The city had a population of 56,800 people in 1860, 150,000 in 1870, 300,000 in 1890 and 450,000 in 1898. San Francisco became a new town born out of the Gold Rush, a city where gold played an important role and whose bay opens onto the Pacific Ocean through a "Golden Gate", so named in 1846. The first ferry to Oakland, the sister city on the other side of the bay, was commissioned in 1852 and ran for more than eighty years. Meanwhile, the urban population of the United States multiplied by 14 between 1820 and 1870, at an extraordinary average growth rate of more than 5.5% a year.

San Francisco from Twin Peaks

Superimposing the orthogonal grid typical of American cities (advocated by a land decree of 1785) on a very hilly site complicated the urbanization process while providing unexpected opportunities. The analytical approach of Florence Lipsky clearly highlights this contradiction, its causes and consequences. The grid plan, dating back to Greco-Roman times and imposed on Hispanic America by the Law of India in 1573, has been criticized for its monotony, its contempt for sites and topography, and its purely commercial logic, but it has also been praised for its neutrality, its refusal to prioritize spaces, its simplicity and the speed with which it can be implemented. In 1854 the hills of San Francisco were recognized as essential to the beauty of the site and integrated in the orthogonal grid, subject to case by case adaptations of the roadways, and some discontinuities and deformations of the theoretical layout. From 1873 onwards many hills became accessible through cable-cars. The brutal superimposition of a horizontal orthogonality over a rough and uneven terrain became an asset and a major dimension of the urban landscape. As a result of the confrontation between humans and nature, San Francisco is a spectacular city of ever-changing perspectives, a coherent city where all transport modes must coexist, and a multifaceted city where America meets the past of Europe and the future of Asia.

Skyscrapers overlooking the bay ©Jenny Solomon/ Shutterstock

The earthquake of 18 April 1906, followed by several days of a terrible fire, destroyed more than half of the city. This earthquake, which lasted 40 seconds and reached a magnitude of 8 on the moment magnitude scale, made 250,000 people homeless and reduced 28,000 buildings to ashes. But the city quickly rebuilt itself on the same layout and this achievement was celebrated at the 1915 Exhibition. By 1920, San Francisco had 500,000 inhabitants. On 26 June 1945 the United Nations Charter was signed there by representatives of fifty nations. It entered into force on 24 October of the same year, with the establishment of the UN headquarters in New York.

San Francisco is known for its forty-two hills, including the challenging Twin Peaks, its cable cars (tramways drawn by underground cables) that ran from 1873 until they were replaced by streetcars (classic trams) after 1906, its Victorian houses, such as the famous "painted ladies" of Alamo Square, its cool climate and its two great bridges. "The most delirious city of America", it attracts hordes of tourists (16 million in 2010) and is the main financial center of the Pacific coast, as well as a center of biotechnology and informatics near Silicon Valley. Although it could still be improved, its public transport network is one of the most efficient in the United States, and is used daily by 35% of the population. Its bridges are powerful symbols of the New Deal of Franklin Delano Roosevelt, who was able to respond to the Great Depression by ambitious infrastructure projects – an example for contemporary governments.

Jean Cocteau wrote in 1937: "San Francisco at night is the most beautiful city in the world." He appreciated the "sublime bay and the two suspension bridges that limit it" but he did not like the style of the buildings, a "terrible mess", too visible during daytime. As we know, cities are always more beautiful at night, when their derelict areas are cloaked in darkness. San Francisco is no exception to this golden rule of urban tourism.

The Embarcadero at twilight with Yerba Buena Island at the back ©Rafael Ramirez Lee/Shutterstock

The city is located in quite an extraordinary environment and has one of the most famous crossings in the world, the Golden Gate Bridge, built between 1933 and 1937. However, this prestigious bridge cannot be considered as fully intra-urban. It is a bridge with a regional purpose along the Pacific Ocean, linking the San Francisco Peninsula in the south to Marin County in the north. The rise of Sausalito on the north side of the bridge is fairly recent. The San Francisco Bay may, in turn, be compared to the bays of Rio de Janeiro and Sydney (a sister city), and its landscape to that of Istanbul. These are four major and fantastic cities sensually occupying magical sites, where water has played a key role in planning and urban design.

A Bridge On The Golden Gate

The Golden Gate Bridge is the archetype of the suspension bridge, probably the most famous in the world. Its construction was launched on 26 February 1933 during a ceremony attended by 200,000 people. It took fifteen years for engineer Joseph Strauss from Chicago, who had built nearly 400 bascule bridges around the world, to convince politicians and bankers that the project was viable. The Golden Gate would immortalize him, although he was not the lead designer (it was Charles Ellis).

The Golden Gate Bridge seen from Baker Beach (South-West)

The Golden Gate Bridge was for 27 years the longest crossing in the world with a suspended span of 1,280 meters, until 1964 when the Verrazano-Narrows Bridge in New York would overtake it by a mere 20 meters. Its two towers rise to 227 meters above sea level, against 154 meters for the Bay Bridge, and its deck to 67 meters. It was funded by bonds issued in 1932 totaling US$ 35 million. The bridge was built in 44 months; eleven workers died during the construction process, ten in a single accident; it required 25 million working hours. The bridge was inaugurated on 27 May 1937 and was walked on that day by more than 200,000 enthusiastic people.

Simple and beautiful, thanks to its perfect proportions and elegant integration into the site, the Golden Gate Bridge was hailed as an impossible sculpture, an architectural poem, a rainbow of steel. This suburban monument, which is self-sufficient, gradually created an urban settlement around its north end. Strauss had fulfilled his dream and died a year after the bridge was completed. Since 1941 his bronze statue welcomes visitors preparing to cross the orange bridge over the "Golden Gate", with barely a thought for the Golden Horn in Istanbul from which the entrance of the bay takes its name. Some of these visitors decide to end their days by jumping off the middle of the bridge – since its opening more than 75 years ago, the bridge has witnessed 1,300 suicides, which probably constitutes a dismal world record.

The Golden Gate International Exposition, held from February 1939, was an opportunity for San Francisco to celebrate its two great bridges. On that occasion Yerba Buena Island was extended with the addition of the artificial Treasure Island, which hosted the exhibition and its 17 million visitors. The theme of the exhibition was "The Pageant of the Pacific" as the U.S. west coast wanted to meet the Pacific (in the broadest sense, the Angkor temples occupied a prominent place) and its civilizations. The attack on Pearl Harbor in 1941 temporarily ruined that dream and although San Francisco detained its Japanese population during the war, the city opened its doors to Asian immigrants in 1945. The airlifts needed over the Pacific Ocean to transport these travellers would attract companies in increasing number, and airports would become the abutments of these "aerial-bridges" and hubs structuring many global cities that some experts now call "aerotropolis" (airport cities).

Postcard of the 1939 exposition

The main urban bridge on the west coast of the USA connects San Francisco in the west of the bay to Oakland and Berkeley in the east. The San Francisco Oakland Bay Bridge was built at the same time as the Golden Gate Bridge. The two major bridges symbolized the New Deal that would get America back on track, in a city which itself symbolized hope. Their impact was immediate on the economy and demography of the urban region. The population increased by 40% between 1940 and 1947. The Bay Bridge cost US$ 77 million and was then the most expensive bridge in the world. The Golden Gate Bridge cost less than half this amount – US$ 35 million.

Zoom on San Francisco and Oakland ©Konstantin Sutyagin/Shutterstock

The construction of the Bay Bridge was decided in 1928 by the State of California. Its necessity was unquestionable, while that of the Golden Gate was more controversial. Financing by the Reconstruction Finance Corporation, a Federal body, posed no problem and President Hoover, a Stanford engineer, played a decisive role in approving the project. As of 1931 Charles Henry Purcell, born in 1883 and a graduate of the University of Nebraska, led the design studies as Chief Engineer of the State of California. He proposed a dual suspension bridge followed by a tunnel and a cantilevered section – a hybrid of a bridge.

U.S. commemorative stamp ©Brendan Howard/ Shutterstock

Started in May 1933, the Bay Bridge was inaugurated on 12 November 1936, two months ahead of schedule. Consisting of two large spans (east and west), it remains one of the longest bridges in the world (7.2 kilometers, and 13.5 kilometers with its approach sections). As a toll bridge, it welcomes nearly 300,000 vehicles per day. This is a complex and heterogeneous metal structure that rests in its middle on Yerba Buena Island. Its western segment, the San Francisco side, is 2,822 meters long. It consists of two beautiful suspension bridges connected by a common anchor, pier W-4, and comprising four steel towers of 5,000 tons each.

The eastern segment, the Oakland side, is 3,101 meters long. Until 2012, it combined a double cantilever (22,500 tons, but cheaper than a suspension bridge), five truss spans and a truss causeway. These two crossings are connected by a huge tunnel (17 meters high, 23 meters wide) running through Yerba Buena Island, 518 meters long. The Bay Bridge has a double deck, and since 1958 it has had five lanes to San Francisco on the upper deck and five lanes to Oakland on the lower deck, which were originally used by trains.

The Bay Bridge and the Business District seen from Yerba Buena ©Andy Z/ Shutterstock

The main difficulty in its construction was building the piers at depths never reached before (more than 70 meters for the western section) in the seismic zone of the San Andreas Fault. The expert in this area was Daniel Moran, who designed the huge W-4 pier as a forty-floor tall building that required 125,000 m³ of concrete, more than the Empire State Building. Many divers were mobilized to work up to fifty meters under water. Their leader Bill Reed acquired a deserved celebrity. In total, 6,500 people contributed to the project, 24 workers were killed on site and 55 million working hours were used. The aura of the bridge was augmented in 1939 with the creation of an artificial island close to Yerba Buena, called Treasure Island, to host the Golden Gate International Exposition.

Bay Bridge, western span seen from Treasure Island

The eastern section of the Bay Bridge, which until recently was the least elegant, has lately been completely rebuilt at a cost of US$ 6.3 billion. The tender took place after lengthy negotiations on funding modalities and technical options. In 2007 the toll increased from US$3 to US$4 during the off-peak period and to US$6 during rush hour. A large self-anchored asymmetrical suspension span (with a 160-metre high tower) was built between 2010 and 2013 on the eastern shore of Yerba Buena. The new span, designed by architect Donald MacDonald, bears some resemblance to the Alamillo Bridge in Seville and the Runyang Bridge inaugurated in 2005 on the Yangtze near Yangzhou, which also relies on a small island – Shiye – and includes a northern cable-stayed portion and a suspended southern section with a 1,490-metre span. The eastern section of the Bay Bridge was affected by the earthquake of 17 October 1989, during which a small portion of the upper deck collapsed. The bridge was then closed for a month, revealing through its absence the key role it played in the functioning of the agglomeration. An important work of retrofitting the western section has also been conducted since that date.

The new eastern span under construction (2012) ©Harris Stiffman/Shutterstock

My friend and former colleague, Mark Hildebrand, who retired in California, raises an important issue: "In the 1930s, San Francisco's new bridges solved major communication problems and were part of an ambitious stimulus plan. They contributed to an economic boom and to a widespread and more balanced urbanization of the bay. Following the current replacement of the eastern span of the Bay Bridge – an enormous investment – we may reach another development stage, probably more secure in terms of seismic resistance but still based on the extensive use of private cars. I wished Caltrans could have added cycling lanes as on the Golden Gate Bridge and a pedestrian promenade as on Brooklyn Bridge. San Francisco missed an opportunity to become a greener city. In my view the decision-making process for such huge infrastructure projects remains as open a question today as it was in the 1930s." This suggestion has indeed been heard: a bike and pedestrian pathway has been added to the south side of the new east span and should be extended over the tunnel before joining the west span. It will soon be possible for bikers to circle the entire bay and to enjoy sweeping views from platforms installed on the bridge.

The previous cantilever eastern span (2011)

Although it broke many records, including in length, weight and price, the Bay Bridge has long suffered an inferiority complex vis-à-vis the Golden Gate, because of its overly ordinary eastern span. It is much less tainted by suicides, being inaccessible to pedestrians, but local connoisseurs appreciate its undeniable charm. It is more urban, more useful but less glamorous than the Golden Gate. Yet it fully deserves the title of "one of the seven wonders of the engineering world" that it was awarded in 1956 by the American Society of Civil Engineers. And it also deserves to be admired for its elegance when the sun sets over San Francisco and artificial lighting illuminates its cables that become necklaces around the skyscrapers of the city. The Bay Bridge was a turning point in the history of San Francisco, fostering the creation of the Greater San Francisco-Oakland region – the transition from city to metropolis – and reducing the distance between two cities that were separated and now complement each other. It may be compared to the bridge linking Rio and Niteroi, which would be built 38 years later, but the look of the Bay Bridge is much more original.

Traffic on the bridge, out of Yerba Buena tunnel ©Vilen Gabrielyan

Old photos of the city and the construction sites of the two bridges, in black and white, are owed to the Moulin dynasty (Gabriel, Raymond, Irving, Thomas). Ideally each city should have its star photographer, like Doisneau in Paris and Güler in Istanbul, capable of recording in artistic clichés and milestones the economic, social and architectural life of their city. In this regard, San Francisco seems ahead because its visual story is fairly well documented. But a museum of the city and its development would need to be established. It should also be noted that the tiny Lake Alvord Bridge, built in 1889 in the Golden Gate Park, was the first reinforced concrete bridge in the United States, a fact that most passers-by who walk under its arch are completely unaware of.

The bridge under construction in 1935 (photo Raymond Moulin)

Today the metropolitan area of San Francisco-Oakland hosts 3.8 million inhabitants. The municipality of San Francisco itself has only 800,000 inhabitants, a figure that has remained fairly stable since 1950. It is dense (6,500 inhabitants per km²), rich and multi-ethnic (43% White, 31% Asian – the highest percentage in the country – and 8% African-American). San Francisco is twinned with Shanghai and Sydney, two other major port cities, and Berkeley with Gao, a historic city on the Niger River in Mali. The Bay Bridge is the only road linking San Francisco to the east of the Bay, via Interstate 80. It has been complemented since 1974 by the Bay Area Rapid Transit (BART, equivalent to Paris RER), which runs under the bay.

The new eastern span inaugurated in September 2013 ©Michael Warwick/ Shutterstock

Downtown San Francisco is ahead of most cities in the world in terms of average per capita income (US$ 62,000 in 2006 in purchasing power parity, according to an OECD study) and also, unfortunately, in terms of high rents and housing prices. However, it also welcomes many homeless people attracted by the available social services. Since the 1960s, San Francisco has been home to counter-culture, pacifism and sexual tolerance. Beatniks and hippies have disappeared but left a few traces, including a strong environmental movement. San Francisco is indeed one of the first "Green Cities" in the United States. Since 2005 it has launched numerous environmentally-friendly initiatives, such as the renovation of Hunters Point and Treasure Island. On 12 November 2011, the city celebrated 75 years of the Bay Bridge, with upgrading works unfortunately not yet finished. The new and beautiful east span (the world's longest self-anchored suspension bridge, 3,670 meters in total) was completed in September 2013, and the cantilever section has thus disappeared in the archives of history, while the Bay Bridge has received a new and younger face.

FACING SEISMIC RISK

The earthquake of 17 October 1989, known as Loma Prieta, which measured 6.9 on the moment magnitude scale, revealed the fragility of the Bay Bridge. In 1934 Charles Purcell had envisioned horizontal accelerations of just one-tenth of the gravity on the San Andreas Fault. This was an underestimation. It was therefore necessary to reinforce the bridge between 1989 and 1992.

Optimizing the relationship between cost and safety is always difficult and a somewhat random task. A large bridge collapses every thirty years, one per generation. And the main technology changes at the same pace, the most recent being that of cable-stayed spans. In terms of earthquake engineering, San Francisco is at the forefront, as evidenced by the recent reconstruction of the eastern span of the Bay Bridge and the continuous renewal of the Golden Gate Bridge.

The work of seismic retrofitting of the Golden Gate and the design of the huge single tower that retains part of the new eastern span of the Bay Bridge are based on two key principles: sacrificial box structures connecting different parts of the bridge, and absorbers to mitigate the impact of shocks. The latter must absorb a part of the seismic energy while sacrificial joins, including between the four columns that make up the new tower of the Bay Bridge, can deform and break without affecting the elements that they combine. Rigidity leaves room for flexibility. As the piers are no longer directly connected to the roadbeds, their movements do not have any serious impact on the deck. In theory, the broken joins can be easily repaired and the bridges can be quickly returned to service following an earthquake.

In the two bridges many metal components, including bracing, are also subject to replacement or reinforcement. The calculations are based on the assumption of an 8.5 moment magnitude earthquake, which may occur in the next thirty years.

The cost of this work is extremely high, in the order of US$2 two billion for the Bay Bridge and also for the Golden Gate Bridge. These amounts are much higher than toll revenues that do not reach US$100 million a year and are only used for routine maintenance works. Significant federal funds and grants from the State of California are mobilized to finance this essential upgrading.

More than a century after the disaster of 1906, the bridges of the west coast are ready for an event that may occur at any time and, of course, could affect all buildings, tunnels and other infrastructure. As in Tokyo on the other side of the Pacific, the full-scale test of the state-of-the-art knowledge in earthquake engineering is approaching.

The tower of the new eastern span designed to resist magnitude-8 earthquakes ©Michael Warwick/Shutterstock

KOLKATA AND ITS RABINDRA SETU

Calcutta, or Kolkata, the capital of West Bengal in the east of India, is a recent city located a few steps from Bangladesh, the former East Bengal. Historically, South Asian urbanization began in the west, in the Indus Valley (now in Pakistan) and continued along the Ganges, towards the east, reaching the delta in the eighteenth century. Calcutta had to wait until 1873 to have a floating bridge on the Hooghly and until 1943 to finally launch a large permanent bridge towards Howrah station. The bridge was renamed Rabindra Setu in 1965, after the most famous Calcuttan in history: Rabindranath Tagore, winner of the Nobel Prize for Literature in 1913.

◀**Rabindra Setu (1943) across Hooghly River, seen from Howrah Railway Station**

KOLKATA AND ITS RABINDRA SETU

In August 1690, the English, under the direction of Job Charnock of the East India Company, settled in three small villages on the banks of the Hooghly: Kalikata, Sutanati and Govindapur. They created Fort William in 1712, and Calcutta emerged on the map of India.

English traders were already present in Madras in the south since 1639 and Bombay on the western coast since 1674, but colonization (in the guise of trade) only began in earnest in Bengal in the eighteenth century. Kalikata was an inhospitable site, 130 kilometers from the sea, yet it seemed ideal for navigation and commerce. Like Saint-Petersburg in the same years, the town was built on floodplains that any reasonable planner would have considered totally unsuitable for the creation of a city. However, from 1760 onwards the revenue from textiles, salt and opium were used to build the first palaces. The impressive Writers Building (more scribes than writers), now the seat of the Government of West Bengal, was inaugurated in 1777. Without a plan, Calcutta grew in the greatest disorder, but with a clear separation between the "white town" in the south and the squalid "black town" in the north.

The Writers Building, designed by Thomas Lion, headquarters of the Government of West Bengal

Bengal, well watered by the Ganges, and known for its rural density and fertility, has been called "the Wonder of India". The English soon controlled its foreign trade, in particular cotton exports. The city of Calcutta became the capital of the British Raj in 1772 and the favorite city of English settlers. It superseded Batavia (the future Jakarta) and became the second city, after London, of the British Empire, with 600,000 inhabitants in 1800.

Charles d'Oyly, Alipore
bridge, first metal bridge in
India, lithograph, 1835

Suspension Bridge at Alipore over Tolly's Nullah, 30.3 x 41.7cn

Many palaces were built throughout the nineteenth century, culminating in the
Anglo-Hindu Victoria Memorial (1906-1921), a rather successful fusion of Victorian
and Indo-Islamic styles with classic and Baroque touches. This monument was the
work of the president of the order of British architects, Sir William Emerson.

At that time, however, Calcutta was starting to resemble a huge shanty town, and
was probably "the largest slum of the world". According to the city's Chief Engineer,
E.P. Richards, 900,000 people were crammed into 45,000 houses and the city had a
normal street system in only two small areas. This poverty of living conditions would
remain the main feature of the city throughout the twentieth century.

Victoria Memorial (1921),
designed by William
Emerson ©Jeremy Richards/
Shutterstock

Calcutta would decline after the transfer of the capital of the Indian Union to New
Delhi in 1912. While this transfer had several goals, it was mainly motivated by political

considerations: the administration feared the consequences of Bengali agitation in a city where 14,000 British civilians were living. Calcutta would then become the victim of repeated famines; that of 1943 caused the death of more than 3 million people, reaching 11,000 deaths per week at the end of that dark year. Calcutta would then see an influx of refugees from East Bengal in 1947 after the partition of India and the creation of Pakistan, and again in 1971, when a war of independence was declared by what was then known as East Pakistan, leading to the establishment of present-day Bangladesh.

Samir Biswas, Howrah Bridge seen from Nandaram Market (1987)

As the capital of West Bengal, where communism had a strong hold, and as the cultural capital of India, home to geniuses such as the writer Rabindranath Tagore and the intimate filmmaker Satyajit Ray, the city is huge, wet, active, proud, both miserable and mesmerizing. Half of its population lives in slums or "bustees", in crumbling buildings and even on sidewalks. The latter are called "pavement dwellers", and do not have an equivalent in other countries, as they are technically "homeless" in the strictest sense of the term. But the "viscous hell" of Calcutta still inspires poets and filmmakers, and the oldest street of the city, Chitpur Road, continues to attract painters and photographers. In fact, Calcutta, a place of terrible contrasts, was and remains an attractive city in many ways, as evidenced by the abundant literature of which it is the object. It has an indefinable mythical dimension. It is a metropolis in perpetual decline, which repels and enchants, an almost inexplicable city.

The Howrah Bridge was renamed Rabindra Setu – Rabindra Bridge – in 1965, after Rabindranath Tagore, the Nobel Prize for Literature winner in 1913, who died in 1941. It was built between 1937 and 1942 to connect the city center, including its hyper-dense Barabaazar, to the dynamic western suburb of Howrah and its large railway station. Until then the Hooghly River (an arm of the Ganges) could only be crossed by way of a pontoon dating back to 1873-1874, designed by Bradford Leslie. Managed by port services, this large floating bridge was originally scheduled to last twenty-five years. It was, in fact, used for seven decades and contributed to the real economic boom of

The floating pontoon in use from 1874 to 1943, designed by Bradford Leslie ©Kolkata Port Trust

the city, which saw the advent of the tramway in 1880, the automobile in 1896, the telephone in 1882 and a Viceroy (that is to say, direct administration) from 1860. By 1900 the city hosted more than one million inhabitants, but the vast majority of the local people continued to live in overcrowded slums.

KOLKATA NOCTURNE

Email from Kolkata, 2 February 2012

Night fell with a thud. I snuck into the next street in the middle of an indescribable crowd, of which I will nevertheless try to sketch a portrait. We are close to New Market, one of the largest bazaars in Kolkata. You can take a stroll here in the beautiful winter evenings. The sticky humidity has not yet hit the city.

Imagine a street almost as wide as 42nd Street in Manhattan, full of people, everywhere, on the sidewalks and on the road. But contrary to appearances, it is not pedestrian. Sometimes a small car emerges, honking to open a passage through the human mass. Surprisingly it receives no kicks or knocks, it moves slowly. Then two pretty girls appear, perched on the seat of a rickshaw. The human horse who pulls them, barefoot, uses his metallic bell and opens a path for himself.

On the sides hundreds of temporary stalls are aligned, selling cheap clothes and varied utensils. Extremely loudly, professional shouters try to attract customers. They yell "ta-ta-ta-ta" with all their might but the deafening noise does not disturb anyone. Kolkata is known locally as the city of screams and chaos. Of course, many street restaurants are open, offering dishes for less than a dollar in plastic plates. People eat and throw the used plates on the ground, much to the delight of stray dogs that share the remains, while barking to get in tune with surrounding bipeds. Sometimes huge piles of stuffed toys remind us that there is no birth control here and that China, the exporting giant, is close by.

Smells of curry mingle with scents of incense; merchants of mobile phones stand alongside garbage heaps. Broken sidewalks are awaiting their batch of concrete blocks. Sometimes the centre of the street turns into a makeshift parking lot. Drowsy drivers in cars. The streets of Kolkata represent a small proportion of the total area of the city (against a third in Western countries), a record of urban density. In this market an average of three people per square meter would be a fair estimate, which is the same as in the corridors of London's Waterloo underground station at 6 p.m., but the human flow is slower, less stressed, almost cool, as fluid as the Hooghly River.

I turn into the avenue and discover the Oberoi Grand Hotel, with its beautiful colonial architecture and its guards dressed as mustachioed maharajas, who filter entries. The contrast is striking but totally ignored by the masses. Clothes stands are attached to the hotel, the screams do not cease, the night is sweet. My friend the book dealer, his books kept well aligned on the sidewalk opens Google on his cell phone and looks for a rare book that he promises the next day. It is 10 p.m. In a few minutes the transactions stop, stalls are packed, light bulbs go off, homeless people try to seize the least uncomfortable shelter, wealthy couples take a taxi, bus, tram, subway. The city falls asleep, satisfied. Tomorrow will be another day.

Samir Biswas, Rabindra Sarani (Chitpur Road), the oldest street in Kolkata, watercolor and ink (2008)

In 1822 the country's first iron bridge was built over the Adi Ganga, or Tolly's Nullah canal. A lithograph of the small suspension bridge, drawn around 1835 by Charles d'Oyly, is displayed at the Victoria Memorial, and gives an idea of the atmosphere of the time in the upmarket Alipore area. The city has a bascule bridge that is still in service, the Nazrul Setu on Karl Marx Sarani, and a swing bridge unfortunately out of order, north of Nazrul Setu.

A permanent bridge over the Hooghly was envisaged at the end of the First World War. In 1921 a committee of engineers chaired by R.N. Mukerjee launched the first feasibility studies and a commission was created in 1922 to oversee the preparatory process. Another committee, established in 1930, recruited a team of designers, the English engineering company R.P.T., and organized the tender. The two halves of the central span were built in 1941 and joined in 1942, during the Second World War.

Howrah Bridge under construction (1942) ©Kolkata Port Trust

Solid metal structure

Inaugurated in February 1943, the bridge is a cantilever steel structure, of 26,500 tons with a main span of 457 meters and two side spans of 99 meters. Both piers are 82 meters high. Bridge maintenance is funded by property taxes collected by the municipalities of Calcutta and Howrah and paid to the owner, the Calcutta Port Trust.

The most frequented (by pedestrians) bridge of the planet

These taxes amount to just 0.5% of the annual value of properties in Calcutta and 0.25% of those in Howrah, and in total they amounted to US$700,000 dollars in 2011 (30 million Indian rupees). Freight trains departing from Howrah station are also taxed because they carry products that have generally crossed the bridge. This original system of revenue collection was established in 1926 by the West Bengal Government to contribute to the construction of a bridge that was then only a sketch, and it remained in place after 1943 to finance the maintenance of the structure.

The Howrah Bridge is probably one of the busiest bridges in the world. It is frequented by buses, cars, rickshaws, all kinds of carts, bicycles, a few cows, donkeys and mules, and, of course, thousands of pedestrians. It is claimed that at peak hours the bridge lengthens by one meter under the weight of traffic. Originally a tramway track was placed in the center.

Place of informal trade

According to Dominique Lapierre, "this bridge is the busiest of the universe. Every day, more than a million people and hundreds of thousands of vehicles cross it in an amazing maelstrom." The six-lane bridge is the lifeline of a huge agglomeration whose population has increased four-fold since 1947. It is now estimated that the traffic averages 100,000 vehicles and 150,000 people per day; the latter figure probably constitutes a world record.

Designed by Rendel, Palmer & Tritton (R.P.T.) and built for the Calcutta Port Trust by the Cleveland Bridge & Engineering Company (which was initially involved in the concept of the Sydney Harbour Bridge), the Howrah Bridge (now Rabindra Setu) was the last great work of British India. It kicked off the post-independence urban explosion and somehow sealed the physical connection of Calcutta to the rest of the country.

Rabindra Setu at sunset

A new bridge, the Vidyasagar Setu, funded by the State of West Bengal, was inaugurated in 1992 near the city center, three kilometers south of Rabindra Setu. It is a beautiful suspension bridge where a modest toll (10 rupees or 0.2 US dollar) is charged, though it is less used than its predecessor because it is less accessible.

Vidyasagar Setu, second bridge in the city center over the Hooghly (1992)

The first railway and road bridge, the Vivekananda Setu (or Bally or Willingdon Bridge), was built in 1931 north of the city. These two bridges are also named after historical personalities: Vidyasagar (1820-1891) was a social reformer while Vivekananda (1863-1902) was a religious reformer. Both are prominent figures of the Bengali Renaissance of the second half of the nineteenth century. Another tolled

suspension bridge, the Nivedita Setu, funded through public-private partnership, was inaugurated in 2007 to complement the Vivekananda Setu, which is located 50 meters upstream. Sister Nivedita (1867-1911) was an Irish disciple of Vivekananda; the neighboring bridges materially remind us of the spiritual closeness between two charismatic leaders.

However, all these bridges are not sufficient to meet the needs of Kolkata and its residents. Dilapidated ferries, therefore, continue to operate quite effectively.

Ferries are still operational

The city built the first subway system in the country in the 1980s, which is gradually extending. Meanwhile, aged trams and thousands of buses, mostly private and more or less maintained, crisscross the town in a raucous concert of horns. Among major Asian cities however, traffic conditions in Kolkata are far from being the worst. In fact, private cars are few, and public transport is subject to fierce competition. Besides public transport, thousands of yellow cabs, pedicabs, tricycles and rickshaws offer low-cost services. Kolkata is the last Indian city to tolerate rickshaws, whose traction by "human mules" is sometimes criticized for violating human rights, but this mode of transportation also creates many jobs and has demonstrated its effectiveness during the monsoon and flooding season.

INDIA, AN URBAN ARCHIPELAGO

If the power of nations depends on the economic policies adopted by their governments, the base must be found in the population, that is, the number of inhabitants and workers that are active and available. History has repeatedly demonstrated that the most populous countries are potentially the most powerful. But this power is also correlated with education and the spatial distribution of populations.

The most recent and official figures[1] provide a glimpse of the current urbanization trends in India. In 1980, there were 690 million Indian people. Fifty years later, in 2030, India will have the same population as China (1.45 billion people), and thereafter overtake China as the most populous country on the planet. In 2013 India had 1.27 billion people. Population growth in China is much slower than in India due to the former's one-child policy and the latter's largely ineffective birth control campaigns. Even so, the current growth rate of India's population is only 1.3% per year.

In 1987 India and China had the same level of urbanization (25%). In 2013 China was 52% urban, while India had only about a third of its population (32%) living in urban areas. India has an annual urban growth rate of 2.47%, which is on the increase. Its urban population is growing by ten million people every year; it has just reached the 400 million threshold.

The population of India has followed the global trend of urban transition, but at a relatively moderate pace. The urban population rose from 63 million in 1950 to 408 million in 2013, a six-fold increase in six decades, while over the same period the multiplier factor was 10 in China and 13 in Africa. In 2030, according to UN projections, India will be 40% urban; the threshold of 50% will only be reached around 2045 when more than 800 million people will be living in urban areas out of a total population of 1.66 billion.

Kolkata, city of commerce: the flower market near Rabindra Setu

1 See United Nations, Population Division, "World Urbanization Prospects: the 2011 Revision". These biennial statistics are the only internationally recognized data, accepted by all UN member states. They are computed in collaboration with national bureaus of statistics. The latest revision has been issued in July 2014.

In 2013 India had 8 cities with more than 5 million people: Delhi (24 million), Mumbai (20 million), Kolkata (15 million), Chennai (9 million), Bangalore (9 million), Hyderabad (8 million), Ahmedabad (7 million) and Pune (5.4 million). Note that the figures correspond to physical agglomerations, only relevant for international comparisons and historical series, and not to administrative boundaries. Also note that the eight most populous Indian cities are fairly well distributed around the country. The Delhi-Kolkata-Chennai-Bangalore-Mumbai-Ahmedabad hexagon reflects this regional balance. The national capital, Delhi, has become the second city in the world in terms of population after Tokyo.

But India also has 40 "millionaire" cities (called "metro-cities"), 60 cities with more than 750,000 inhabitants and 400 cities with over 100,000 inhabitants. India remains a country of towns and large villages that are poorly interconnected.

The history of India's urbanization is fundamentally exogenous, beginning in the basins of the Indus and the Ganges but mainly determined by invaders from Central Asia in the thirteenth century who created the Delhi Sultanate and the Mughal empire from 1526, and finally by the British colonization in the eighteenth and nineteenth centuries. The urban wave moved from North to South over the centuries.

After history, the economy is the second explanatory factor of urbanization, and can be partially explained by urban dynamics. The annual economic growth rate in India is around 7%, driven by large private firms. Cities already provide about 60% of GDP. Despite poor infrastructure, urban productivity is significantly higher than in rural areas and cities attract the most dynamic people. But this productivity also depends on local policies. The estimated GDP of Mumbai is double that of Kolkata, with a population that is only 30% larger.

The central government remains weak, both in terms of investment, regulations, control and monitoring of companies. This has resulted in a liberal laissez-faire accompanied by the constant search for consensus (a British heritage?) and thus an essentially spontaneous process of urbanization. However, the federal government seems to be awakening slowly in recent years, not only to defend the interests of big Indian companies in international negotiations, but also to help the States of the Federation to better meet the infrastructural needs of these firms. Cities, on their part, are also joining the trend, trying to become "world class" in an increasingly competitive globalized economy.

Indeed, national, regional and municipal infrastructure is still underdeveloped. This is due to investment rates that remain far too low (25%). Similarly, foreign direct investments are highly targeted and insufficient. It is becoming increasingly urgent for India to drastically increase its investments in infrastructure. The McKinsey Global Institute has estimated that India should invest US$ 1.2 trillion in urban infrastructure by 2030, averaging US$ 134 per capita per year, a significant increase from the US$ 17 per capita that was invested in 2007. An enormous challenge.

Political and fiscal decentralization is quite uneven in the country despite the 74th Amendment to the Constitution, adopted in 1992, while Indian politicians loudly proclaim their quasi-philosophical commitment to "local" virtues. It may be noted – this is the best criterion for judging effective decentralization – that local government revenues are dependent on the fluctuating whims of States. The average annual income of municipalities barely reaches US$ 25 per capita.

In India States are strong but cities are weak. In such a context, rural interests often outweigh those of urban areas, as has been observed for decades in West Bengal, a state of 90 million people, of which only 26 million are urban residents, and also in Maharashtra, home to India's economic powerhouse and second largest city, Mumbai.

Kolkata, city of culture: the annual book fair (2012)

Income poverty has steadily declined but poverty of living conditions persists. This poverty is reflected in the high density of the urban fabric, and the importance of informal settlements, which represent between 30% and 50% of urban housing. Social inequalities are glaring and denounced by all sociologists, while economists are confident and rely on the expected benefits of economic growth, a domino effect that has yet to be realized.

Launched in 2005, the National Urban Renewal Mission (JNNURM) aimed at reducing poverty in 63 cities. Supported by a federal budget of US$ 12 billion over six years, it has helped to build major infrastructure. As in other countries, however, there is a reduction in the production of social housing by public agencies and an inexorable evolution of developers toward high-end speculative real estate and "gated communities".

Indian businessmen and some visionary politicians generally see cities as engines of innovation, growth and exports in a global economy from which they intend to derive maximum benefits. But they remain silent about this shared vision as they must take into account strong rural traditions and hundreds of millions of people who will continue to (over-)populate the countryside for two or three generations.

Kolkata, city of demonstrations: an electoral campaign (2011) ©Arindambanerjee/Shutterstock

Regional disparities, lack of adequate natural and energy resources, and environmental problems (pollution of air and water in urban areas, power-hungry production methods, obsolete industries, etc.) are constraints and threats that policymakers and the public are slowly becoming aware of.

The rapid development of capital markets and mortgages, as the last missing link to fully enter the market economy, can be observed in a more or less chaotic but cautious way. It is generally accepted that Indian financial institutions are quite transparent and efficient but above all seek short-term profitability.

Finally, the growing adherence to Western models of consumption through some local adaptation (private cars, fast food, supermarkets, modernist architecture, skyscrapers etc.) contrasts with a strong national pride, and among the middle and upper classes, with faith in the future and the unlimited benefits of Asian capitalism.

The country's mode of spatial development looks a bit like that of continental Europe at the dawn of the nineteenth century, with a rather hierarchical urban network, pockets of underdevelopment corresponding to the most rural areas, and deficient infrastructure. In fact, Indian urbanization reflects an archipelago economy, made of "high-tech" islands emerging from a still under-equipped territory. An extrovert until 1947, India became an introvert for over forty years, until the 1991 reforms that introduced a large movement towards liberalization, which is still ongoing.

Indian cities are gradually abolishing the center-periphery dichotomy that characterizes many European cities that have a wealthy center, as well as those in North America where the rich live in suburbs. With a few exceptions (such as Bangalore) Indian cities are increasingly multi-centered because of the invisible hand of land markets and the strategies of investors.

In terms of urban management, the Indian authorities are fully aware of the necessary steps they need to take: they must decentralize more, invest more in infrastructure, adopt modern administrative procedures and the latest technologies, try to improve the urban "quality" to make cities more attractive, and promote metropolitan regions, that is, corridors amalgamating urban and rural areas and promoting intra-regional synergies. If the various stakeholders are able to translate these goals into action, the current process of "glocalization" (more political localism together with more economic globalization) may be beneficial to India as to other emerging economies.

All over Asia, cities are indeed the engines of new growth models. Despite some heavy wagons, they effectively pull the economy in the right direction, which is not only reflected in trade figures but also in the reduction of poverty and a new – though still insufficient – respect for the environment. China and India ("Chindia") are good examples of this evolution that will mark the twenty-first century and the world.

According to Alexander Frater, "Calcutta has the merit of showing to the rest of India what to expect if all Indians realize their anarchistic tendencies" – a one-sided view, because the patchwork of urban Kolkata is not that deplorable. One should not forget that the Howrah Bridge was opened discreetly in 1943, during the Second World War, when the city was gripped by a severe famine, only four years before independence. Anarchy Bengali style is certainly preferable to war.

A ghat, ablution site close to Rabindra Setu

The winner of the 2001 Nobel Prize for Literature, V.S. Naipaul, is also very critical of Calcutta in his book "India, A Million Mutinies Now" (1998). He admires the Anglo-Bengali architecture and the monuments built by the British, "emblems of a conquering civilization", but dates the city's decline from independence in 1947 and the partition of Bengal in 1971. In 1962 he experienced the sensation of visiting a real metropolis. In 1988, he no longer recognized a ghost town, a mere campground for millions of migrants. For him, the diagnosis looked clear: "When the British ceased to rule, the city began to die." He predicted that the agony of the city will be endless. The Howrah Bridge marks in this dark vision the beginning of the end of a world. Or the birth of contemporary India ... a land of extremes, if any there is. A local adage says: "Kolkata is a city of screams, headaches and chaos"... Typical Bengali self-mockery.

Calcutta has long represented a certain synthesis between East and West, creating a cultural and architectural fusion illustrated by imperial monuments standing majestically amid urban chaos. It expresses horror and misery, yet manages to incubate a highly intellectual and educated middle class, and a literary tradition. Its slums and pavement dwellers are at the forefront of human resilience, in daily contact with more privileged residents. Visitors' first impressions of Calcutta are of an intolerable and repulsive hell. "And yet they live", to paraphrase Galileo... Then the intelligent outsider, or the Bengali writer himself, tries to understand, and the less he succeeds, the more subdued and doubtful he becomes. The conclusion is often the same: a city that is horrible but charming, a city of records – now in competition with Karachi and Dhaka – in the areas of pollution, traffic, noise, dirt, ... but also a champion of survival, vitality and innovation. Cosmic, surreal, Brechtian, an improbable city, impossible to understand rationally. It deserves the title of most fascinating city in the world. According to poet Dinesh Das, Calcutta is "a black snake, tail twisting in the lake, with its head on the Howrah Bridge" ... One can easily imagine the city as a hypnotic reptile.

In an admiring journal ("Show your tongue," 1989), the great German writer Günter Grass proposed to transfer the UN headquarters to Calcutta, a city that he hated but that attracted him like a magnet. He discovered the beauty of its shameful misery: "The aesthetics of poverty shocks me: how every detail of the huts made of rags, sheets of plastic, cardboard and jute sacks is so terribly palpable and cries out for a name. This ultimate beauty challenges to the extreme everything that is recognized as beautiful." Louis Malle's film about the city (1968) reflects the same paradox. In addition, old British buildings badly affected by tropical weather conditions constitute an excellent science fiction decor, creepy and oozing, seducing every visitor.

Calcutta became Kolkata in 2001 to comply with the Bengali pronunciation of Kolikata, the original village. After thirty-four years of apathetic and ruralist communist rule (1977-2011), the city is now led by the Congress Party (TMC), which would like to boost investment, on the model of Delhi and Mumbai. A major project could be to renovate the banks of the river, an amalgam of crumbling warehouses, dumps, and buildings in poor condition. Already a riverbank road is being revitalized, on the Howrah side, between the two bridges. Since 2006, the Rabindra Setu has been illuminated at night, in two alternating colors, gold and magenta, and must be repainted

Painting the bridge (2005)
©Kolkata Port Trust

periodically, with 26 tons of paint. A perceptible tremor appears in the management of this metropolis of 15 million inhabitants. There is similarly concern, according to a recent BBC article, to protect the metal structure of Rabindra Setu, which is deteriorating due to spit containing areca nut and betel leaf, which appear to be terribly corrosive...

In terms of territory, an interesting parallel can be drawn between India and Brazil, two prominent members of the BRICS group of emerging economies. Both countries have, in fact, three capitals: a political capital originally conceived as a new city (New Delhi / Brasilia); a large economic capital (Mumbai / Sao Paulo); and a cultural capital, a former political capital that has been decommissioned (Kolkata / Rio de Janeiro). The slums of Kolkata are more sordid and denser than the favelas of Rio, but they are less dangerous. Although the differences between the two cities are obvious, Kolkata might be inspired by Rio in terms of economic revitalization and international positioning.

My friend Sudipto Mukerjee, an international development expert who grew up in the capital of West Bengal, likes to say that the Rabindra Setu is the actual heart of the city, its backbone, its gateway, but that dozens of bridges (and other investments) would be needed to transform Kolkata into a twenty-first century metropolis. He underlines that the city witnesses one of the highest spot densities in the world (200,000 inhabitants per km² in some areas) while having one of the lowest ratios of streets and roads vis-a-vis the total urban area (10%).

Will Kolkata become a competitive metropolis and move beyond survival, odd jobs and self-help? Local politicians would like to believe so, but the poor do not really have time to think about it. No one can predict the future of this extraordinary metropolis. A city to be watched…

Enlightened Rabindra Setu, signal of Kolkata renaissance?
©Kolkata Port Trust

HIROSHIMA AND ITS HEIWA OHASHI

While Japan has some historical cities, such as Kyoto, its overall urbanization process has been slow and gradual. It began in the sixteenth century, at a time when the country was opening up to Western explorers, notably Portuguese and Dutch traders. The real growth of the cities started during the Edo period and under the Tokugawa dynasty, which took power in 1603. Most major Japanese cities were castle towns (Tokyo, Hiroshima, Osaka, Nagoya) and ports, but with limited external links. They were autonomous, much like Italian city-states. The city of Hiroshima, the largest in the Chugoku region, is a pleasant city, with numerous waterways. It hosts many bridges, some of which having a strong symbolic character.

◀ **The Peace Bridge (Heiwa Ohashi) across Motoyasu River**

HIROSHIMA AND ITS HEIWA OHASHI

Edo (now called Tokyo) had about one million inhabitants in 1720, Osaka 380,000 and Kyoto 340,000. Japan's population had by then reached some 30 million. Even as cities stagnated in the eighteenth century the general urbanization process continued endogenously, as in China, and was directly linked to the increase in agricultural production. Towns and countryside lived in harmony, and industry developed in relative autarky, thanks to a rice surplus. Japan entered its modern age in 1868, with the start of the Meiji era, and thereafter plunged into modernization with determination.

As an urban planner one can hardly fail to be amazed by the dismal appearance of Japanese cities. To quote the astute description of Alain Basset: "Japanese cities are in shambles, endlessly displaying styles that nothing holds together, a succession of areas dedicated to the worship of business and commerce." He writes about layer after layer of shopping malls, gray suburbs and the proliferation of concrete and neon, of entrenched temples and supermarkets, of an urban chaos with limited efficiency, but with incredible politeness and courtesy, and also of the presence of the homeless and real estate speculators, airtight architecture, declining security, and Americanized, even tribalized, adolescents in extravagant outfits. Japanese cities are as ugly as they are hyperactive.

The contrast in Japan between the refinement of the culture and traditional architecture and the ugliness and heterogeneity of contemporary cities just seems inexplicable. Why has Japan not produced a planning worthy of the name? Is it due to a strong corporate spirit opposed to a limited civic interest in public goods? Or is it the brevity of the urban culture compared to the long history of rural values (the rice-field

Tokyo, a typical district
©rudiuk/Shutterstock

cult)? In the words of Robert Guillain: "The Japanese love beauty, but are very often blind to ugliness." Japanese cities may illustrate in their own way the principle of the unity of opposites: elegant tatami, yukata and bonsai indoors, in striking contrast with a monotonous architecture dominated by land speculation on the outside, a dualism which the practical citizens of the land of the Rising Sun seem resigned to accept.

My friend, the planner Toshi Noda, acknowledges: "In Japan, we can admire beautiful scenes of hills and fields in rural areas, yet it is rare to find attractive urban landscapes. Of course, the effort to conserve historic townscapes is based on specific planning acts while the importance of urban quality is emphasized in the City Planning Act and in the Building Standard Act. However the authorities are not strictly sticking to such acts and land use regulations are still weak. As a result, it is difficult to observe a homogeneous urban fabric."

Hiroshima, the "wide island" on the Otagawa delta, is not the most beautiful city in Japan simply because there are no truly beautiful cities in Japan. Endearing Kyoto, which could claim that title, gives the impression of a patchwork of parks and magnificent palaces surrounded by hundreds of gray, anonymous buildings. It is hardly a homogeneous city.

Hiroshima was born in the late sixteenth century as a bailey town around the Rijo castle (1589-1591) and developed further from the late eighteenth century onward by reclaiming land on the delta. It housed a military complex until 1945 – and paid a terrible price for it.

A-Bomb dome ©Sean Pavone Photo/Shutterstock

Hiroshima today has become a universal symbol of peace. If the T-Bridge (Aioi Ohashi) was the target of the first atomic bomb on that fateful 6 August 1945, then the Peace Bridge (Heiwa Ohashi), built in 1952, has tried to exorcise the ghost of 150,000 dead that haunted the city. It is a small bridge of 80 meters, a simple steel beam, almost Zen-like, with curved balustrades designed by the famous Japanese-American sculptor Isamu Noguchi (born in Los Angeles in 1904, died in 1988). It symbolizes sunrise, the future.

The bridge spans the Motoyasu River, one of the six rivers of Hiroshima, providing access to the 100-metre-wide Peace Avenue, the ultimate meeting place in the city, and to the Peace Museum, an important memorial designed by Kenzo Tange. On the other side of the island, the West Peace Bridge (Heiwa Nishi Ohashi) crosses the Honkawa River, symbolizing sunset, the past.

Downtown Hiroshima with its memorial spots: 1. Honkawa Bridge, 2. Aioi Bridge (T- Bridge), 3. Peace Museum, 4. Peace Bridge, 5. Monument to the old T-bridge, 6. A-Bomb dome, 7. Motoyasu Bridge ©Michio Ide

PAST AND PRESENT JAPANESE BRIDGES

Japan is a land of many bridges, large and small, crossing streams as well as stretches of sea. In ancient Japanese mythology a floating bridge – probably a rainbow – connected heaven and earth at the very moment of creation, thus allowing the gods to establish the country's first island. A beautiful suspension crossing called the Rainbow Bridge, 798 meters long, became in 1993 the symbol of modern Tokyo and its bay. Once again, the idea of a rainbow...

Japan is an archipelago, consisting of four main islands and thousands of smaller islets, and is rich in large bridges. These suspension and cable-stayed bridges, including those leading to artificial islands created during the last thirty years to decongest major coastal cities like Kobe, or linking islands, are by and large impressive. Many were built during the 1990s.

Kobe, Akashi Kaikyo Ohashi (1998), the longest suspended bridge in the world ©Sean Pavone Photo/Shutterstock

The most spectacular structures are located in the Inland Sea, between southern Honshu (notably the Chugoku region where Hiroshima is located) and the island of Shikoku. Many embody real technical prowess. There are seven bridges over the scenic Shimanami-Kaido route, a road of bridges. One of the most famous is the Kurushima Kaikyo Ohashi (4 kilometers long), located in Ehime Prefecture near Hiroshima, a three-span suspension bridge. The Akashi Kaikyo Ohashi in Kobe, on its part, remained in 2013 the longest suspension bridge in the world. It opened in 1998, crossing the busy Akashi Straits. Its center span measures 1,991 meters, although it was originally designed to be 1990 meters – the 1995 Hanshin earthquake, the epicenter of which was just under the bridge that was then under construction, extended it by a full meter (the deck was, fortunately, not yet completed).

One should, however, not ignore Japan's old stone and wooden bridges, such as the beautiful five-arched Kintai-kyo Bridge, which is 225 meters long, in Iwakuni, Yamaguchi Prefecture, near Hiroshima. The bridge, built in 1673, was originally reserved for Samurais. Meganebashi, the small Chinese-style "spectacles bridge" (1634) located in Nagasaki and crossing the Nakashima River is also well-known throughout the country. Hundreds of masonry bridges, well integrated in their environment, were built throughout the nineteenth century in various localities and rural areas.

Kurushima, Kaikyo Ohashi (1999), 4105 meters ©Teruo Hirano

Most bridges in Tokyo were built in the twentieth century, especially over the Sumida River, which is crossed by several steel bridges. Kiyosu (suspended, and modeled after a bridge in Cologne, 1928, 186 meters), Kachidoki (bascule in its central part), Eidai, Kuramae and Shirahige, were all rebuilt after the Great Kantō earthquake (1923).

The arc-shaped Naya bridge in Nagoya is worth a detour for its balconies and parapets, as is the Asahi, also arc-shaped, crossing the Asahikawa in the northern island of Hokkaido (see photo). It was inaugurated in 1932 and is a contemporary of New York's Bayonne Bridge and Sydney's Harbour Bridge. It was constructed with German steel and is 225 meters long.

Iwakuni, Kintaikyo (1673) ©Teruo Hirano

Gifu, Musai Kyo, traditional bridge ©Goyu Sato

For centuries, landscape gardeners have been passionate about garden bridges, in painted wood, usually red, and always impeccable. The garden bridges ("hashi") of ancient Japan have been researched extensively by Jean-Pierre Giraud of the University of Paris-Sorbonne. He writes that the hashi were traditionally related to religion, and frequently built by Buddhist monks – that of Nagasaki, for example, was built by the monks of Kofukuji temple. Paving the way for light and salvation, these wooden bridges, made of a flexible material, were earthquake-resistant. They required constant maintenance but were easily removable in case of conflict. They marked a boundary between two spaces, or between life and death. The classic "soribashi" – small arch-shaped wooden bridge – is the most typical in Japanese gardens. The curvature of the bridge is supposed to hinder demons which, unsurprisingly, dislike steep slopes.

Finally, one must refer to the Nihonbashi, "Bridge of Japan", built in 1603 at the beginning of the Tokugawa dynasty (Edo) as the starting point for measuring all distances in the country. It is an essential reference point, located in the central ward of Chūō in Tokyo, surrounded today by modern buildings.

Asahikawa, Asahi Bridge (1932) ©Teruo Hirano

The writer Tamiki Hara, a native of the city who was in Hiroshima on 6 August 1945, wrote: "In the silvery emptiness which lay in the hot, blinding sun, there was a road, a river, a bridge, and here and there swollen and bare bodies. The smell of death filled the air. Every time we passed a river, I found it extraordinary that the bridge had not collapsed." In fact, many surviving bridges were to be washed away a few weeks later due to a devastating hurricane. The city was utterly destroyed.

T. Hara committed suicide in 1951. And a few years later, the French writer Marguerite Duras chose to stage, with director Alain Resnais, a trivial, fleeting and wonderful love story rather than deliver a fictionalized documentary about the city, noting aptly: "One cannot talk about Hiroshima. All one can do is talk about the impossibility of talking about Hiroshima." She would, therefore, attempt to sublimate the horror by telling it through an "enchanting" love story. The result was the movie Hiroshima, Mon Amour.

Today the agglomeration has 2 million inhabitants, compared to 350,000 in July 1945. It is quite a pleasant city, thanks in part to its rivers, but also to its parks. My good friend, the urbanist and former UN official Nassrine Azimi, who has worked there for many years, is convinced that "the many parks and trees of Hiroshima, particularly those which survived the bomb and its pernicious radiation, are teaching the world a lesson about nature's resilience and are a warning against the threat of nuclear weapons". She has started a global campaign, Green Legacy Hiroshima, which aims to distribute seeds and saplings from the 170 "A-bombed survivor trees" within the 2-km radius of the bomb's epicenter, officially registered by the municipality, around the world. Indeed the city was rebuilt soon after the war and has played a significant role, alongside Nagasaki, its sister-city in nuclear martyrdom, in the global peace movement. Each year, on the night of 6 August, thousands of multi-colored paper lanterns, lit in memory of the missing, are floated on the rivers towards the sea.

TOKYO, THE MEGACITY PAR EXCELLENCE

Tokyo is by far the world's most populous city. Defined physically, rather than administratively, the Greater Tokyo megalopolis, which includes the three prefectures of Saitama, Kanagawa (with Yokohama as the capital) and Chiba, has a population of 37 million (in comparison, the population of the world's second largest city, Delhi, is "only" 24 million). Tokyo is also the first city in the world, ahead of New York, in terms of production of goods and services.

Tokyo's planning began during the Meiji era, and it was modeled after Western cities. Its first railroad tracks date back to 1872. The Japanese urban planning style has at times been referred to as organic, that is to say, respecting natural conditions as in traditional villages. Tokyo's development took off significantly after the 1923 earthquake, focusing on transport infrastructure, land zoning and building regulations. Its development model has always been highly centralized and hierarchical. Tokyo is not laid out in a grid pattern, nor does it have a real centre. Above all else functional, it has placed jobs in the city centre and residences in the suburbs. Mobility, therefore, is essential and transit networks, including trains and subways, are highly developed. Accommodation is generally cramped and expensive, and land speculation reaches frequent heights, with real estate bubbles occurring regularly.

Tokyo's GDP is around US$ 2 trillion per year, higher than that of many large countries, such as India and Russia, and roughly comparable to the GDP of Brazil and Italy. With 28% of the nation's population, the city provides 35% of national GDP. It is the third largest financial centre in the world, after London and New York. Curiously it was ranked in 2011 as the world's fifth most romantic city (Paris being the first) and the third most hedonistic (New York being at the top) by the estate agency Knight Frank. Invasive advertisements, multi-colored neon lights, unconcealed electric cables and excessive decibels do not seem to affect the urban pleasures of Tokyoites, gastronomy, being one of them – preparing and eating good food reduces the city's frenetic pace, and may well be cause of Tokyoites' apparent euphoria.

Tokyo, Rainbow Bridge (1993) ©Teruo Hirano

According to official statistics, the conurbation or megalopolis of Tokyo had 11.2 million people in 1950. It surpassed New York in 1955 with 13.7 million, rose to 16.7 million in 1960, 28.5 million in 1980, 35 million in 2000 and has now stabilized at around 37 million. Japan has only eight cities with over 750,000 inhabitants. Osaka-Kobe is the second largest agglomeration with 11.3 million inhabitants, and Hiroshima comes seventh, with 2 million. The urbanization level in Japan reached 92% in 2013, making the country one of the most urbanized in the world.

Tokyo, Kabukicho, district of night life ©Sean Pavone Photo/Shutterstock

Tokyo, Kiyosu Bashi (1928) ©Teruo Hirano

It is interesting to note that Japan had a population of 100 million in 1967. Its population peaked at the beginning of this century with 127 million but its decline began in 2006 and it is expected to return to 100 million by 2060. There were officially 126,659,683 people in March 2012, or 263,729 less people than the previous year, reflecting the on-going demographic crisis prevalent also in other industrialized nations. Tokyo accounted for 13.5% of the country's population in 1950, 27.6% in 2000 and could reach 36% in 2050. Its importance will only increase and the city may one day concentrate half of the national economy. Tokyo, however, should also be prepared to cope with future earthquakes, which could disrupt its undoubted dynamism.

With the Peace Memorial Museum nearby, the Heiwa Ohashi is a powerful symbol. Silent witness to a terrifying twentieth century, it shows both the brutality and cruelty of war and the resilience of men and women in the most tragic of circumstances. The Peace Bridge is not grandiose; it would almost go unnoticed. But its significance to the collective human memory is immense. Typical of Japan and its traditional sense of discretion – but also as a symbol of restored pride – this bridge echoes other works that are just as modest and symbolic, like the Stari Most in Mostar.

In Nagasaki, one can observe the Meganebashi ("Spectacles Bridge"), an old stone bridge with two arches that was spared by the atomic bomb of 9 August 1945, the epicenter of which was the Urakami Catholic Cathedral, and which left more than 70,000 dead. Located on the west coast of the southern island of Kyushu, Nagasaki has long been the Japanese city most open to outside influence. Perhaps by coincidence, in a city where the Dutch were so present, the Meganebashi resembles a bridge on the Leidsegracht in Amsterdam. Nagasaki, a warm and welcoming city, today has a population of 500,000.

Nagasaki, Meganebashi (1634) ©Toshiyasu Towatari

Hiroshima may be the most beautiful city in Japan after all, alongside Fukuoka, repeatedly nominated as "best city in Asia" by the regional press. In that regard, one may remember that in 1965 Fukuoka still looked like a very ordinary third world city. Reconstructed and modernized in less than three decades, Japanese cities did not have time to adopt sophisticated development strategies. Speed and quantity prevailed over quality, durability and aesthetics. The current demographic decline of the country could actually provide an opportunity for revisiting urban development options and gradually improving the appearance of Japanese cities.

Kitakyushu, Kanmon Kyo, 712 meters (1973) ©Katsuko Matsuda

ISTANBUL AND ITS BOĞAZIÇI KÖPRÜSÜ

Istanbul is one of four "mega-cities" of Europe, together with Moscow, Paris and London. It is also one of the most attractive cities in the world due to its unique location and its 3,000-year history. Until 1453 the city was called Constantinople, the city of Constantine. Westerners called it Constantinople until 1923 but the Turkish people referred to it as Istanbul. And before the fourth century and its rebuilding by Emperor Constantine, it was known as Byzantium. Istanbul extends on both sides of the Bosphorus strait ("passage of the ox"). Turkey is both European and Asiatic or Anatolian, Istanbul being the only city in the world built on two continents. Since 1973 these two parts of Eurasia have been connected by a suspension bridge that is the transcontinental complement of the historic Galata Bridge, itself present on the Golden Horn since 1845.

ISTANBUL AND ITS BOĞAZIÇI KÖPRÜSÜ

The small town of Byzantium was founded by the Greeks on the European shore of the Bosphorus, between the Golden Horn and the Sea of Marmara. It replaced decadent Rome to become the second global city in history after the fall of the Western Roman Empire, as the capital of the Eastern Roman (or Byzantine) Empire and much later, after the schism of 1054, of the Orthodox religion. In 330 Constantine made the city his capital, which became the sole capital of the Empire in 476 after the conquest of Rome by the Barbarians. He converted to Christianity and imposed the new religion on all his subjects. He transformed the infrastructure and invested in multiple buildings. Aqueducts and cisterns were built to supply water to the city. Constantinople had 400,000 inhabitants in the year 500 and was the largest city of the medieval world several times between 500 and 1700, with terrible eclipses, especially between 1204 and 1453.

The Golden Horn and Galata Bridge, with the Bosphorus Bridge in the background ©IBB Kultur AS

Byzantium-Constantinople was a city of Greek language and culture. One of the oldest buildings in the world, the Byzantine cathedral, mosque and now a museum, Hagia Sofia or Aya Sofia (Divine Wisdom), is the best testimony of this first sumptuous age. It was built by Constantine and completely rebuilt in the sixth century under Justinian (532-537) by Isidore of Miletus and Anthemius of Tralles. It is nearly 1,500 years old and has held for almost a millennium the record for the largest dome in the world (the dome – el Duomo – in Florence only surpassed it in 1436). It holds the absolute record of architectural longevity, despite all the earthquakes that have tried to destroy it.

Ayasofia, one of the oldest covered building in the world (537)

The climax of the Byzantine Empire happened between the tenth and twelfth centuries as Constantinople was the crossroads of trade between East and West. The capture of this (Greek) Christian city and its looting by the (Latin) Christian Crusaders in April 1204 reflected the growing interest in the West for the riches of the East and the influence of rival Venetian merchants. The Latin occupation (1204-1261) was disastrous for Constantinople but allowed the takeoff of Venice. The bronze Quadriga (looted from Constantinople) that adorns the facade of St Mark's Basilica in Venice symbolizes this transfer of power.

Under the immense dome of Ayasofia

Only the Galata district grew, thanks to the Genoese. During the next two centuries the Ottomans gradually advanced in Asia Minor towards Constantinople and dealt repeated blows to the Byzantine Empire, which finally fell in 1453. It was soon replaced by a new empire. Indeed the Ottomans took Belgrade in 1521, Buda in 1526, Baghdad in 1534, but they failed twice before Vienna, in 1529 and 1683.

The second period of Constantinople's glory started when it became the capital of the Ottoman Empire after the capture of the city by Mehmet II on 29 May 1453. At the time it had only 50,000 inhabitants. Istanbul in the local Turkish language means "to the city" (bul being derived from the Greek polis), a term used for years by the population to refer to Constantinople. Its golden age was reached during the reign of Suleiman the Magnificent, in the sixteenth century. The city then had 500,000 inhabitants while remaining very cosmopolitan. Beautiful mosques were built, such as the Süleymaniye (1557), designed by the great Sinan, chief architect of three successive sultans, and author of 79 mosques, 34 palaces and more than 300 other buildings, including 12 bridges (see chapter on Mostar) between 1538 and 1588. A floating bridge was built during the siege of the city in 1453 and Leonardo da Vinci designed a permanent masonry structure on the Golden Horn, which was not realized (but which was simplified and built in wood in 2001, in Ås, Norway). Michelangelo received the same order from the Sultan in 1506, without more success.

Night over Galata Bridge
©MarkIII Photonics/
Shutterstock

The Asian shore of the Bosphorus began to urbanize as the Ottoman Empire went into decline in the late seventeenth century, after the failure of the siege of Vienna (1683). The first detailed map of Istanbul was prepared by two French engineers, F. Kauffer and J.B. Lechevallier, in 1786. But the empire gradually disintegrated, while its cities were modernizing. Istanbul's population increased from 400,000 to 900,000 between 1840 and 1890, and a municipality was established in 1854. Western banks appeared in numbers in the district of Galata. Tens of steamers cruised on the Bosphorus while a tram and a funicular were installed in Pera in 1870.

Constantinople, End Of Empire, Or The French Writers' Melancholy

Gérard de Nerval visited Istanbul and Cairo in 1843 and described his experiences in Voyage en Orient. He lived in Beyoğlu and enjoyed the city and its nights of Ramadan. He even forgot his recurrent depression and natural melancholy and found out that the city looked like a beautiful theatre surrounded by squalid slums. He admired its tolerance. Gustave Flaubert came to Istanbul in 1850 (after visiting Cairo, as Nerval) and tried to treat a syphilis caught in Beirut. He stayed five weeks, visited brothels and cemeteries but, being a narcissist, showed little interest in urban culture. He preferred the desert and the nomads. Thus, from the mid-nineteenth century, the journey to Constantinople became a sort of "rite of passage" for some French writers in search of exoticism.

A friend of Nerval, Théophile Gautier visited Istanbul-Constantinople in 1852 and stayed in the city for 72 days, enough to write Constantinople (1856), a detailed description of a capital whose decay was imminent. He rendered the customs and traditions with the melancholy (hüzün) that would become the leitmotif of the literature on Istanbul (well analyzed by Orhan Pamuk in his Memories and the City). The author of Captain Fracasse was a traveller who knew London, Venice, Constantine and Granada. He appreciated the "nights of the Alhambra." He was also a journalist, a serial writer, a "literary daguerreotypist", in his own words. His book on the Turkish city that caught his imagination is not a fiction, for which he is better known, but a poetic and personal report.

Gautier regretted that Turkey began to civilize "in the worst sense of the word," that is to say, by imitating Western countries. He considered himself an Orientalist and sketched with humor the

Théophile Gautier by Nadar (1856)

picturesque scenery of Istanbul life. His enthusiasm was measured and without illusion; he noted "the squalor and hideous decay" of some neighborhoods where paradise turned into a cesspool. He dutifully visited the three parts of the city: the modern Pera ("Marseille of the Orient"); the traditional Stamboul; and the Asian Scutari. He got lost in cemeteries ("in the Orient, life cannot be easily separated from death as we usually do, death mingles casually with life ...") and in the ruins. He loved the wild "baroquerie" of streets and the inextricable labyrinth of the Grand Bazaar that he carefully described.

On his way Gautier had stopped at Smyrna and visited the Bridge of Caravans "disfigured by an ugly cast iron balustrade." He compared the Bosphorus to a great river, a marine river, and spotted the place where Xerxes made a bridge for the passage of his army. Where banks were significantly closer (Rumeli-Hisar fortress), he recalled Herodotus: "Darius made his army cross here in his expedition against the Scythians, on a bridge built by Mandrocles of Samos. Seven hundred thousand men marched, gigantic mass of Asian hordes." He insisted on the difference between Arabic and Turkish architecture, the first being gorgeous (he cited repeatedly the Alhambra), the second being at best "agreeable" ("the art so fine, so elegant and pure of the Arabs has left few traces in the Turks").

However, at the entrance of the Golden Horn "a marvelous panorama unfolds before my eyes like an opera décor in a magical play." The city, built as an amphitheater on both sides of this cornucopia, beautifully rugged, silvered with a white light where the smoke of steamboats on the Bosphorus floats like transparent gauze, impressed him upon arrival and excited his curiosity. He observed "three pontoon bridges that join the two shores of the Golden Horn, and allow a continuous communication between the Turkish city and its suburbs of mixed populations." He emphasized that Constantinople was "a real Tower of Babel" and specified that the latest bridge of boats, recently completed, was built at the expense of a rich Armenian. He wanted to "take the risk to cross the Galata Bridge and go eis tin polin, as the Greeks said."

Gautier noted that wooden houses made the city of Constantinople highly combustible. He witnessed several fires and deplored the fatalism of the population. He was ironical about "the Turkish-rococo taste of the arabesques in the Bazaar arcades which resembles the kind of ornament in use under Louis XV." He travelled by caïque, "the most graceful boat, next to it the Venetian gondola is a coarse chest", essential "when you're too far away from one of the three bridges of boats across the harbor" but threatened by the competition from steamboats that had begun to circulate on the Bosphorus. He often crossed the Golden Horn "on the bridge of boats, throwing four paras to the toll office" before plunging into a maze of Turkish alleys. He hated the Jewish Quarter, "the foulest, most disgusting and most purulent" ("what a difference from the splendid Jewish women of Constantine, as beautiful as the Queen of Sheba!"). He attended Mahmoud's hammam and enjoyed its comfort. He admired the Dolmabahce Palace, hybrid and majestic, "where one feels the intention to imitate the splendor of Versailles". The waves of sweet hills along the Bosphorus, the light "soft and clear as a ceiling of Paul Veronese," richly adorned women "heads starry with diamonds and jewels shining through their muslin veil" fed his imagination. But he left the city on a frustrated note: "The everlasting bal masqué of the streets has begun to weary me. I had seen enough of veils; I wished to see a few faces." Orientalism met its limits here, the mysteries yielded some prejudices and Gautier looked at Constantinople fading on the horizon with "an indefinable melancholy".

Unlike Gautier, Pierre Loti described more than the city. He lived it lovingly and uses it as a backdrop for a romance. In 1879 Loti, whose real name was Julien Viaud, published Aziyadé in memory of his abandoned mistress, a beautiful Circassian seen in a harem of Salonika, who he tried in vain to re-contact later. The hero of Aziyadé is called Loti, "lieutenant of the British navy". While the European Pera annoyed him, he loved old Stamboul, especially the "holy Eyüp

Galata Bridge at the end of the nineteenth century ©Keskincolor

suburb, picturesque as possible". Like Gautier, Loti was a real reporter who enjoyed smoking the nargileh in traditional neighborhoods. From Pera he crossed the Galata Bridge to get to Eyüp with his friend Ahmet: "The crowd gathers under a scorching sun. The high noon light streams throughout this grouping of walls, domes and minarets, that crowns up there Stamboul, it is scattered on a motley crowd, dressed in the most conspicuous colors of the rainbow. Boats arrive and depart, loaded with a picturesque public; peddlers shout loudly, knocking the crowd. We know all these boats that transported us to all points of the Bosphorus, we know on the bridge of Stamboul all the shops, all passers-by, even all the beggars, the entire collection of cripples."

Pierre Loti has his own street and his café in Istanbul

And at night, he observed the silhouette of the Oriental city: "The minarets, domes of mosques stand high out against a starry sky where a thin moon crescent is suspended; the horizon is fringed with towers and minarets slightly drawn as bluish silhouettes in the pale tint of the night. Major superimposed domes of mosques rise in shaded colors to the moon, and produce in the imagination the impression of hugeness." What a declaration of love!

Twenty-five years later, when he had become a member of the French Academy, Loti rediscovered this mythical city in The Disenchanted. Upon his arrival, "suddenly thrilled by the emotion, always the same, and of a kind essentially impossible to put into words, as he had always experienced whenever Stamboul was unexpectedly brought before him from the depths of his memory after many days of oblivion," he exclaims: "Stamboul! What powers of evocation lay in the mere name! The city of minarets and domes, majestic and unique, unrivalled still even in its irredeemable decay, standing out high against the sky, with the blue waters of the Sea of Marmara circling the horizon. (...) It was a ghost, a magnificent ghost of the past, this city, still standing, with its endless spindles of stone, so slender, so light, that how they have lasted is a marvel". He would sit there and dream, smoking his nargileh, "with all that dying magnificence around him, and all that decrepitude and religious silence and prayer," observing "the red fez men and veiled ladies , the tangle of wooden houses, the long caravan of sailing vessels on the Bosphorus, huge modern steamers or beautiful yachts of yesteryear," and of course at night, "the incomparable skyline of the illuminated city, and its minarets, gigantic spindles of shade wearing, at different heights in the air, their rings of fire."

Loti, a naval officer for forty years, "whose eyes had seen the whole world" is totally captivated by Stamboul, the incomparable Oriental city, including "by those two opposite shores, Europe and Asia, displaying to each other's eyes minarets and palaces along the banks of the Bosphorus, under constantly changing aspects in the play of the eastern light".

According to Orhan Pamuk, Loti loved Eyüp as a sentimentally perfect image of an Oriental dream, traditional and exotic, rejected by modernist intellectuals of his time. Istanbul was actually a dream shared by many Western writers of the nineteenth century, a dream of the Orient, of mystery and decadence, a powerful invitation to travel, an irresistible attraction towards a supposed otherness and the strange beauty of a setting that raises again and again a gentle melancholy. Several other French writers (Chateaubriand, Lamartine, Gide ...) gave their impressions of the city, as well as major European authors, including the Norwegian Nobel laureate Knut Hamsun, not to mention the many Turkish writers, such as Ahmet Tanpinar. Istanbul and literature seem to have been made for each other.

Public lighting appeared in 1857, followed by water and sewer networks. The quay was constructed in Galata in 1893-1894. As in other countries, the city was equipped and westernized, at least in some upscale neighborhoods, throughout the second half of the nineteenth century.

Galata Bridge and Eminönü Mosque ©Tomas Sereda/ Shutterstock

In 1845 the first Galata Bridge was finally built, at the mouth of the Golden Horn, in the place which was closed by a chain during the siege of 1453. This wooden and tolled bridge (a "bridge of boats", wrote Théophile Gautier in 1853 in Constantinople) established a permanent link between the old Muslim Istanbul (Eminönü) and the much more cosmopolitan districts of Galata, Beyoğlu and Harbiye. This crossing became essential to the growth of Istanbul, which would see the doubling of its population over the next four decades. The Galata Bridge was the catalyst of a revival that would not last beyond the century. Today the Golden Horn hosts its fifth Galata Bridge (after those of 1845, 1863, 1875, 1912), a central bascule bridge 465 meters long

Galata Bridge, seen from Beyoğlu ©Sailorr / Shutterstock

and 42 meters wide, built in 1994, at the center of one of the most spectacular urban landscapes on the planet. The Galata Bridge consists of two floors: the top floor is used by cars, trams and hundreds of fishermen, the lower floor by restaurants. This is a social bond and a social spot par excellence, the true heart of Istanbul.

Ara Güler's photos reveal the soul of Istanbul in the 1950s and 1960s, at the turning point of its development. His multiple shots of the Galata Bridge, from 1952 to 1965, are simply immortal. They show the structure that was rebuilt in 1912 between Karakoy and Eminönü, which suffered a fire in 1992 and was dragged up the Golden Horn to serve as a cultural space. Güler's black-and-white photos have lit up my office for years.

Daydreaming on the bridge, towards Süleymaniye Mosque

As imperial capital, Istanbul declined slowly throughout the nineteenth century, as well described by Nobel Prize laureate Orhan Pamuk in a masterly essay which emphasizes the melancholy of the site and the role of the Bosphorus: "The city evokes destruction and poverty while the Bosphorus expresses life and joy, Istanbul draws its strength from the Bosphorus." After the fall of the Ottoman Empire during the First World War, followed by the Allied Forces occupation and the proclamation of the Turkish Republic by Mustafa Kemal on 29 October 1923, Istanbul lost its status as a political capital in favor of Ankara but remained the economic driving force of the country. Its master plan, prepared in 1934-1937 by the French urban planner Henri Prost, was implemented twenty years later. The city stagnated and reached one million inhabitants in 1951. Growing gradually after the Second World War, it then suffered from a lack of crossing over the Bosphorus.

Fishermen on the bridge, daily
scene in Galata

In 1957, therefore, Prime Minister Adnan Menderes decided to launch preliminary studies for the first intercontinental bridge of the planet. In 1968, a British firm, under the direction of engineers Gilbert Roberts and William Brown, won the design contract and construction started in February 1970. The first bridge over the Bosphorus (Boğaziçi Köprüsü) was built very quickly and opened in October 1973 between Beylerbeyi (in Asia) and Ortaköy (in Europe) for the 50th anniversary of the founding of the Republic. It cost US$ 200 million. This suspension bridge, which is entirely metallic, is 1,510 meters long and 39 meters wide, the distance between the two piers being 1,074 meters (it was the longest span in Europe in 1974). Towers, built on the shore, dominate the deck by 105 meters, the clearance between the bridge and the sea being 64 meters. A toll bridge of six lanes, plus two security lanes, it is visited by 180,000 vehicles each day (more to Europe in the morning, to Anatolia in the evening). It is home to many cultural and sporting events, and has, like other bridges across the world, been the site of many suicides. The second highway bridge over the Bosphorus (Fatih Sultan Mehmet Köprüsü, further north-east, on the narrowest part of the strait) is more technically advanced but less symbolic from a historical perspective. Located where armies coming from the south had once built a floating bridge in 513 BCE (Darius) as in 1453 CE (Sultan Mehmet), it was inaugurated in 1988.

The Bosphorus, one of the most frequented avenue of Istanbul ©IBB Kultur AS

A third transcontinental bridge is being designed in the north-east, at the mouth of the Black Sea. Unveiled in 2010, this US$ 6 billion project sparked an outcry among Istanbulites, particularly among environmentalists, because it would destroy hectares of forest and already encourages land speculation along the route of the future highway. But it will be soon under construction. A third international airport is also planned, as well as a canal parallel to the Bosphorus between the Marmara Sea and the Black Sea. Pharaoh-type works.

During the last sixty years Istanbul has grown very fast. Its population fell between 1910 and 1930 because of the First World War and the transfer of the capital to Ankara, but increased from 700,000 in 1930 and 967,000 people in 1950 to 2,772,000 in 1970, 6,552,000 in 1990 and 12,700,000 in 2010. It has grown thirteen times in sixty years and quadrupled from the opening of the first intercontinental bridge. While many migrants still live in gecekondus (informal settlements), the city has hosted prestigious events, such as the UN City Summit in June 1996 and intends to host other world conferences. It perfectly plays its role as a bridge between Europe and Asia.

Satellite view of the Bosphorus between the Sea of Marmara, South, and the Black Sea, North. Two bridges on the Bosphorus and three on the Golden Horn can be spotted ©Earth Observatory, Nasa

While the first Galata Bridge (1845) announced the opening of the city to the West (French writers then rushed to Constantinople, see box), the two bridges across the Bosphorus symbolize the entry of Turkey into economic modernity and the first steps towards its inevitable membership in the European Union.

Istanbul is a maritime city built on two continents, whose heart is torn between modernity and conservatism, religion and secularism, East and West. It is divided by a large salty river, the Bosphorus Strait, 36 kilometers long, where 50,000 ships pass each year carrying 120 million tons of dangerous goods, one of the busiest avenues of the city. But from the cemetery and the lovely Ortaköy Mosque in Europe, people can admire the imposing Bosphorus Bridge that links forever the two banks and think about the greatness of two civilizations that have been in competition and synergy from the time of the Silk Road.

The Bosphorus Bridge with Fatih Sultan Mehmet Bridge at the back

Sunset over the city,
seen from Beylerbeyi
©fulili/Shutterstock

Today a tunnel under the Bosphorus has been built as part of the Marmaray transport project and a port buried for over 2,000 years has been uncovered. A new metro bridge is controversially under completion over the Golden Horn, near the Atatürk Bridge. Istanbul is more than ever a bridge-city and a world city, the polis par excellence, in constant renewal, a productive city whose GDP is in the same range as that of Barcelona, Sydney, Rio de Janeiro and Mumbai.

My friend Nefise Bazoglu, a sociologist living in Istanbul, is very critical vis-à-vis the recent acceleration in infrastructure construction. Her opinion is clear: "I have nothing against bridges which in principle should bring people together. But how they are determined and programmed here ignores the need for impact studies. Therefore, communities must accept new buildings, roads, bridges and tunnels, which disturb rather than improve their lives and do not reflect their priorities."

In Istanbul, as elsewhere, participatory governance remains to be invented, and the balance between economic, social and environmental objectives requires complex mediations. Cities are never simple; historic towns and cities, meeting points of civilizations, are even more complicated. The future of Istanbul is in the hands of both its inhabitants, who want to preserve their way of life and public spaces, and the political leaders of Turkey, keen to cut corners. Finding common grounds and accepting compromises are challenges that have to be met to access a sustainable modernity respecting the exceptional history and geography that constitute the most valuable assets of this booming city.

Bosphorus Bridge and the European side of Istanbul ©IBB Kultur AS

Shanghai And Its Nanpu Da Qiao

Shanghai had more than 21 million inhabitants in 2013. This figure includes permanent and temporary registered residents, as well as the "floating" population estimated at more than 3 million workers. Shanghai is the largest city in China and the economic capital of a country that has enjoyed an annual growth rate of 10% for the last twenty years. Located in the Yangtze River Delta, Shanghai is becoming the largest port in the world. With a demographic growth rate of 2.5% per annum, it is now the third largest city in the world. Its bridges of the 1990s allowed the city to initiate the development of Pudong on the eastern bank of the Huangpu River, and to make a

◄Huangpu River
and Nanpu Bridge
with Pudong in the
background ©Philip
Lange/Shutterstock

SHANGHAI AND ITS NANPU DA QIAO

For centuries Shanghai was a big fishing village on the west bank of the Huangpu (Shang 上 = towards, hai 海 = sea, Shang-hai = place where the river meets the sea), which was fortified in the sixteenth century to resist Japanese pirates. It gained prominence in the nineteenth century after the Opium Wars conducted by the European powers to force the Chinese to open their markets, including letting in the opium from India. Although Shanghai was born during the Song dynasty in the eleventh century and became an administrative center in 1291, the city was officially founded in 1843 after the first Opium War. It had, however, stone and wooden bridges on Suzhou Creek, such as the Xin Zha Bridge, and over other nearby rivers, since the seventeenth century.

The English, attracted by its ideal location for import-export, attacked the city, as well as four other Chinese harbors, in June 1842. Following the unequal Treaty of Nanjing, Shanghai then became the seat of British, American and French concessions. Industries and commerce developed rapidly around the river that connects Shanghai to Suzhou, the Venice of China, fifty kilometers away.

During the second half of the nineteenth century the first modern bridges emerged. The very first was built in 1856 by the English engineer L.S. Wills at the mouth of Suzhou Creek. It was a wooden bridge whose toll caused great discontent among Chinese pedestrians. The toll was abolished and the "Garden Bridge" was rebuilt, still in wood, in 1873. This Waibaidu Qiao was permanently rebuilt in 1907 and inaugurated in January 1908 as the first steel bridge in China. It is still in service and occupies a special place in Shanghai's memories.

The Waibaidu Qiao (1908)
©Yao Rusheng/Shutterstock

In 1863 Shanghai was divided into three parts: the International (Anglo-American) Settlement, the French Concession and the Chinese city. This division lasted until the Second World War. In 1900 the city had a million people, including 350,000 in international areas, but only 7,000 foreigners. In the 1920s it became the major financial center of Asia, and the capital of the underworld of racketeers and gangsters.

Li Zili, Waibaidu Qiao (Garden Bridge), Souvenirs (2009), oil on canvas, 162x130 cm

Popular housing built at that time consisted of terrace houses, usually on two stories, overlooking a narrow path. These lanes, called Li Long, hosting a few dozen families, constituted for nearly a century (1880-1980) the main habitat of Shanghai, a tenement housing of very high density (1,500 persons per hectare). The constructions, called Shi Ku Men, allied bricks, stone and wood. They offered different levels of comfort depending on their location and rents. Li Long favored a rich social life and neighborly relations that disappeared in the vertical social housing of the 1970s. Most of this traditional housing was destroyed to make way for thousands of skyscrapers that characterize Shanghai today.

HISTORIC BRIDGES OF CHINA

"Bridge" in traditional characters

An ancient civilization, China has a rich architectural heritage, which includes many bridges that were described by Prof. Ronald Knapp in a beautiful book published in 2008: Chinese Bridges, Living Architecture from China's Past.

Chinese crossing tradition dates back several millennia, with suspension bridges of ropes and bamboo in the mountainous regions and step-on block bridges to cross shallow streams. The Anlan Bridge in Sichuan, rebuilt in 1975, offers a good example of a traditional suspension bridge (steel wire cables now replacing bamboo ropes); it has eight suspended spans and a length of 320 meters.

The founder of the Zhou dynasty launched the first floating bridge across the Wei He River (near Xi'an) 3,000 years ago while the Huang He (Yellow River) was crossed by the same technique in 541 BCE, 28 years before Darius' pontoon on the Bosphorus. Note that the evolution of Chinese technologies did not benefit from outside influence until the eighteenth century. Surprisingly bridge-building techniques were developed in parallel and almost simultaneously in both the Indo-European world and East Asia, two civilizations separated by the impassable barrier of the Himalayas.

Also on the Wei He, a large girder bridge, 544 meters long and 18 meters wide, was built under the first emperor of unified China, Qin Shihuang, in 210 BCE. It included sixty-eight wooden spans resting on stone piers. Many beam bridges followed, including those of megalithic stones in Fujian. Arch bridges would later appear, in wood and then in stone, as evidenced by numerous engravings of the Han Dynasty. A big technological leap occurred in the early seventh century with the famous Zhaozhou Bridge, a superb low arch still in place. The multiple arch stone bridge long remained the dominant type in the country. There are many examples in provinces of the lower Yangtze. In particular, the historic city of Shaoxing (Yue's capital) in the southern part of the Gulf of Hangzhou hosts all kinds of ancient bridges over its canals, including one built during the Song dynasty (Bazi, 1256).

Among the bridges known to all Chinese specialists, the most famous are mentioned below:

The Zhaozhou Qiao (605, Sui Dynasty) in Hebei, also known by the name of Anji, has celebrated its 1400th anniversary. It was the first segmental arch bridge in the world. Its single arch, pierced with four open spandrels, is impressively thin. Instead of the traditional semi-circle, the arc is a segment of a circle (of 27 meters in diameter), a technique which would re-appear in 1345 in Florence in the Ponte Vecchio. Built on the Xiao river to allow north-south transport of goods to Chang'an, this bridge was designed by a master builder called Li Chun who should deserve international recognition. Among the innovations that should be noted are not only the flattened shape and open spandrels that reduce the weight, but also the stabilization of arches by X-shaped metal reinforcements (as in Mostar), shallow foundations, carved parapets. The span has a length of 37 meters and a width of 9 meters. This work of art in the true sense of the word remains an insufficiently known step in the evolution of construction techniques.

The Lugou Qiao or Marco Polo Bridge (1189-1192, Jin Dynasty) is historic for several reasons. Located in Wanping in the southwest suburbs of Beijing, this stone bridge on the Yongding (or Lugou), which is 266 meters long and 9 meters wide, strongly impressed Marco Polo during his visit to the site in 1280. It has 11 semi-circular arches, averaging 13 meters of internal width, and is adorned with 500 carved lions seated atop marble balustrades in a variety of poses. This bridge is famous not only for its age and aesthetics, but also because it was the site of the outbreak of the invasion of China by Japan, on 7 July 1937. In fact, the battle on Marco Polo Bridge that day marked the beginning of the Second World War in Asia. Beijing fell a few days later.

Small stone bridge in Zhouzhuang in the Yangtse delta ©Rodho/Shutterstock

Lugou Bridge near Beijing (1192) ©Jianguo Shen

Garden bridges were built during the Ming and Qing dynasties in Beijing and copied in many other cities. In addition to those in the Forbidden City and its surrounding lakes, the most beautiful may be the Seventeen Arches Bridge built in the eighteenth century in the "Garden of Gardens" (or Summer Palace) northwest of Beijing, across Kunming Lake. It is a 150-metre long structure, 8 meters wide, that accommodates 128 statues of lions. A marvel of marble and grace. Nearby the Yudai (Jade Belt) bridge constitutes the archetypal Chinese hump-backed bridge. Very steep, it is reflected in the lake to evoke the full moon. The Zigzag Bridge in downtown Shanghai and the stylish Wuting (five pavilions) Bridge on Yangzhou's lake can also be categorized as garden bridges.

Covered bridges, especially in southern Zhejiang, northern Fujian and Sichuan, are more numerous in China than in North America. Several thousand "fengyuqiao" still exist. Built mostly with timber, they support a corridor or pavilion which can serve as a toll booth. Baling Bridge in Weiyuan, Gansu, is so graceful that it adorns the cover of Ronald Knapp's book. A cantilevered wooden bridge or rainbow bridge, it is 45 meters long and 6 meters wide and rises 15 meters above the river. It is modeled after a much older and similar bridge built in Lanzhou during the Tang dynasty. The bridge of five pavilions in Yangzhou (1757) is also spectacular in its charm, its complexity and its position as an observatory on the slender lake. In Zhejiang, the neighboring Xidong (1570) and Beijian (1674) bridges in Sixi, each with a span of thirty meters, represent the archetypal wooden covered bridge. In Fujian the long and flat Wan'an Bridge was rebuilt several times since the Song; it rests on five piers and spans 100 meters.

The seventeen-arched Bridge in the park of the Summer Palace (1722) ©Buddhadl/Shutterstock

In South China the Dong ethnic group, of unparalleled carpenters, has also built magnificent covered bridges in Guangxi, such as the grandiose Chengyang Bridge (78 meters long) with four arches and five pavilions, built between 1912 and 1924 in Sanjiang district and recently renovated. The interest in covered bridges is still alive in China as evidenced by the new Anshun Bridge in Chengdu, whose deck supports a large restaurant.

Luding Bridge in Sichuan was crossed by the Long March in May 1935. It is a narrow iron chain suspension bridge across the Dadu River. The bridge was built in the eighteenth century on the trade route from India and Tibet to Beijing. The bridge was stormed by the Liberation Army and allowed thousands of soldiers of the Long March to defeat a nationalist blockade; this was a decisive step towards Yan'an (Shaanxi) that they reached in October 1935. Luding Bridge today symbolizes the struggle of the Chinese people for its liberation.

Wuting (five pavilions) Bridge in Yangzhou (1757)

Yong An Bridge at the entrance of Beihai Park in Beijing, thirteenth century ©Fashon Studio/Shutterstock

Nanjing Bridge across the Yangtse River (1968)

Finally the Nanjing Bridge across the Yangtze (or Changjiang) River symbolizes the new China. Built between 1960 and 1968, it reflects the technological independence gained at that time by China, when Russian technicians had left the country. A steel truss bridge, it crosses the river over 1,577 meters in ten spans. Its lower deck carries a dual rail track (6,772 meters long, 14 meters wide), the upper deck being dedicated to road traffic (4,589 meters long, 20 meters wide). It resembles the much shorter Waibaidu Qiao in Shanghai, built sixty years earlier. A bridge of the Cultural Revolution, it is admired and visited by thousands of Chinese citizens and has appeared in dozens of films.

The agglomeration grew from 6 million inhabitants in 1950 to 7 million in 1970, 8.2 million in 1990, 13.2 million in 2000 and 21.5 million in 2013. From the late 1980s Shanghai experienced an unprecedented economic boom, as evidenced by an increase of 5 million people in ten years i.e. more than 60%, after 40 years of slow growth. Having exceeded its former limits, the authorities decided to urbanize the eastern shore of the Huangpu River, which was then completely rural. The new town of Pudong (Pudong means "east bank") was born and grew at a frenetic pace. Hundreds of skyscrapers, huge avenues, a giant TV tower (The Pearl of the Orient, 486 meters high) were built in a few years. But the absence of a bridge to connect downtown Shanghai with Pudong was a major obstacle to the growth of the city. As in Saint-Petersburg a century earlier with the Neva, local authorities made a decision to cross the Huangpu and to build several major bridges across the busy river, using the most modern techniques.

Model of Shanghai (700 m2) at the Town Planning Museum

The first of these works was the Nanpu Bridge, inaugurated by Prime Minister Li Peng in December 1991, one year before schedule. It was designed and built in three years. The second was the Yangpu Bridge, opened in 1993.

Yangpu Bridge (1993)

Both are composite (steel-concrete) cable-stayed bridges. They were designed and built by subsidiary bodies (such as the Shanghai Infrastructure Company) of the Municipality of Shanghai.

The Nanpu Da Qiao (or Great Nanpu Bridge, 南浦 大桥) has a central span of 423 meters and a total length of 765 meters. It has seven lanes (four west-east and three east-west). Its two H-shaped towers, built on the banks, are 150 meters high. It looks like a more elegant version of the Alexander Fraser Bridge in Vancouver. The chief engineer of Shanghai Municipal Engineering Design Institute (SMEDI) who piloted the project, Lin Yuan Pei, now retired, is highly respected by his peers. His colleague Yue Gui Ping, welcoming us on 8 November 2006, emphasized that the Nanpu Da Qiao was undoubtedly the most symbolic of the four major urban bridges of Shanghai, while the Yangpu Da Qiao had held a world record for its central span of 602 meters.

Nanpu Bridge in the city, an artist view

The third bridge, the Xupu Da Qiao, opened in 1997, is also a cable-stayed bridge (590 meters of main span, with piers on the shore). The fourth and final bridge, the Lupu Da Qiao, inaugurated in 2003, is an arch bridge that broke the world record in its class, previously held by the Sydney Harbour Bridge and the Bayonne Bridge in New York, with 550 meters. Like its counterpart in Sydney, it can be climbed. Although arch bridges belong to an endangered species (as they are too expensive), the idea was to demonstrate that in the twenty-first century Chinese engineers could master all technologies. The cable-stayed span remains the dominant technique in China, a good example being provided by the Runyang Da Qiao, opened in 2005 near Yangzhou, which combines harmoniously across the Yangtze River a southern suspension bridge spanning 1,490 meters and a northern cable-stayed bridge. The Lupu Bridge, with its multicolored lighting, was meanwhile at the center of the Shanghai Expo 2010 and admired by millions of visitors.

The Asian Development Bank (ADB) provided funding for the first two bridges amounting to a total of US$ 155 million. The Nanpu Da Qiao cost a total of US$ 227 million, including US$70 million lent by the ADB. Of this amount, US$ 91 million was used for evacuating and resettling hundreds of people. Traffic on the bridge quickly reached an average of 120,000 vehicles per day, far exceeding expectations. Maintenance of the bridge costs US$ 500,000 per year, a continuous monitoring of the work and traffic being ensured by two dozen cameras connected to an ultra-modern control room.

Control room of the Nanpu Da Qiao

Since 1997, the bridge has been beautifully illuminated at night. The toll initially in place was removed in May 2000 and substituted by a tax on vehicles. Meanwhile, Pudong's GDP has increased 18-fold between 1990 and 2001, from US$ 740 million to $US 13.3 billion! In 2013 the population of the east (or right) bank of the Huangpu had reached 6 million, which represents more than a quarter of the agglomeration.

Pudong district now plays a major role in the Greater Shanghai, in both the financial, commercial and industrial fields. Many residents of Puxi (Puxi 浦 西 means "west bank of the river", i.e. the old city) are moving to Pudong, as housing, infrastructure and services become available. Shanghai built 560 kilometers of an underground metro between 1995 and 2013, a world record for efficiency in the realization of complex infrastructure.

The western access to Nanpu Da Qiao has a very elegant spiral shape, which allows traffic to rise 46 meters above the river in a minimum of space. All around this access a huge urban renewal project was implemented in preparation for the 2010 World Expo.

Spiral entrance to Nanpu Bridge from Puxi (west bank) ©Philip Lange/Shutterstock

Shanghai has four major urban bridges on the Huangpu, which are called, upstream to downstream: Xupu, Lupu, Nanpu and Yangpu. These names systematically associate the first character of the Western District (like Nan 南 or Yang 杨) and the first character of the Eastern District (always the "Pu" 浦 of Pudong, knowing that Pu means river and Dong 东 means east), districts connected by the bridges in question. Now tunnels instead of bridges are constructed in dense urban sites, because they require less demolition. However the double-deck Mingpu Da Qiao was recently built upstream.

In downtown Puxi, one should not forget to visit and admire the Zigzag Bridge in the heart of the old city. Pedestrian, it is made of nine orthogonal sections and was built in 1559-1577 in the beautiful Yu Yuan Garden. Many tourists, both Chinese and Foreign, meet there at lunchtime. The Zigzag Bridge is not far from the Nanpu Bridge, about two miles away. China is a country of streams, rivers and deltas, hosting tens of thousands of bridges of all kinds.

Li Zili, Flamboyant waltz (Yuyuan, Zigzag Bridge), oil on canvas, 146x114 cm (2009)
Li Zili is a contemporary painter who works in Paris and Shanghai and has exposed several times in the two cities. He is a leader of modern post-impressionism.

Residents of Shanghai and Beijing, the economic and political capitals, like to compare their respective cities. Shanghai does not have the magnificent historical monuments that Beijing can rightly be proud of. It is a new city. But another difference is that Beijing has no significant river, only artificial lakes surrounded by beautiful gardens and parks, while Shanghai has developed a symbiotic relationship with the Huangpu.

As my friend and colleague Jianguo Shen, a native of Shanghai, but married to Beijing-born Ling, underlines: "Beijing is beautiful and orderly, Shanghai is progressive, explosive and always looking for new challenges." The city's GDP reached US$ 300 billion in 2011, or about US$ 15,000 per capita. A quarter of China's foreign trade passes through the port of Shanghai. This economic dynamism explains the enormous investment capacity of a city which builds nearly 100,000 flats per year.

The Zigzag Bridge (1577)
©Jianguo Shen

Five hundred years before our era, Confucius noted that "time flows like a river's water". Apollinaire poetically developed the same idea in his "Pont Mirabeau." Another Chinese philosopher, Xun Kuang, added in 250 BCE a maxim that is still valid today: "The water of a river is like people, it can hold a boat, but it can also overturn it." Water and rivers have been at the heart of Chinese civilization for millennia and have fueled popular wisdom from generation to generation. An old saying from Shandong is also known throughout China: "If you want to be rich, you must first build roads" (equivalent of "when the building industry goes, everything goes"). This is truer than ever in the twenty-first century. The Chinese government seems to have adopted this principle: if you want better cities, start by providing them with good transportation infrastructure, as well as proper water supply, sanitation and communication services. So Xun Kuang's boat will not sink and will move forward, carried by running water.

Shanghai's bridges took their full part in the remarkable success of this metropolis over the past two decades. They could join the list of great Chinese innovations and should be acknowledged in the long history of Chinese bridges.

CHINA, 3,000 YEARS OF URBANIZATION

The history of China, an immense country, is often described as a succession of order and chaos, of multiple kingdoms in a permanent state of war among themselves and of centralized and stable empires, of fantastic achievements and of disastrous backward moves, of progress at the beginning of a new dynasty followed by stagnation, decline and anarchy, opening the way to the next dynasty. Indeed, the history of Chinese urbanization alternates between phases of centralization and autonomy, of pyramidal and rigid structuring and involuntary liberalism. This process was entirely endogenous i.e. it was not affected by any external influence until the nineteenth century.

China's urban history started with the Shang (1,500-1,050 BCE, capital Anyang in present-day Henan) and effectively with the Western Zhou (1,050-770 BCE). The Zhou developed the first ceremonial cities and the division between agricultural and urban labour. They founded the two cities which would be the capitals during almost two millennia: Chang'ān, presently Xi'ān (City of the West) and Luoyang (City of the East), separated by only 300 kilometers, in the fertile basin of the Yellow River. However, they were unable to unify the country. Out of anarchy appeared the great Chinese philosophies of Confucianism and Taoism, and literature, astronomy, medicine, at the time when Greece discovered or invented the same arts, the same sciences. An interesting coincidence (Confucius preceded Socrates by eighty years). Large walled cities with big earth fortifications and tiled roofs were developed. With more than 100,000 inhabitants (the size of Athens at the time), these seats of decentralized power competed with each other. And they benefitted from the increasing surplus of a dynamic agriculture.

Xi'an, the first imperial capital ©bbbar/Shutterstock

With the very short (but long in the making) Qin dynasty (221-202 BCE), the country reached a turning point as it was unified for the first time. The cities lost their autonomy; they became administrative prefectures (in total more than one thousand) which stabilized the country and provided a solid hierarchical structure.

The Han dynasty constituted the first great dynasty. It brought about economic prosperity through a centralization of decisions and lasted four centuries (206 BCE – 220 CE). It continued the pendulum swing by transferring the capital from Xi'ān (Western Han until 8 CE) to Luoyang in 25 CE (Eastern Han until 220 CE). Luoyang then had 300,000 inhabitants. The Han invented paper, seismography, chemistry and general anesthesia. The Han could be considered the Chinese equivalent of the Roman Empire. Successive dynasties (Wei, Shu, Wu, Jin, Song, Qi, Liang, Northern Wei) were weak and unstable; their capitals moved from Luoyang (which fell in 316 to the Barbarians) to Nanjing. Many cities took advantage of their increased autonomy. The Sui, a new transition dynasty (581-618), brought back stability, dug the Grand Canal (about 2,000 kilometers) and built beautiful marble bridges.

Then the Tang took over. They were the second great dynasty, which lasted three centuries (618-907). Under the Tang, the city of Xi'ān, still under the name of Chang'ān, was probably the largest city in the world (around one million people in the year 700). Modern town planning was invented there, in an area of 84 km², with a lay-out which would be used as a model for the emerging Korean and Japanese cities. After a first phase of expansion, chaos and fragmentation restarted in the middle of the eighth century. The Arabs defeated the Tang armies in 751 in Central Asia.

The Song stabilized the southern bank of the Yellow River, taking Kaifeng (east of Luoyang) as their capital. These Northern Song remained in power for 166 years (960-1126). Simultaneously, the Liao (916-1125) dominated the region of Beijing while the Xia (1034-1227) occupied the north-west. This was a time of territory sharing among major ethnic groups and of moving internal borders. In 1115 the Manchus arrived from the north-east and created the Jin state; they attacked the Song capital, which then had 400,000 people. The dynasty tottered; this was the very end of the Yellow River capitals. The Song abandoned the Yellow River for the Yangtse, thus becoming the Southern Song (1127-1279). After Yangzhou, Hangzhou became their new capital in 1138. But the North-South confrontation deepened. In 1153 the Manchus established their capital in Beijing (renamed Zhongdu). The country was split in two parts but the Song remained a great dynasty, particularly at the cultural and scientific levels. Four essential inventions reflect the scientific supremacy of China during this period: the compass, gunpowder, papermaking and printing. More than 10% of the population lived in urban areas, a slightly higher rate than in Europe. Between the eighth and twelfth centuries China witnessed a shift of population from North to South, due to recurrent instability in the North. The centre of gravity of urbanization also moved towards the South.

The thirteenth century saw the birth of the third great dynasty, the Yuan (Mongols), which began with Gengis Khan (1206-1227) and reached its peak with Kublai Khan (1260-1294). In only seventy years the Mongols unified the country by force and went much beyond, up to India and the Black Sea. In 1234 they defeated the Jin. In 1272 Kublai Khan decided to make Beijing (under the name of Dadu) his capital and launched enormous renovation and construction works. Dadu became the capital of the world while Hangzhou (which had half a million people) finally fell in 1276. At the time when dozens of cathedrals were being built in Europe, at the end of the Middle Ages, Paris, the largest European city, had only 200,000 inhabitants. In both East and West the thirteenth century was a period of builders. The Yuan dynasty (1206-1368) should be remembered for its achievements in architecture and urban development, as well as in textile and agriculture. However, the fourteenth century was more chaotic and witnessed many revolts. As always, the dynasty which was progressive in its first phase degenerated in its second phase.

The fourth great Chinese dynasty was the Ming (i.e. lights), which was in power from 1368 to 1644. It emerged out of popular discontent against Mongol domination and taxes. Zhu Yuanzhang founded the new dynasty in Nanjing and conquered Beijing where his son Zhu Di retransferred the capital in 1421, after building the most splendid monuments (Forbidden City, Temple of Heaven, etc). Beijing had more than 600,000 inhabitants in the year 1500 but the glory of the Ming was by then already declining. The Mongols remained a formidable presence in the North; they defeated the Ming army in 1449 and harassed the dynasty for decades. Ming's decline continued throughout the sixteenth century. China lost ground while Europe woke up, but its arts and sciences remained dynamic and of the highest calibre. This is, in fact one, of the most interesting features of Chinese history: the periods of political trouble are not synonymous with scientific and cultural decline; on the contrary, it seems that scientists and artists, essentially in urban areas, took advantage of the weakened central control to move forward, to innovate, to liberate their imagination and talents.

The fifth and last hereditary dynasty was the Manchus or Qing who, coming from the north-east (Shenyang), progressively eliminated the Ming forces by taking advantage of peasant insurrections. They crossed the Great Wall and took Beijing. They pushed away the Ming to the south, up to Taiwan. Emperor Kang Xi, the last great Chinese emperor (in power from 1661 to 1722) stabilized and unified the whole country in 1683 and signed a treaty with Russia to define the common border. His grandson Qian Long brought Tibet under Chinese control in the 1780s.

The Forbidden City in Beijing ©06photo/Shutterstock

At the end of the eighteenth century, the Chinese economy looked prosperous. Beijing was the most populous city in the world with one million people; it would be overtaken by London around 1820. The country's population had exploded, increasing from 150 million in 1700 to 320 million in 1800. Exports were growing but the imperial administration tried to limit imports through regulatory measures. China closed its doors and this isolationism worked against its economic and technological development. The productivity gap between China and Europe increased during 1750-1840 and China missed the industrial revolution. For once Chinese cities were unable to replace the collapsing State.

Chinese capitalism remained focused on trade. In spite of agricultural surpluses the urban bourgeoisie did not invest in the industrial sector and did not make use of technical innovations. Urban potential initiatives were discouraged by the central bureaucracy. Stagnation and decline started. And, as usual, corruption replaced good governance. The Manchus became unpopular and the Western powers, led by the British, took advantage of this situation to force the Chinese to open their markets. There were two Opium Wars (1840-42 and 1856-60) aimed at introducing Indian opium into the Chinese territory. The British occupied Hong Kong and shared Shanghai with the French. The great China (430 million people in 1850) became a semi-colony while the last Qing collaborated with foreign forces. But a new class of modern intellectuals appeared at the turn of the century; they called for independence and democracy. The dynasty collapsed after the uprising of 10 October 1911. In 1912 in Nanjing Sun Yat-Sen was elected President of the new Republic.

The last (and present) Chinese "dynasty" is therefore republican. Its first 37 years were marked by many conflicts, civil wars (between communists and Kuomintang forces) and the war against the Japanese invaders (1937-45), then by the liberation and the creation of the People's Republic in 1949. This was followed by the achievements and chaos of the construction of an independent country under the leadership of Mao Zedong until 1976, and the economic boom of the 1990s, which is still on-going.

Despite its political unity, China has gone through a process of administrative and financial decentralization over the last two decades. Chinese cities of the twenty-first century are rich and autonomous, high incomes resulting from market-oriented land policies allow them to rapidly improve urban infrastructure and to address progressively the enormous environmental problems inherited from a forced industrialization. For the first time in history, the idea that political decentralization and socio-economic progress can go hand-in-hand is gaining legitimacy. The State no longer fears centrifugal forces.

Skyscrapers in Pudong ©zhangyang/Shutterstock

It is possible to briefly draw some lessons from this 3,000-year history and from its continuous moves between progress and recession, stability and anarchy, centralization and fragmentation. Over 3,000 years one could claim that imperial stability dominated for 1,800 years while divisions and chaos affected the country for 1,200 years. These troubled decades or centuries cover approximately the following periods: 300 years at the end of the Zhou dynasty, 400 years at the end of Han, 150 years at the end of Tang, 70 years at the end of Yuan, 150 years at the end of Ming and 110 years at the end of Qing (1839-1949). In fact these periods of political and military turmoil have often been those of great economic and cultural progress and success. This "mystery" of Chinese history can be easily explained if we note that quite often cities have replaced the failing State to ensure the vigor of the Chinese civilization. And, thanks to close relations with their hinterland, they have brought about an almost uninterrupted growth of the economy. The cities have grown like one hundred flowers on the vast Chinese territory and they have structured the Chinese space through a dynamic interaction between centralism and autonomy, bureaucracy and initiative, unity and diversity. The main exception to this rule occurred at the end of the eighteenth century when the Qing State prevented all possible attempts to bring the country into the industrial era. However, Chinese cities remain, today as yesterday, the engines of development and an essential sphere of the state machinery. Spending only a few weeks in Shanghai and in other cities of the Yangtse delta is enough to be convinced of this reality.

Suzhou Creek and Waibaidu Bridge seen from the Pearl of Orient

In 2013 China had a population of 1.35 billion, including 720 million living in urban areas (53% of the total population) and 100 cities with more than one million people. These 100 cities produce three-quarters of the GDP. The ancient capitals Xi'ān and Luoyang regroup, respectively, 5.2 and 1.7 million inhabitants. Shanghai agglomeration, with 21.5 million people, is the third largest city in the world and Beijing has 17 million inhabitants. The urban network of eastern China is dense and quite balanced but the country is still under-urbanized in relation to its fast growing GDP. The cities in the west of the country are less dynamic, but are receiving increasing attention from the central government, including through the improvement of transport infrastructure between the interior and the coast. The issues of equity or "harmony", both social and spatial, are also high on the agenda.

China's urbanization process is expected to continue for at least the next 40 years. The one-billion-urban threshold will probably be reached before 2050. Chinese cities of the twenty-first century will have to be economically productive, socially inclusive, environmentally sustainable and politically democratic—a serious challenge that the lessons from history can help address, provided they are combined with a bold vision for the future.

POSTFACE

GEPHYROPHILIA OR THE LOVE OF BRIDGES

At the mere mention of the word "bridge[1]", you feel faint, you pant, your heart is pounding. You are a victim of gephyrophobia – the phobia of bridges - and you are not alone. In the United States, some states come to the rescue of terrified drivers. The State of New York employs a driver to transport phobics across the Tappan Zee Bridge, which rises at almost 50 meters above the Hudson. The same service is provided at Mackinac Bridge, the suspension bridge over the Mackinac strait in Michigan, and at the endless Chesapeake Bay Bridge in Maryland. On the San Francisco-Oakland Bay Bridge, the authorities prefer prevention to cure: a tow truck pulls terrified drivers across.

As misfortune never comes alone, gephyrophobia is often associated with other disorders: vertigo and fear of tunnels, of air travel, of spiders, of darkness, of confined spaces, of medical care, of contact with others ... the list goes on. Beyond their great diversity, phobias have one thing in common: they come from an inability to separate from the mother.

According to the psychoanalyst Irene Diamantis, one of their key components is "the impossibility to get out from a known place or familiar situation to join an unknown world which is a source of panic." An interesting explanation which sheds new light on a spreading disease. In ancient Greek, "phobia" means "fear". Rational thought is brutally stopped, time is suspended, and the person feels no recourse against a danger that threatens to destroy his or her very existence. The person is paralyzed, inhibited, unable to move, to love, to enjoy life. This is the case for Jared, for whom all medical examination means a death sentence; Anil, who uses only national roads to avoid terrifyingly empty highways; Miguel, who imagines the eyes of birds are filled with evil intentions; Sara, who believes that if she meets a rat, it will jump on her; Caitlin, panicking in aircrafts because she has the feeling that only her vigilance could prevent it from crashing ... Some tremble at the thought of looking into the eyes of others at the company cafeteria. Phobia arises when we feel that our familiar environment wobbles: the rat, bird, spider, or the glance from someone else will be used as frightening support to our inner discomfort. Is it a coincidence if the famous painting by Edvard Munch, The Scream[2], has a rectilinear bridge stretching into the background?

---

1 In ancient Greek gephyra, in modern Greek gefura
2 A version of this painting has been auctioned, in May 2012, for the record price of USD 120 Million.

Edvard Munch,
a version of the
famous Scream, 1893,
private collection

And gephyrophilia? It is much more common than gephyrophobia because many people love and often adore bridges. They include photographers, poets, painters, designers of stamps and posters, engineers and architects, popes (Sovereign Pontiffs), military engineers, and, of course, politicians. Bridges are powerful symbols of peace and human creativity. Dozens of cities have bridges as symbols. The Mayors of London are systematically photographed in front of Tower Bridge. We recommend that their peers follow suit, even if it means losing the votes of some unfortunate gephyrophobes. Paradoxically the very common condition of gephyrophilia does not find any entry in dictionaries, unlike its antonym!

This book should help combat the phobia of bridges, which is similar to the fear of others, who we imagine to be threatening, standing on the opposite shore. It is dedicated to the millions of budding gephyrophiles who have yet to truly recognize their chance, and to all those who are open to exchanges with people on the opposite bank and with other cultures.

BIBLIOGRAPHY

Ackroyd P., *London, the Biography*, New York, First Anchor Books Edition, 2003.

Ackroyd P., *Venice: Pure City*, Chatto and Windus, 2009.

Adao da Fonseca A., *Los puentes de Oporto*, Porto, 2003

Aidara Abdoul Hadir, *Saint-Louis du Sénégal, d'hier à aujourd'hui*, Paris, Grandvaux, 2004.

American University in Cairo, *Cairo: A City in Transition,* UN-Habitat, Nairobi 2011.

Andrić I., *The Bridge on the Drina*, University of Chicago Press, 1977.

Angel S., *Planet of Cities*, Lincoln Institute of Land Policy, Cambridge, Massachusetts, 2012.

Antonov B., *Les Ponts de Saint-Pétersbourg*, Editions d'Art, Saint-Pétersbourg, 2007.

Autrement, *Le Caire : Mille et Une villes*, Paris, 1985.

Autrement, *Shanghai, Rires et Fantômes*, Paris, 1987

Bairoch P., *Cities and economic development: from the dawn of history to the present*, University of Chicago Press, 1991.

Balabnev V., *Amsterdam-Petersburg*, Saint-Petersburg, 2003.

Balabnev V., *Venezia-San Pietroburgo*, Saint-Petersburg, 2003.

Basset A., *Japon, les délices de l'extrême*, Bruxelles, La Renaissance du Livre, 2006.

Baussy-Oulianoff D., *La déchirure jaune*, Gallimard, 1983.

Beren P. et Moulin Studios, *Vintage San Francisco,* Welcome Books, New York, 2003.

Bergère M-C., *Histoire de Shanghai*, Paris, Fayard, 2002.

Bernard M., *Histoire de Prague*, Fayard, 1998.

Bernard-Gely A. et Calgaro J-A., *Conception des ponts*, Paris, Presses de l'E.N.P.C., 1994.

Bettini S., *Venise, naissance d'une* ville, L'Eclat, 1978-2006.

Bialobrzeski P., Calcutta : Chitpur Road Neighborhoods, Hatje Cantz, Ostfildern, 2007.

Biarnes P., *Les Français en Afrique, de Richelieu à Mitterrand*, Armand Colin, 1987.

Biau, D., « L'ONU et le développement urbain : un voyage de Vancouver à Nairobi, Istanbul et Naples », in Lieberherr-Gardiol, F. Solinis, G. (dir.), *Quelles villes pour le 21ᵉsiècle ?,* Gollion, éd. Infolio, 2012

Biswas S., *Calcutta, Portraits*, Goodricke Group Ltd., Calcutta, 1995.

Bomati Y. and Nahavandi H., *Shah Abbas, Empereur de Perse* (1587-1629), Paris, Perrin, 1998.

Boriaud J.-Y., *Histoire de Rome*, Paris, Perrin, 2012.

Braudel F., *The Mediterranean and the Mediterranean world in the Age of Philip II*, University of California Press, 1996.

Braudel F., *Civilization and Capitalism, 15ᵗʰ-18ᵗʰ Century, Vol. 1*, University of California Press, 1992.

Braudel F., *Venice*, Paris, Arthaud, 1984.

Brown D., *Bridges : Three Thousand Years of Defying Nature*, New York, MBI, 2001.

Burdett R., Sudjic D., *The Endless City,* London, Phaidon, 2010.

Burns R. and Sanders J., *New York: an illustrated history*, New York, Alfred A. Knopf, 2003

Chaudhuri S. (dir.), *Calcutta: the Living City*, New Delhi, Oxford University Press, 1990.

Cigic A. and Miškovic A., *The Old Bridge in Mostar*, Intsitut za strojarstvo, 2004.

Collectif, *L'art mamelouk, splendeur et magie des sultans*, Aix-en-Provence, EDISUD, 2001.

Cortright R., *Bridging the World*, Wilsonville, Bridge Ink, 2003.

Cote M., *Constantine, cité antique et ville nouvelle*, Constantine, Media-Plus, 2006.

Coulais, J.F. and Gentelle P., *San Francisco*, Paris, Belin, 2003.

D'Araujo Al., *Rio colonial*, Quartet Editora, Rio de Janeiro, 2006.

Drake Boehm B. et Fajt J., *Prague, the Crown of Bohemia*, 1347-1437, New York, Metropolitan Museum, 2005.

Covi M. and Rigon F., *Palladio*, Citadelles et Mazenod, 2009.

De Freitas Pinheiro, *Encantos do Rio*, Rio de Janeiro, Salamandra, 1995.

De Meaux L., *Saint-Pétersbourg*, Paris, Robert Laffont, 2003.

Denison E. and Guang Yu Ren, *Building Shanghai, the story of China's gateway*, Londres, Wiley, 2006.

De Voogd C., *Histoire des Pays-Bas*, Paris, Fayard, 2003.

Diba D., Revault P. and Santelli S., *Maisons d'Ispahan*, Maisonneuve et Larose, Paris 2001.

Dillon R., *High Steel, Building the bridges across San Francisco Bay*, Berkeley, Celestial Arts, 1979.

Djament-Tran G., *Rome éternelle, les métamorphoses de la capitale*, Paris, Belin, 2011.

Drieskens, B., Mermier, F., Wimmen, H. (dir.), *Cities of the South, Citizenship and Exclusion in the 21st Century,* Beyrouth, SAQI-ifpo, 2007.

Dudak V. et Podrazil J., *Charles Bridge*, Prague, Baset, 2003.

Dumont-Le Cornec E., *Les ponts mythiques*, Paris, Belin, 2011.

Duras M., *Hiroshima, mon amour*, Gallimard, Paris, 1960.

Dupré J., *Bridges: a History of the World's Most Famous and Important Spans*, New York, Black Dog and Leventhal Publishers, 1997.

Enard M., *Parle-leur de batailles, de rois et d'éléphants*, Actes Sud, 2010.

Enders A., *Histoire de Rio de Janeiro*, Paris, Fayard, 2000.

Gautier T., *Constantinople of Today (1854)*, Kessinger Publishing, 2009

Giraud J-P., « Les ponts dans la société et l'imaginaire de l'ancien Japon », » in James-Raoul D. and Thomasset C. (dir.) *Les ponts au Moyen-Âge*, PUPS, Paris, 2006.

Grattesat G., *Ponts de France*, Paris, Presses de l'E.N.P.C., Paris, 1982.

Gasponi G., *Visages de Rome*, Rome, Euroedit-Trento, 2000.

Ghorra-Gobin C., *Los Angeles et San Francisco, différences et ressemblances*, in Hérodote n° 101, 2001.

Glaeser, E., *Triumph of the City*, New York, The Penguin Press, 2011.

Gordon A., *A Modern history of Japan*, Oxford University Press, 2009.

Graf B., *Bridges that Changed the World*, New York, Prestel, 2002.

Grass G., *Show your tongue*, Mariner Books, 1989.

Gréco, J., *Ça se traverse et c'est beau*, Paris, Deutsche Grammophon, 2012

Guechi F.Z., (Dir.), *Constantine : une ville, des héritages*, Constantine, Media-Plus, 2004.

Guillain R., *Orient Extrême, une vie en Asie*, Le Seuil, Paris, 1986.

Güler A., text from Orhan Pamuk, *Istanbul*, Paris, Editions du Pacifique, 2009.

Günay R., *Sinan, the Architect and his Works,* Istanbul, Yem Yayin, 1998.

Halasz Z., *La Hongrie*, Budapest, Corvina, 1991.

Hara T., Summer Flowers, in Minear R., *Hiroshima: Three Witnesses*, Princeton University Press, 1990.

Harvey D., *Paris, Capital of modernity*, Routledge, 2005.

Hattstein, M. et Delius P., *Islam, Art and Architecture*, Cologne, Könemann, 2000.

Haw R., *The Brooklyn Bridge, a cultural history,* New Jersey, Rutgers University Press, 2005.

Hazan E., *L'invention de Paris*, Paris, Seuil, 2002.

Hobsbawm E., *The Age of Empire: 1875-1914*, Vintage, 1989.

Horel C., *Histoire de Budapest*, Paris, Fayard, 1999.

Hoskins I., *Sydney Harbour*, Sydney, University of New South Wales Press, 2010.

Hughes A., *Michelangelo*, Phaidon, 1997.

IplanRio (1991), Arcos da carioca, 1755/1988, Rio de Janeiro

Kadaré I., *The Three-arched Bridge,* Arcade Publishing, 1997.

Kasarda J. D. et Lindsay G., *Aerotropolis*, Penguin Books, New York, 2012.

Khelifa A., *Cirta-Constantine, la capitale céleste*, Alger, Colorset, 2011

Knapp R. G., *Chinese Bridges*, Oxford University Press, 2008.

Korb L. and Lefèvre L., *Le Pont-Neuf à travers les siècles*, Paris, Flammarion, 1998.

Krob M. & Jr., *Prague*, Ed. Kvarta, 2005.

Kuban D., *Istanbul, an urban history,* Istanbul, Türkiye Bankasi, 2010.

Lacombe R., *Budapest en mouvement*, Paris, Autrement, 2004.

Lalor P., *Bridge : The epic story of an Australian icon – The Sydney Harbour Bridge,* 2006.

Lambert G., *Les Ponts de Paris*, Action artistique de la Ville de Paris, 1999.

Lane F. C., *Venise, une république maritime*, Paris, Flammarion, 1985.

Leuven J- M., *La Sérénissime et la Sublime, comparaison entre les deux renaissances*, in Paris, Autrement, 1988.

Levy M. et Salvadori M., *Why Buildings fall down*, Norton & Company, New York, 2002.

Lipsky F., *San Francisco, la grille sur les collines*, Paris, Parenthèses, 1999.

Loti P., *A Spahi's Love Story*, BiblioBazaar, 2009.

Loti P., *Aziyadé,* T. Werner Laurie, 1927.

Loti P., *Disenchanted*, Ulan Press, 2012

MacDonald D. and Nadel I., *Bay Bridge: History and Design of a New Icon,* San Francisco, Chronicle Books, 2013

Magne E., *L'esthétique des villes*, Infolio éditions, 2012

Mantran R., *Histoire d'Istanbul*, Paris, Fayard, 1996.

Manucci N., *Un Vénitien chez les Moghols*, Phébus libretto, 2005.

Mc Cullough D., *The Great Bridge, the Epic Story of the Building of the Brooklyn Bridge*, New York, Simon and Schuster Paperbacks, 1972.

Merdaci M., *Constantine, Citadelle des vertiges*, Constantine, Edif 2000, Media Plus, Paris-Med, 2005.

Michel B., *Histoire de Prague*, Paris, Fayard, 1998.

Mitra, R., *Calcutta Then and Now*, Calcutta, Amanda Publishers Limited, 2004

Moorhouse G., *Calcutta, the City Revealed*, Penguin Books India, 1994.

Mostar Project Coordination Unit, *A Bridge Towards a shared Future: Proceedings of the International Conference of Ministers Responsible for Culture in South-East Europe*, World Bank, UNESCO, 2004.

Mostar Project Coordination Unit, *Mostar, a Bridge Story*, World Bank, UNESCO, 2004.

Mosteghanemi A., *Memory in the Flesh*, The American University in Cairo Press, 2003.

Mumford L., *The City in history*, Mariner Books, 1968.

Myasnikov A. and Razdolgin A., *Saint-Petersburg, History of the City*, Saint-Petersburg, 1998.

Naipaul V.S., *India, A Million Mutinies Now*, Londres, Vintage, 1998.

Nocky D. (Dir.), *Amours de villes, villes africaines,* Paris, Dapper, 2001.

Oe K., *Hiroshima notes*, Grove Press, 1996.

Ouettar T., *Le séisme,* Algiers, SNED, 1981

Pamuk O., *Istanbul, Memories and the City*, Vintage 2006.

Panda C., *Charles D'Oyly's Calcutta*, Victoria Memorial, Kolkata, 2011.

Papin P., *Histoire de Hanoi*, Paris, Fayard, 2001.

Perlman J., *Favelas, Four decades of Living on the Edge in Rio de Janeiro*, Oxford University Press, New York 2010.

Peroncel-Hugoz J-P., *Villes du Sud*, Paris, Payot, 1993.

Petitguillaume L. and Bourdet I., *Les coulisses du Pont-Neuf*, Editions du Chêne, Paris, 2010.

Pérouse, J.F., Istanbul, entre Paris et Dubaï : mise en conformité « internationale », nettoyage et résistances, in *Villes Internationales*, Paris, La Découverte, 2007.

Perrier J-C., *Le goût des villes de l'Inde*, Paris, Mercure de France, 2005.

Petrovski H., *Engineers of Dreams*, New York, First Vintage Books, 1996.

Pétuaud-Létang M., *Bordeaux, Saint-Pétersbourg, Chronique comparée de deux villes du*

18ème siècle, Bordeaux, A éditions, 2003.

Pierce P., *Old London Bridge, the story of the longest inhabited bridge in Europe*, Londres, Headline, 2002.

Pitte J-R., *Paris : histoire d'une ville*, Paris, Hachette, 1993.

Poncioni C., *Louis-Léger Vauthier, un ingénieur fouriériste au Brésil*, Michel Houdiard, Paris, 2009.

Popova N., *Saint-Pétersbourg et ses environs : 300 ans d'une histoire glorieuse*, Saint-Pétersbourg, Ivan Fedorov, 2005.

Prade M., *Les Ponts, Monuments Historiques*, Editions Brissaud, Poitiers, 1986.

Punin A. and Pliukhin Y., *And Bridges Spanned the Waters' Width*, Leningrad, Aurora Art Publishers, 1977.

Racine J-L and Al., *Calcutta 1905-1971*, Paris, Autrement, 1997.

Rand R., *Historic San Francisco*, San Francisco, Heritage House, 2007.

Raymond A., *Cairo*, Rizzoli Universe Promotional Books, 2003

Reader J., *Cities: A magisterial exploration of the nature and impact of the City from its beginnings to the Mega-conurbations of today*, Atlantic Monthly Press, 2005.

Recouvrance S., *Les Ponts de Paris*, Paris, Ed. Jean-Paul Gisserot, 2007.

Reier S., *The Bridges of New York*, New York, Dover Publications, 1977.

Renouard Y., *Histoire de Florence*, Paris, Ed. J. P.Gisserot, 2006.

Rezapour S. and Hosainzadeh H-R., *Isfahan, Pearl of Iran*, Teheran, Yassavoli, 2006.

Robb G., *Parisians: an Adventure History of Paris*, Norton, 2010.

Rodenbeck M., *Cairo : the city victorious*, The American University in Cairo Press, 1999.

Richard F., *Le siècle d'Ispahan*, Paris, Découvertes Gallimard, 2007.

Royal Academy of Arts, *Living Bridges: the Inhabited Bridge, Past, Present and Future*, London, Prestel, 1996.

Saraiva J. H., *Portugal, a Companion History*, Carcanet, 1997.

Savet, J-M., *Les Ponts d'hier et d'aujourd'hui*, Paris, Editions MAE, 2006.

Serres M., *L'art des ponts – Homo Pontifex*, Paris, Le Pommier, 2006.

Sevilla J-J., *Rio de Janeiro en mouvement*, Paris, Autrement, 2005.

Simmel G., *Rome, Florence, Venise*, Paris, Allia, 2006.

Sollers P., *Dictionnaire amoureux de Venise*, Plon, Paris 2000.

Souyri P-F., *Nouvelle histoire du Japon*, Paris, Perrin, 2009.

Souyri P-F., *Moderne sans être occidental, aux origines du Japon d'aujourd'hui*, 2009.

Starr K., *Golden Gate*, Bloomsbury Press, New York, 2010.

Stendhal, *Rome, Naples et Florence*, Gallimard, Paris, 1987

Stierlin H., *Ispahan, image du paradis*, Paris, 1976.

Stierlin H., *L'art de l'islam en Orient, d'Ispahan au Taj Mahal*, Paris, Gründ, 2002.

Stierlin H, *L'Art Persan*, Editions Imprimerie Nationale, Paris, 2011.

Sutherland C. A., *Bridges of New York City*, New York, Barnes and Noble Books, 2003.

Švábová J. and Rygl T., *Prague, Detailed picture guide*, Prague, ATP Publishing, 2005.

Talese G., *The Bridge*, New York, Walker and Company, 2003.

Taylor R., *Tiber River Bridges and the Development of the Ancient City of Rome*, Internet, 2002.

Thilmans G., « Les Ponts de Saint-Louis, le Pont Faidherbe », in *Revue Saint-Louis-Lille-Liège* n° 4, 1999 et n° 5, 2006.

Thomasset C., « La construction du pont médiéval dans deux romans contemporains » in James-Raoul D. et Thomasset C. (dir.), *Les ponts au Moyen--Âge*, PUPS, Paris, 2006.

Tiziano R., *I Ponti di Venezia*, Newton Compton Editori, 1983.

Toman R., *Baroque: Architecture, Sculpture, Painting,* Ullmann, 2013.

Toman R., *Gothic: Architecture, Sculpture, Painting,* Ullmann, 2011.

Toman R., *The Art of Italian Renaissance*, Ullmann, 2011.

Trimble P. et Alioto J., *The Bay Bridge*, Images of America, 2005

Tzonis, A. et Caso Donadei, R., *Calatrava Bridges*, Thames & Hudson, Londres, 2005

UN-DESA, Population Division, World Urbanization Prospects: the 2011 Revision, New York, 2012

UN-Habitat, State of the World's Cities, Biennial Reports, Nairobi, 2010, 2012

UN-Habitat, Regional State of Cities Reports, Nairobi, 2008, 2010, 2012

Vacant C., *Jean Rodolphe Perronet (1708-1794),* Presses de l'E.N.P.C., 2006.

Van Loo A. and Brouwier M-C., *Héliopolis*, Fonds Mercator, Bruxelles, 2010.

Vidal-Bué M., *L'Algérie des Peintres 1830-1960,* Alger, EDIF 2000- Paris Méditerranée, 2002.

Weil F., *Histoire de New York*, Paris, Fayard, 2005.

Welch A., *Shah'Abbas and the Arts of Isfahan*, The Asia House Society, New York, 1993.

Whitfield P., *Cities of the World: a History in Maps*, Berkeley, University of California Press, 2005.

Whitney C. S., *Bridges of the world*, New York, Dover publications, 2003.

Winchester S. and Rupert, *Calcutta,* Melbourne, Lonely Planet Publications, 2004.

Yuan M. Speaker, *The London Tower Bridge*, London, Blackbirch Press, 2004.

Zuffi S., *Venise*, Leonardo Arte, Milan, 1999.

Zucchetta G.,*Venezia Ponte per Ponte*, Stamperia de Venezia, 1992.